D1482114

COLOSSAL
BOOK OF
CROSSWORDS

COLOSSAL
BOOK OF
CROSSWORDS

Compiled by Peter Coupe

Capella

Published by Arcturus Publishing Limited

For Bookmart Limited
Registered number 2372865
Trading as Bookmart Limited
Desford Road, Enderby, Leicester LE19 4AD

This edition published 2003

©2003 Arcturus Publishing Limited

All rights reserved. No part of this publication may be
reproduced, stored in a retrieval system, or transmitted
in any form or by any means, electronic, mechanical,
photocopying, recording or otherwise, without written
permission or in accordance with the Copyright Act
1956 (as amended). Any person or persons who do any
unauthorised act in relation to this publication may be
liable to criminal prosecution and civil claims for damages.

British Library Cataloguing-in-Publication Data: a catalogue
record for this book is available from the British Library

Arcturus Publishing Limited
26/27 Bickels Yard, 151–153 Bermondsey Street, London SE1 3HA

ISBN 1-84193-162-4

Jacket design: Steve Flight Studio

Printed in India

THE PUZZLES

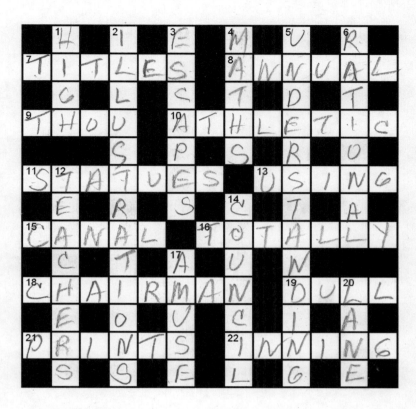

The completed crossword grid (handwritten answers):

Across:
7 TITLES
8 ANNUAL
9 THOU
10 ATHLETIC
11 STATUES
13 USING
15 CANAL
16 TOTALLY
18 CHAIRMAN
19 DULL
21 PRINTS
22 INNING

Down:
1 HEMOUR (HUMOUR)
2 ILLUSTRATIONS
3 ESCAPES
4 MATHS
5 UNDERSTANDING
6 RATIONAL
12 TEACHERS
14 COUNCIL
17 AMUSE
20 LANE

ACROSS

7 Found on front of books, also Lady, Sir etc (6)
8 Every year this book comes out! (6)
9 You in olde english ? (4)
10 Fit and strong (8)
11 Carved figures (7)
13 Making use of (5)
15 Man made waterway (5)
16 Completely (7)
18 Male company boss (8)
19 Boring or uninspiring (4)
21 Photographs or lithographs maybe (6)
22 Cricketer's batting session (6)

DOWN

1 In the air (4)
2 Drawings (13)
3 Gets away (7)
4 Number based school subject (5)
5 Comprehension (13)
6 Sensible, based on measured thought (8)
12 School employees (8)
14 Could be local, borough or county (7)
17 Make laugh (5)
20 Country road (4)

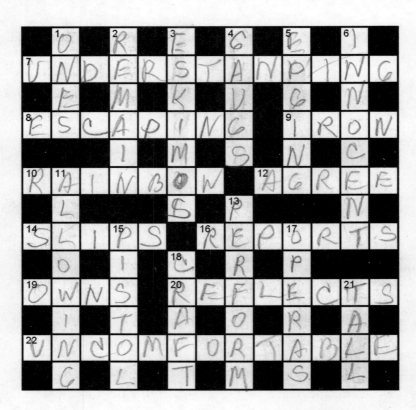

ACROSS

7 Comprehension (13)
8 Breaking Free (8)
9 Metal or press clothes (4)
10 ROYGBIV (7)
12 Concur (5)
14 Underwear or betting papers (5)
16 Given out at school - progress indicators (7)
19 Possesses (4)
20 Bounces light specularly (8)
22 Ill at ease (13)

DOWN

1 One is without an apostrophe ? (4)
2 Stay (6)
3 Igloo dwellers, properly called Inuit (7)
4 Measuring device - depth maybe ? (5)
5 Sidling along, finishing strip (6)
6 Not Guilty! (8)
11 Permitting (8)
13 Do something - like an operation (7)
15 hand gun (6)
17 Plays with songs, can be grand (6)
18 Stealth or hand making (5)
21 Certainly not short! (4)

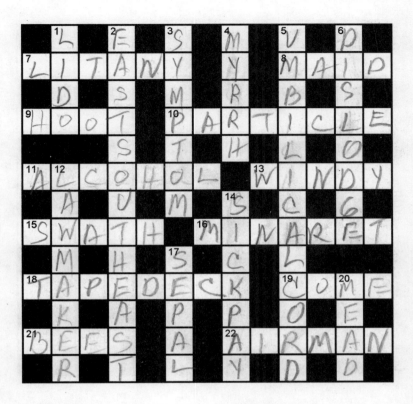

ACROSS

7 Long and tedious list (6)
8 Female servant (4)
9 Owl noise (4)
10 Small part of something (8)
11 Wine, beer and spirits (7)
13 Blustery (5)
15 Cut strip as in mowing (5)
16 Slender tower with balconies (7)
18 Recording and playback device (4,4)
19 Oh! .... all ye faithful (4)
21 Stingers with great knees? (4)
22 Flyer, male (6)

DOWN

1 Recreation area with swimming pool (4)
2 Compass direction (4-5-4)
3 Indication of illness (7)
4 Came with gold and frankincense (5)
5 Joins mother to child (9,4)
6 Knock or shake loose (8)
12 One who gives laws (8)
14 Remuneration for illness (4,3)
17 Part of a flower, when shaken leaps! (5)
20 Fermented honey and water (4)

ACROSS

7 Girls name (4)
8 Items for discussion ? (6)
9 Cold treats (4)
10 Business (8)
11 In disgrace (7)
13 Totalled up numbers (5)
15 Underwear is confused lisps ! (5)
17 Computer software or glazing devices! (7)
20 Arrange (8)
21 Trial (4)
22 Do it again (6)
23 Taken without owner's consent (6)

DOWN

1 Foxtrot, waltz, jive, bop, tango (6)
2 Containers - sometimes for tea (4)
3 Nipped between finger and thumb (7)
4 Receipt for postage paid ? (5)
5 Wonderful (8)
6 Frozen drip ? (6)
12 Asked for reconsideration - plead ape! (8)
14 Illness (7)
16 Bigger (6)
18 Misuses (6)
19 In perfect condition (4)
21 Saw or screwdriver or hammer for example (4)

ACROSS

7 Fix something to something else (6)
8 Number less than 100 (6)
9 Measured space (4)
10 Brolly (8)
11 OK (7)
13 Say something - US area (5)
15 Frequently (5)
17 Topic (7)
20 Seen (8)
21 Soil maybe - can be dished ? (4)
23 Bigger (6)
24 Spread to an equal thickness (6)

DOWN

1 Rotate spoon in pan for example (4)
2 Girl's name (4)
3 Idea in head (7)
4 Door handles ? (5)
5 Small creature (6)
6 Fit and strong (8)
12 Sea rescue craft (8)
14 Century (7)
16 Electricity is one form of this (6)
18 Pronounced, gauged, estimated (6)
19 Each and all (5)
22 Swiss, bread or even heads! (4)

ACROSS

7 Having less heat - device to make wine chilled (6)
8 Staffing bureau - possibly secret ? (6)
9 Remain (4)
10 Day of the week (8)
11 Propelled boat (7)
13 From floor to floor in a case? (5)
15 Country - of the pyramids ? (5)
17 Occupation on the land (7)
20 Feelings (8)
21 Armed force (4)
23 Say bless you after this (6)
24 Not so far away as before ? (6)

DOWN

1 Run off - metal fastener (4)
2 Took part in game (6)
3 Thwarts, intersects or Christian emblems (7)
4 Of the sea - as a dog might be ? (5)
5 Memorised (6)
6 Special day (8)
12 Dispute (8)
14 Lifting - sometimes bread ? (7)
16 Planted - maybe like beef ? (6)
18 In the mind like arithmetic (6)
19 Hues or musical notes (5)
22 Aspect (4)

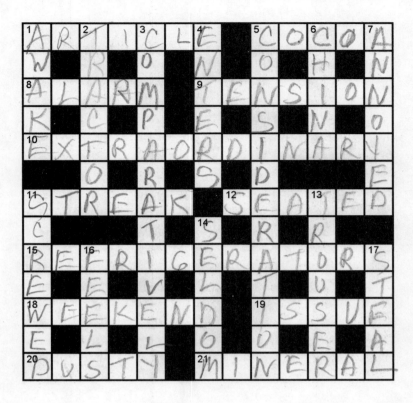

ACROSS

1 Item or newspaper piece (7)
5 Late night drink - I should! (5)
8 Fear, panic or clock! (5)
9 Taughtness, latent hostility (7)
10 Far more than usual or expected (13)
11 Run around naked! (6)
12 Sitting down (6)
15 Coolboxes (13)
18 Two day period after Friday (7)
19 Hand out (5)
20 Covered in fine particles (5)
21 Not animal or vegetable! (7)

DOWN

1 Not asleep (5)
2 Farm machine (7)
3 Relative to something else (13)
4 Goes or comes in (6)
5 Thoughtfulness (13)
6 Country or pot (5)
7 Irritated (7)
11 Penetrated with a circular motion (7)
13 Half a pair of gents pants? (7)
14 Rarely (6)
16 Senses (5)
17 Take without owner's consent (5)

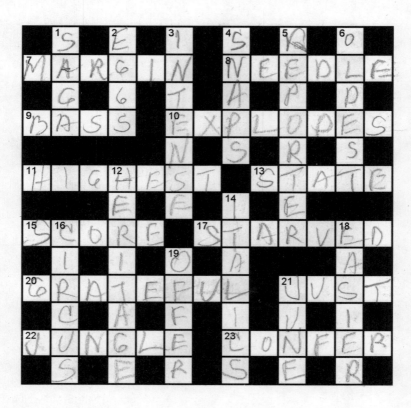

ACROSS

7 Border or edge (6)
8 Difficult to find in a haystack! (6)
9 Lowest part of musical range (4)
10 Blows up (8)
11 Topmost (7)
13 Say something (5)
15 Get a goal (5)
17 Deprived of food (7)
20 Thankful (8)
21 Only - fair! (4)
22 Impenetrable equatorial forest (6)
23 Transfer to someone (6)

DOWN

1 Old story (4)
2 Chicken product (4)
3 Acute (7)
4 Photographs - breaks off (5)
5 Journalist (8)
6 Most senior (6)
12 Practices that are handed down from the past by tradition (8)
14 Letters leaning forward (7)
16 Entertainment - could have three rings ? (6)
18 Least difficult (6)
19 Propose (5)
21 Month and girl's name (4)

Colossal Book of Crosswords

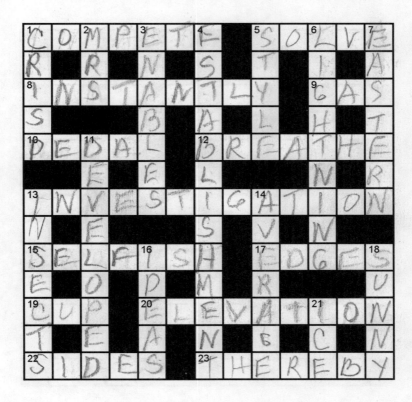

ACROSS

1 With no parts missing (7)
5 Work out puzzle (5)
8 Straight away (9)
9 Matter in non liquid or solid state (3)
10 Bicycle propulsion device (5)
12 Pass air through lungs (7)
13 Search for truth (13)
15 Concerned about oneself only (7)
17 Borders or boundarys (5)
19 Drinking vessel (3)
20 Height or act of raising something (9)
22 Faces or contesting groups (5)
23 Because of that - thy beer! (7)

DOWN

1 Not soggy and sometimes potato! (5)
2 Married female salutation (3)
3 Makes possible (7)
4 The act of forming something (13)
5 Manner of performance or flair (5)
6 Electricity from the heavens (9)
7 From the East (7)
11 Film made into negatives (9)
13 Small air-breathing arthropod (7)
14 Around the middle of the scale (7)
16 Notions (5)
18 Cheerful disposition ? (5)
21 Frozen water (3)

Colossal Book of Crosswords

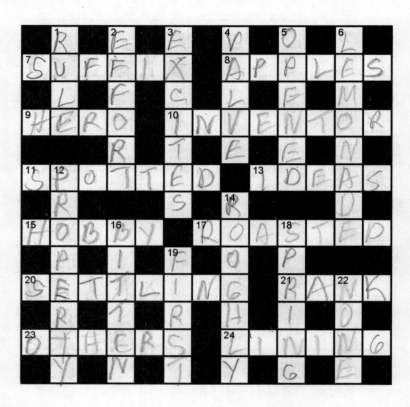

ACROSS

7 Attached to the end of a word (6)
8 Fruits (6)
9 Courageous champion (4)
10 One who devises new things (8)
11 Seen - splashed with paint? (7)
13 Thoughts (5)
15 Pastime (5)
17 Cooked in oven (7)
20 Calming down (8)
21 Position in forces (4)
23 Additional persons (6)
24 Inner protective covering (6)

DOWN

1 Law or measuring stick (4)
2 Exertion (6)
3 Gets going - turns on! (7)
4 Opens and closes (5)
5 Not closed! (6)
6 Drink made with sharp fruit (8)
12 House perhaps (8)
14 Approximately (7)
16 Grabbed by the teeth! (6)
18 Type of onion or water outlet (6)
19 Just before second (5)
22 How many are left in an empty box? (4)

Colossal Book of Crosswords

ACROSS

7 Holy building (6)
8 American state (6)
9 Weather - frozen rain? (4)
10 Look like (8)
11 Looked up to (7)
13 Book of the year! (5)
15 Higher (5)
17 Doctors' workplace? (7)
20 Breaking open (8)
21 Kept in place (4)
22 Returning sounds-little sir! (6)
23 Found responsible for crime (6)

DOWN

1 Called up (6)
2 Made picture with pencil? (4)
3 Having more point or edge (7)
4 Run after and try to catch (5)
5 Propelling one's body through water (8)
6 Person responsible for murder (6)
12 Encroachment, intrusion into another's land (8)
14 Suitcases (7)
16 Rebound from impact (6)
18 Get on with (6)
19 Number one! (5)
21 60s musical stuff grows on head! (4)

Colossal Book of Crosswords

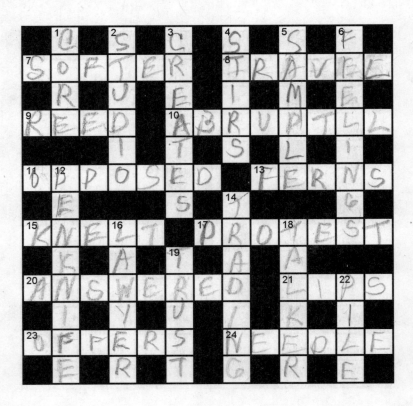

ACROSS

7 Less hard (6)
8 Broadens the mind (6)
9 Wind instrument component (4)
10 Suddenly, with no warning (8)
11 Anti, against (7)
13 Nonflowering frondy plants (5)
15 Went down on knees (5)
17 Declare objection (7)
20 Gave reply or response to (8)
21 Outer edge of mouth (4)
23 Bids (6)
24 Hypodermic (6)

DOWN

1 Apple centre, earth centre? (4)
2 Artist's workplace (6)
3 Makes (7)
4 Agitates coffee with spoon (5)
5 I representative selection (6)
6 Emotions (8)
12 Small pocket cutting device (8)
14 Buying, dealing or selling (7)
16 Attorney (6)
18 Speaker, verbaliser (6)
19 Complete confidence or fund (5)
22 Heap or stack (4)

Colossal Book of Crosswords

ACROSS

1 Pals turn round for a blow across face! (4)
3 Possibility or expectation (8)
9 Said in church (7)
10 Swimming stroke - back or front (5)
11 Goes on for some time - cobblers? (5)
12 Without difficulty (6)
14 Mistakes (6)
16 Baby resting place (6)
19 Throws away, spends thoughtlessly (6)
21 Topic for discussion? (5)
24 Enlarge, like a heavy sea? (5)
25 In the middle (7)
26 Catastrophe (8)
27 Aircraft engines (4)

DOWN

1 Provided or furnished with (8)
2 People from Arabia (5)
4 Done in a hurry (6)
5 Hits, put onto feet? (5)
6 Made possible (7)
7 Expressed a story in words (4)
8 Of lower value (6)
13 Football match men in black? (8)
15 Persons who read (7)
17 Lifted up (6)
18 Large area of land (6)
20 Discussions (5)
22 Distance between (5)
23 Second hand (4)

Colossal Book of Crosswords

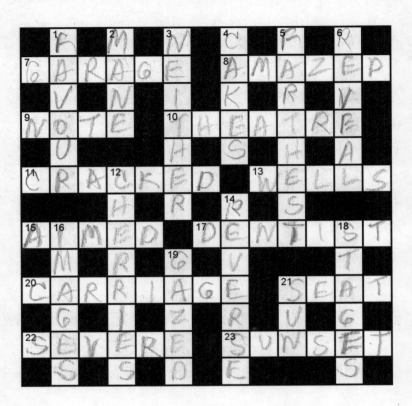

ACROSS

7 Car home (6)
8 Astonished (6)
9 Short letter (4)
10 Playhouse (7)
11 Made a joke or damaged vase? (7)
13 Water holes (5)
15 Pointed at (5)
17 Tooth doctor (7)
20 Conveyance - could be horseless! (8)
21 Place to sit (4)
22 Extreme (6)
23 Red sky at night - tessun! (6)

DOWN

1 Kindness, privilege (6)
2 Horse's neck hair (4)
3 Not one or the other (7)
4 Buns (5)
5 Most distant (8)
6 Show (6)
12 Fruits- life is a bowl of them? (8)
14 Turn backwards, negative (7)
16 Pictures, photographs (6)
18 Parts of a rally (6)
19 Looked at with fixed eyes (5)
21 Source of Earth's light and heat (3)

Colossal Book of Crosswords

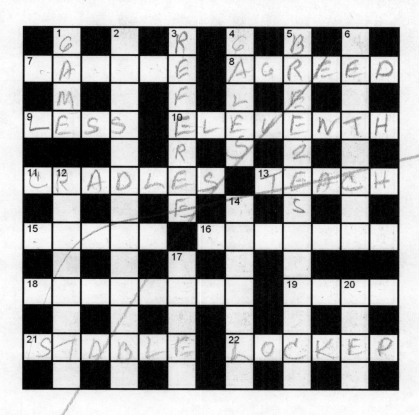

ACROSS

7 Car repair depot (6)
8 Achieved consensus (6)
9 Fewer than (4)
10 After tenth, before twelfth (8)
11 Baby beds, holds gently (7)
13 Pass on knowledge (5)
15 Chance to buy at reduced prices (5)
17 She - flesher! (7)
20 Do not concur (8)
21 Farm animal house or storage (4)
23 Intense or extreme (6)
24 Fixed shut (6)

DOWN

1 Amusement or pastime (4)
2 Stopped for a short time (6)
3 Sports controller with whistle! (7)
4 Strong winds (5)
5 gentle winds (6)
6 Going up, or down? (8)
12 Understood, Leeds air confused! (8)
14 Go the opposite way (7)
16 Rubber (6)
18 Underground (6)
19 Attempted (5)
22 Oliver, actor (4)

Colossal Book of Crosswords

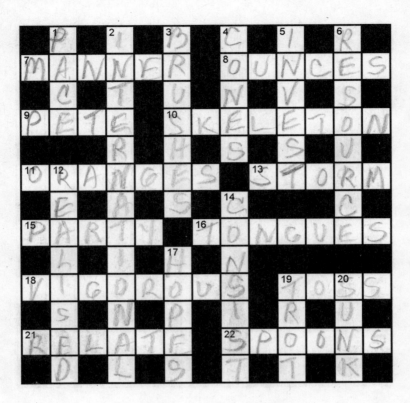

ACROSS

7 Way, style, fashion (6)
8 Imperial measures (6)
9 Male name (4)
10 Bones (8)
11 Fruit (7)
13 Bad weather (5)
15 Celebration or political group (5)
16 Parts of a shoe found under the lace (7)
18 Forceful and energetic (8)
19 Throw carelessly (4)
21 Tell a tale or story (6)
22 Used for eating or can be played! (6)

DOWN

1 The rate of moving (especially running) (4)
2 From or between other countries (13)
3 Artists and cleaners both use these (7)
4 Temporary motorway lane markers (5)
5 Place money to make profit (6)
6 Wealth that can be drawn upon if needed (8)
12 Successfully completed (8)
14 Made up of (7)
17 Desires (5)
19 Between walk and canter, short communist ? (4)
20 Buried below ground or sea? (4)

Colossal Book of Crosswords

ACROSS

7 Pigments suspended in liquid (6)
8 Right and suitable (6)
9 Like Larch or Chestnut (4)
10 Utmost, highest, final (8)
11 Bath aids? (7)
13 Come in (5)
15 Opposite North (5)
16 Accurate (7)
18 Lacking general education or knowledge (8)
19 (archaic) you, objective case of thou (4)
21 Fix or mend (6)
22 Hand tool for digging or lifting (6)

DOWN

1 In an evenhanded manner (4)
2 Between one or more countries (13)
3 Guaranteed (7)
4 Small skin blemishes (5)
5 Exchange of speech (13)
6 Unable to settle (8)
12 Broken up and turned over earth (8)
14 Say no! (7)
17 Take a wife or husband (5)
20 Look at - usually with desire! (4)

Colossal Book of Crosswords

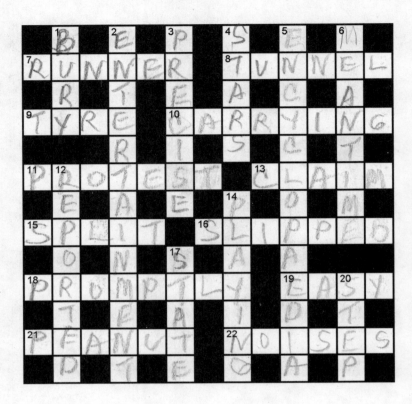

ACROSS

7 Jogger (6)
8 Underground passage (6)
9 A car touches the road through this (4)
10 Conveying (8)
11 Dissent or Objection (7
13 Demand for something as rightful or due (5)
15 A lengthwise crack in wood (5)
16 Skidded or slued (7)
18 Immediately when asked or due (8)
19 Simple (4)
21 Groundnut (6)
22 Sounds (6)

DOWN

1 Inter (4)
2 Amusement (13)
3 Accurate (7)
4 Heavenly bodies (5)
5 Reference work - often alphabetical (13)
6 During the intervening time (8)
12 Made known, described an event (8)
14 Having fun (7)
17 Express an idea or position (5)
20 Pest is found to be part of stairs! (4)

Colossal Book of Crosswords

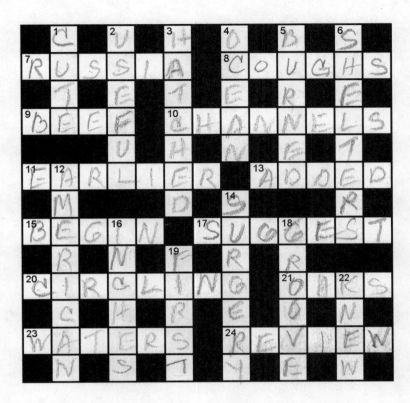

ACROSS

7 Former communist country (6)
8 Exhales abruptly - when one has a chest cold? (6)
9 Meat eaten by royal guards ? (4)
10 Official routes of communication (8)
11 In a previous part of the day or week ? (7)
13 Totalled up numbers (5)
15 Start (5)
17 Imply as a possibility (7)
20 Going round and round (8)
21 Old trees (4)
23 Adds liquid to plants ? (6)
24 A new appraisal or evaluation (6)

DOWN

1 Attractive in a sweet way ? (4)
2 Having a function or service (6)
3 Came out of egg - idea perhaps ? (7)
4 Large body of water (5)
5 Thrown into fire (6)
6 Protective structures (8)
12 From the USA (8)
14 Medical practice (7)
16 Imperial measures (6)
18 Long narrow furrow (6)
19 Before anything else (5)
22 Had the knowledge (4)

Colossal Book of Crosswords

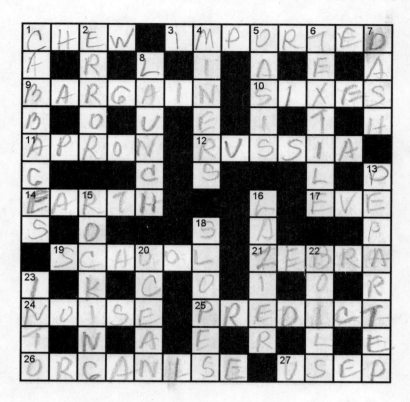

ACROSS

1 Break up with teeth (4)
3 Brought in from another country (8)
9 Good buy! (7)
10 What cricketers hit? (5)
11 Kitchen wear (5)
12 Country (6)
14 Soil (5)
17 First lady? (3)
19 Place of learning for fish? (6)
21 Striped animal (5)
24 Unwanted sound (5)
25 Look into the future (7)
26 Get people together (8)
27 Secondhand - mixed dues! (4)

DOWN

1 Vegetables, green (8)
2 Mistake (5)
4 Coal workers (6)
5 Pop group and water hole (5)
6 Fabric, cloth, material (7)
7 Rush - (4)
8 Lift off (6)
13 Gone (8)
15 Type of chair (7)
16 More idle (6)
18 Places where skiing is done? (6)
20 Sea (5)
22 Water reaching 100 centigrade does this (5)
23 Changing from one to another, keen on... (4)

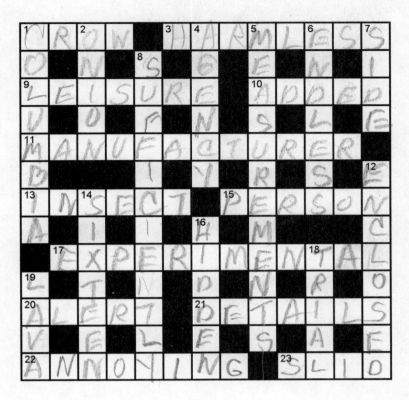

ACROSS

1 Black bird (4)
3 Unlikely to hurt or disturb anyone (8)
9 Spare time (7)
10 Brought together - possibly numbers? (5)
11 Maker (12)
13 Small creature (6)
15 A human being (6)
17 Not yet perfected ? (12)
20 On guard (5)
21 Small concerns - contains the devil ? (7)
22 Irritating (8)
23 Skidded (4)

DOWN

1 North American river (8)
2 Pungent bulb (5)
4 Federal or Criminal Investigation (US) (6)
5 Sizes obtained by tapes or rules ? (12)
6 Never ending (7)
7 One face of something (4)
8 To the required degree - is tuff nicely ? (12)
12 Within, contained (8)
14 Baker's dozen plus three! (7)
16 Out of sight (6)
18 Court case - free test period ? (5)
19 Volcanic liquid (4)

Colossal Book of Crosswords

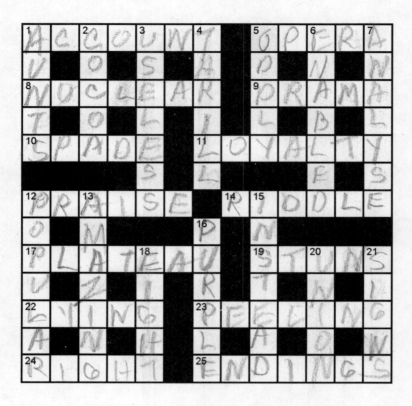

ACROSS

1 Bank record of transactions (7)
5 Singing play (5)
8 Atomic (7)
9 Play (5)
10 Digging implement (5)
11 Feelings of allegiance (7)
12 Expression of approval (6)
14 Puzzle (6)
17 Flat mountain top (7)
19 Knocks out (5)
22 Not being truthful (5)
23 Preparing potatoes for cooking maybe ? (7)
24 Conservative wing ? (5)
25 Finishes, conclusions (7)

DOWN

1 Mother's sisters (5)
2 Chocolate drink (5)
3 Of no value (7)
4 Fill with sublime emotion (6)
5 Strangely - uneven maybe ? (5)
6 Allowed or made capable (7)
7 Consider in detail (7)
12 Well liked by the majority (7)
13 Astonishing, awesome... (7)
15 In place of (7)
16 Colour (6)
18 Number (5)
20 Trade group (5)
21 Roadside directions and instructions (5)

Colossal Book of Crosswords

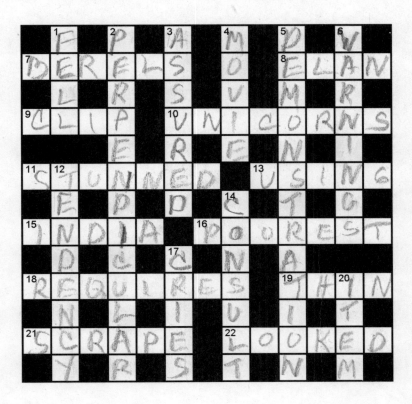

ACROSS

7 Valuable gems (6)
8 Distinctive and stylish elegance (4)
9 Short piece of movie ? (4)
10 Horned horses of mythology (8)
11 Dazed (7)
13 Making use of (5)
15 Country (5)
16 Least wealthy (7)
18 Needs (8)
19 Not thick (4)
21 Abrade (6)
22 Searched (for) (6)

DOWN

1 Tumbled (4)
2 Straight up from the horizon (13)
3 Guaranteed (7)
4 Film (5)
5 Protest (13)
6 Cautionary messages (8)
12 Leaning towards (8)
14 Seek information from (7)
17 Shouts (5)
20 Thing in rabbit emporium (4)

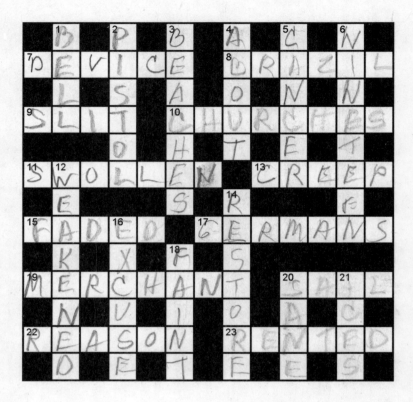

ACROSS

7 Machine (6)
8 Country and nut (6)
9 Long narrow opening (4)
10 Places of worship (8)
11 Puffed up - distended (7)
13 Unpleasant character (5)
15 Colour bleached with time (5)
17 A European people (7)
19 Business person (8)
20 Boat propulsion method (4)
22 Sense - rational motive (6)
23 Let out for money (6)

DOWN

1 Ringer! (4)
2 Hand gun (6)
3 Lands boat on shore (7)
4 On the move - out and ..... (5)
5 Disease (6)
6 Number (8)
12 Lessened the strength of (8)
14 Bring back to health (7)
16 Poor reason for doing
   something (6)
18 Collapse (5)
20 Not mad (4)
21 Summer treats (4)

Colossal Book of Crosswords

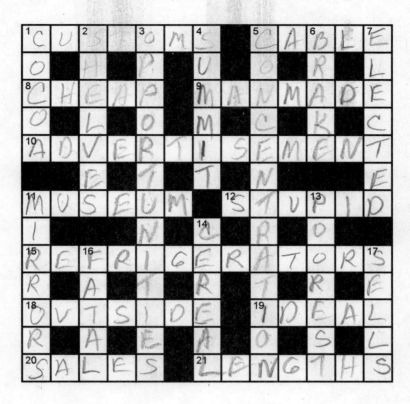

ACROSS

1 Accepted habit or practice (7)
5 Wire (5)
8 Inexpensive (5)
9 Not natural - produced by humans ? (3-4)
10 Promotion of something - I am rented vets ! (13)
11 Place for display of antiquities (6)
12 Idiotic (6)
15 Coolboxes (13)
18 Not inside (7)
19 Perfect (5)
20 Periods of reduced price (5)
21 What extents one might go to ? (7)

DOWN

1 Chocolately drink (5)
2 Storage slats on wall or cupboard (7)
3 Chances or possibility (13)
4 Top of the hill (6)
5 Intense mental effort (13)
6 Stopping device in car (5)
7 Put in office by voters (7)
11 Reflecting devices (7)
13 Least wealthy (7)
14 Breakfast food (6)
16 Deadly (5)
17 Hands over for a price! (5)

Colossal Book of Crosswords

ACROSS

7 Pop group and constables! (6)
8 Beast (6)
9 Domestic swine (4)
10 Places of performance (8)
11 Catching fish ? - tin gent! (7)
13 Put down in words (5)
15 Finished (5)
17 Craziest (7)
20 Could be level if used for trains! (8)
21 Bottom (4)
22 Not openly made known (6)
23 Demonstrated or presented (6)

DOWN

1 A sign posted in a public place (6)
2 Ceases to exist (4)
3 Taking a break - maybe on laurels ? (7)
4 Foundations, stands, army camps ? (5)
5 Imagined in the mind (8)
6 Mother or father (6)
12 Buried gold ? reuse tar! (8)
14 Largest (7)
16 Brought back to health (6)
18 Gaps (6)
19 Unclean (5)
21 Not fast! (4)

ACROSS

1 Absolute requirement to do (4)
3 Day of the week (8)
9 Least attractive (7)
10 Type of cheese (5)
11 Diagnostic trials (5)
12 Fortified building (6)
14 Small area of land surrounded by water (6)
16 Predatory arachnid (6)
19 Car storage or repair place (6)
21 Number (5)
24 Highest part in choral music (5)
25 Gouda, stilton, cheddar are all these (7)
26 Without warning (8)
27 Treat skin or hide (3)

DOWN

1 Higher than a hill - could be debt? (8)
2 Vends (5)
4 Roof spaces (6)
5 Encourages someone to do something (5)
6 Times 2? (7)
7 365 days is one! (4)
8 A human being! (6)
13 Son's son or daughter's son (8)
15 Knowledgeable - highly educated (7)
17 Shoves (6)
18 Writing or drawing device (6)
20 By oneself (5)
22 Go to see someone (5)
23 Pretends (4)

Colossal Book of Crosswords

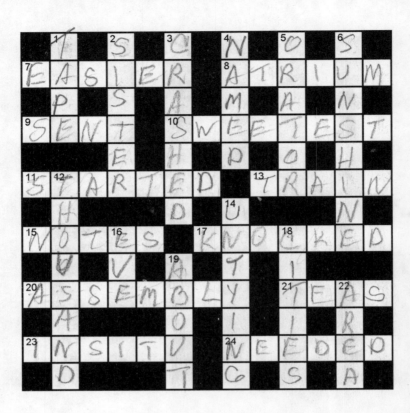

ACROSS

7 Less difficult (6)
8 The central area in a building; open to the sky (6)
9 Caused to go somewhere (4)
10 Most sugary (8)
11 Got going (7)
13 Series of events - also transport device! (5)
15 Jottings (5)
17 Banged - possibly at a door? (7)
20 Morning gathering in school (8)
21 Seat confused for hot drinks (4)
23 In the original or natural place or site (2,4)
24 Required (6)

DOWN

1 Recording or sticky media (4)
2 Female sibling (6)
3 Fall or come down violently (7)
4 Mentioned and identified by name (5)
5 Public speaker (6)
6 The rays of the sun (8)
12 Number (8)
14 Loosening the ties that fasten something (7)
16 First lady ? (3)
18 Large inhabited places (6)
19 Approximately (5)
22 A particular geographical region (4)

Colossal Book of Crosswords

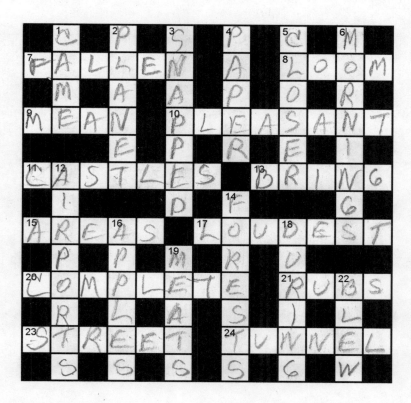

ACROSS

7 Killed in battle (6)
8 Weaving machine (4)
9 Tight fisted (4)
10 Nice to look at - I spangle (8)
11 Chess piece or makes chess move? (7)
13 Take something with oneself somewhere (5)
15 Geographical regions (5)
17 Making the most sound (7)
20 In total - nothing further required (8)
21 Chafes, wipes (4)
23 Road lined with buildings (6)
24 Underground passage - Like the channel ? (6)

DOWN

1 Arrived (4)
2 Celestial body (6)
3 Closed sharply - broke twig ? (7)
4 Printing support - daily news bringer ? (5)
5 Nearer (6)
6 Before midday (8)
12 Places to take off and land (8)
14 Wooded places (7)
16 Fruits (6)
18 Whilst (6)
19 Flesh used as food (5)
22 Expelled air, possibly into a balloon ? (4)

Colossal Book of Crosswords

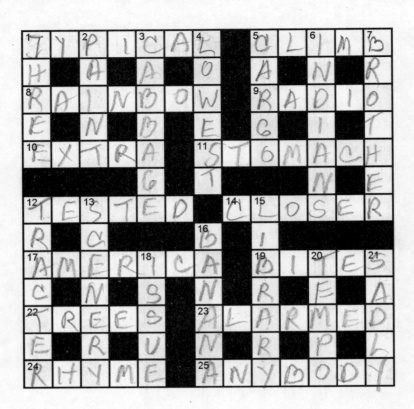

ACROSS

1 Of a type or group (7)
5 Go up mountain (5)
8 Arc of coloured light in sky (7)
9 Wireless (5)
10 More than required - as in films? (5)
11 Put up with (digestive organ) (7)
12 Had a try (6)
14 Nearer (6)
17 Country (7)
19 Sinks teeth into - sit be! (5)
22 Perennial woody plants (5)
23 Frightened, possibly by bell? (7)
24 Sound alike - as in poetry? (5)
25 Applies to anyone (7)

DOWN

1 After two, before four (5)
2 Pigment for walls, etc (5)
3 Green vegetable, brassica (7)
4 At the bottom (6)
5 Goods carried by vessel (5)
6 Natives of India (7)
7 Sibling (7)
12 Farm machine (7)
13 Painted background for stage show (7)
15 Book store (7)
16 Yellow fruit, providing trip? (6)
18 Question or dispute (5)
20 Time signature (5)
21 With unhappiness (5)

Colossal Book of Crosswords

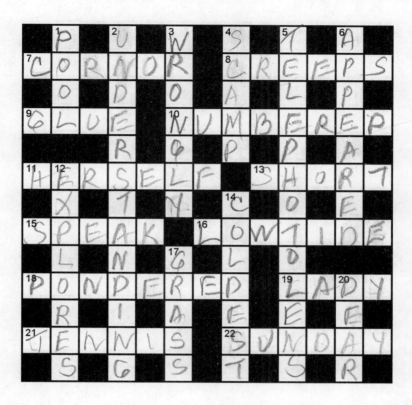

ACROSS

7 Bend in the road or path (6)
8 Moves stealthily (6)
9 Adhesive (4)
10 In a sequence, numerically arranged (8)
11 She - re shelf! (7)
13 Not long (5)
15 Verbalise (5)
16 Farthest ebb of the sea at the beach (3,4)
18 Thought about, considered (8)
19 Female (4)
21 Ball game with service (6)
22 Day of the week (6)

DOWN

1 Swimming place (4)
2 Comprehension (13)
3 Incorrectly (7)
4 Little tinker! Mischief maker! (5)
5 Long camera lens (9,4)
6 Came into sight or view (8)
12 Delves into...spree lox! (8)
14 Having the lowest temperature (7)
17 Green herbage grown as lawns (5)
20 Term of endearment (4)

Colossal Book of Crosswords

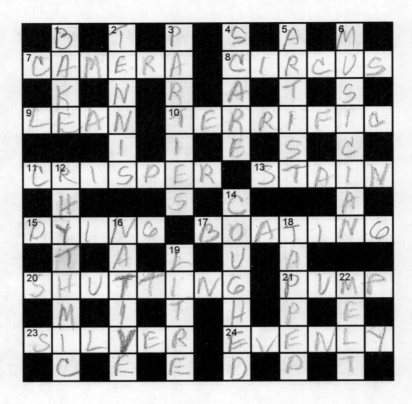

ACROSS

7 Photographic device (6)
8 Entertainment in a tent! (6)
9 Rest against something (4)
10 Great! (8)
11 Crunchier - per risc! (7)
13 Mark or blemish (5)
15 Passing on or desirous to try something (5)
17 Being on the water (7)
20 Closing (8)
21 Heart ? Liquid moving device (4)
23 Precious metal and Lone Ranger's horse! (6)
24 With a consistent coating (6)

DOWN

1 Make bread (4)
2 Racket game (6)
3 Birthday or anniversary celebrations? (7)
4 Frighten (5)
5 Painter or sculptor (6)
6 Instrument player (8)
12 In time with a beat (8)
14 Expelled air suddenly (7)
16 From the place - indigenous (6)
18 Struck lightly - with a screw thread ? (6)
19 Metric measure (5)
22 Liquify by applied heat (4)

Colossal Book of Crosswords

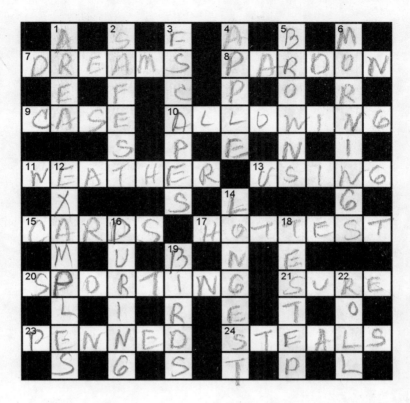

ACROSS

7 Visions seen in sleep (6)
8 Forgiveness, what ? (6)
9 Holiday clothes container (4)
10 Permitting (8)
11 The meteorological conditions (7)
13 Making use of (5)
15 Playing, greeting or on the ..... (5)
17 Highest temperature (7)
20 Willingness to take a risk (8)
21 Certain (4)
23 Wrote (6)
24 Robs (6)

DOWN

1 Measured space (4)
2 Most secure place (6)
3 Gets away from custody (7)
4 Fruit (5)
5 Fries in a pan until colour changes (6)
6 Early parts of days (8)
12 Punishments intended as warnings (8)
14 Having the greatest length (7)
16 Whilst (6)
18 Checked to ensure fitness or safety (6)
19 Flying creatures (5)
22 Swiss, perhaps, or on a winner? (4)

Colossal Book of Crosswords

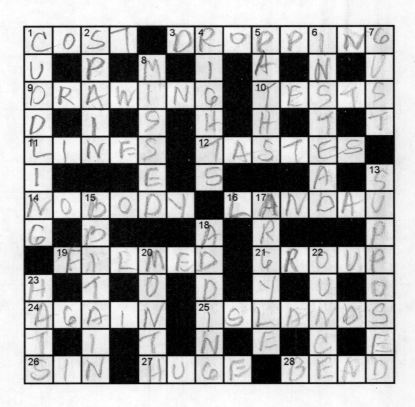

ACROSS

1 Price to pay (4)
3 Allowing to fall (8)
9 Artistic output (7)
10 Checks - for driving perhaps ? (5)
11 Tracks (5)
12 Samples - food or drink ? (6)
14 A person of no influence (6)
16 A four-wheel covered carriage (6)
19 Captured on film - or video (6)
21 Pop combo - or other gathering (5)
24 Once more (5)
25 Small land areas surrounded by sea (7)
26 Bad behaviour - could be cardinal ? (3)
27 Very large (4)
28 Modify a rule without actually breaking it! (4)

DOWN

1 Hugging (8)
2 European country (5)
4 Individual freedoms (6)
5 Lines of travel or access (5)
6 In place of (7)
7 Burst of wind (4)
8 Failed to catch (6)
13 Thought to be (8)
15 European country (7)
17 Diamond shaped sock pattern (6)
18 Making by combining numbers (6)
20 Period of 28, 29, 30 or 31 days (5)
22 Imperial weight (5)
23 Headgear (4)

ACROSS

7 Inflict harm upon (6)
8 Made noise like a lion (6)
9 We have lost our apostrophe! (4)
10 Teeth doctors (8)
11 Spring and Summer (7)
13 Once more (5)
15 Ecclesiastical garments (5)
17 A journey usually by ship (7)
20 Controlling - tin Damon! (8)
21 Secure against leakage (4)
23 Small (6)
24 Up and down playground toy (6)

DOWN

1 Recording or sticky media (4)
2 Descriptive or identifying tags (6)
3 Requiring (7)
4 Reduce to powder by abrasion, mill (5)
5 Looking toward (6)
6 Pain of growing teeth (8)
12 Using the minimum of time or resources (8)
14 Most corpulent (7)
16 has an existence (6)
18 Female sibling (6)
19 Art support in tripod form (5)
22 Put in reserve - not for immediate use (4)

ACROSS

7 Weight or british currency (6)
8 Cure all liquid (6)
9 Obtain with difficulty....out! (3)
10 Responded to (8)
11 Hidden stuff - secret stores! (7)
12 Held dear (5)
14 Normal - maybe suspects? (5)
15 Accommodation (7)
17 Average - down the centre (8)
19 From cows (4)
21 Woodwork tools or jets ? (6)
22 Tidy (4)

DOWN

1 Reach a destination of decision (4)
2 Agreement - transuding end! (13)
3 Broke free (7)
4 Plural of goose (5)
5 Takes up a lot of time - miscounting me! (4-9)
6 Number - final teen year! (8)
13 Having the greatest length (7)
16 Before all others (5)
18 Small island (4)
20 Go in front - heavy metal! (4)

Colossal Book of Crosswords

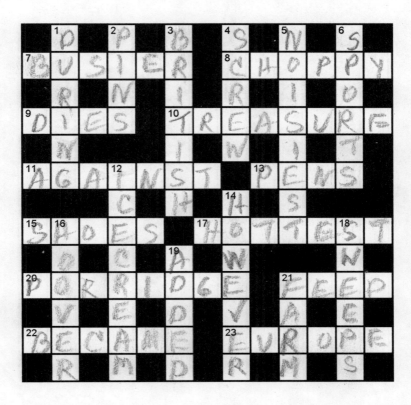

ACROSS

7 More occupied - confused bruise! (6)
8 Rough sea (6)
9 Passes on (4)
10 Buried by pirates it is often thought! (8)
11 Anti, contrary stand (7)
13 Animal cages, writing implements (4)
15 Footwear (5)
17 Highest temperature (7)
20 Breakfast dish - Scots (8)
21 Give food to (4)
22 Turned into (6)
23 Continent (6)

DOWN

1 In the course of, whilst (6)
2 Often with needles when a limb goes to sleep! (4)
3 From Britain (7)
4 Woodworking component, needs a driver (5)
5 Making the most noise! (8)
6 Wears, good losers, games (6)
12 Frozen dessert containing cream (3,5)
14 By contrast; on the other hand (7)
16 Vacuum cleaner (6)
18 Brushes and chimney cleaners (6)
19 Supplemented (5)
21 Agricultural business (4)

Colossal Book of Crosswords

ACROSS

7 Noises - suns do! (6)
8 Petition or prayer - or sion! (6)
9 Garden party or fair (4)
10 Responded to question (8)
11 She, reflexive form of her (7)
13 Sides - cafes? (5)
15 Steel is, as is brass, and also iron (5)
16 Plants cultivated for blooms or blossoms (7)
18 Nuptial ceremonies (8)
19 Cooperative group, like football ? (4)
21 Supports for teapots or hats perhaps (6)
22 Not out of the ordinary (6)

DOWN

1 Humorous anecdote or quip (4)
2 Comprehension (13)
3 Under normal circumstances (7)
4 Coming undone or flowing garment (5)
5 Soft drink - with natural additives (12)
6 From whom you are descended (8)
12 War ending hour, day and month (8)
14 Shutting (7)
17 Anxiety feeling - possibly teenage ? (5)
20 Not present, having left, gone .... (4)

Colossal Book of Crosswords

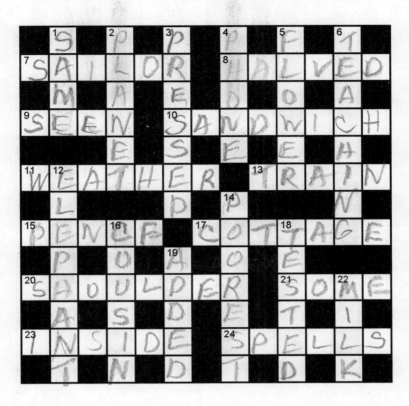

ACROSS

7 Boat person ? matelot ? (6)
8 Cut in two - equally! (6)
9 Viewed (4)
10 Bread slices containing fillings (8)
11 Rain, snow, sleet, mist, for example (7)
13 Track based transport device (5)
15 Coppers - 100 to the pound (5)
17 Small house - also pie! (7)
20 Carry a burden - so hurdle! (8)
21 Unknown or unspecified (4)
23 Where you are after entering? (6)
24 Periods of time or magic chants (6)

DOWN

1 Not different (4)
2 Mars is one (6)
3 Pushed, as a doorbell might be ? (7)
4 Short telephone (5)
5 Blossom (6)
6 Educating or instructing (8)
12 Five-toed pachyderm (8)
14 Least wealthy (7)
16 Relative (6)
18 Tried out (6)
19 Numbers brought together in a total (5)
22 The liquid of human kindness! (4)

Colossal Book of Crosswords

ACROSS

- **1** Happens (6)
- **4** Soft fabric (6)
- **9** Have joining in (7)
- **10** Measuring stick and king! (5)
- **11** Body part - courage! (5)
- **12** Funnel shaped wind (7)
- **13** Deciding - entering dim! (11)
- **18** Honoured or esteemed (7)
- **20** Grouping - sometimes in trade! (5)
- **22** Not friend! (5)
- **23** Solemn, sincere belief (7)
- **24** Type of car, area of land (6)
- **25** Shut (6)

DOWN

- **1** Allium Cepa - edible plant makes tears! (6)
- **2** Hide - front or back of a book? (5)
- **3** Take over and give rest (7)
- **5** Mistake (5)
- **6** Baddie! (7)
- **7** Overwhelming fear (6)
- **8** Decimal measures (11)
- **14** Least difficult (7)
- **15** Neither positive nor negative? (7)
- **16** Gentle wind (6)
- **17** Together (6)
- **19** Country (5)
- **21** Thoughts (5)

Colossal Book of Crosswords

ACROSS

7 Colours - pigment based (6)
8 Place something or someone came from (6)
9 Earlier in time than... (3)
10 Made a respone to a question (8)
11 Estimates (7)
13 More than one woman (5)
15 Normal (5)
16 No longer where it should be ? (7)
18 Touching stolen goods ? (8)
19 Unmarried female, wide of target ? (4)
21 Son of King ? (6)
22 Day of rest ? (6)

DOWN

1 Holiday container, legal proceeding (4)
2 Comprehension - transuding end ? (13)
3 Gets away, maybe from prison (7)
4 Aquatic bird - pinch bottom ? (5)
5 Needing time to complete (4-9)
6 Number (8)
12 On the next floor (8)
14 Largest (7)
17 Dismissed, like a gun ? (5)
20 Cleaning bar (4)

Colossal Book of Crosswords

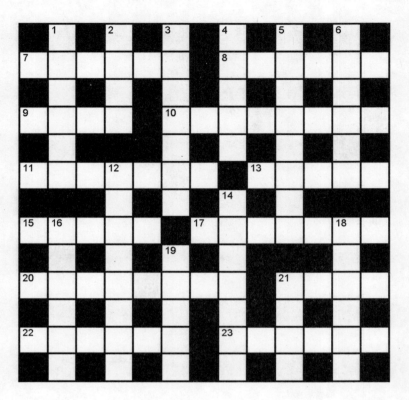

ACROSS

7 Yellow fruit (6)
8 Damaged, hurt (6)
9 Fabricated (4)
10 Shaking with fear ? (8)
11 Playfully vexing (especially by ridicule) (7)
13 Last ball in a cricket over (5)
15 Number of feet in a yard (5)
17 Altitudes - could be dizzy ? (7)
20 Farm vehicles (8)
21 Shellfish - seen dressed mainly ? (4)
22 Building adhesive - make firm friendship (6)
23 Health care workers (6)

DOWN

1 A ceremonial procession (6)
2 Can be audio, sello, or red ? (4)
3 Durable, as some friendships ? (7)
4 Straight up or down without a break (5)
5 Grasping hold of (8)
6 Say again (6)
12 Formal speaking to audience (8)
14 Learning periods, possibly at school (7)
16 More durable, more difficult (6)
18 Dealer - works on stock exchange ? (6)
19 Clothes for outdoor wear (5)
21 Foot complaint - cereal ! (4)

Colossal Book of Crosswords

ACROSS

7 Serious lack of food (6)
8 Tooth or bath coating (6)
9 Ice crystals forming white deposit - back emir ! (4)
10 Covering - often large flat areas (8)
11 Troops trained to fight on horseback (7)
13 Incorrect (5)
15 Donut shaped bread roll (5)
17 Huge (7)
20 Chemical used in fumigating (8)
21 Exchange (4)
22 Next to - like the sea ? (6)
23 Money lender who overcharges ! (6)

DOWN

1 A fancy dock for small yachts (6)
2 Huge heap - possibly of cash ? (4)
3 Time available for ease and relaxation (7)
4 Measure use of something, perhaps parking ? (5)
5 An ornamental flower garden (8)
6 A long flag; often tapering (6)
12 Taken before a meal as an appetizer (8)
14 Non professional (7)
16 Shrewdness shown by keen insight (6)
18 Cocktail mixer (6)
19 Place of security and rest (5)
21 Wrapped up tight and warm - like a rug bug ? (4)

ACROSS

7 Find (6)
8 Brave, larger than life (6)
9 Capital of Italy (4)
10 Digestive organs, puts up with (8)
11 Broke free (7)
13 Here is without apostrophe ! (5)
15 Before all others (5)
17 Statement that expresses opinion (7)
20 Taking top layer off - possibly financially ? (8)
21 Make reference to, and shame ? (4)
23 Father's brothers, to father's son (6)
24 Moving carefully, finishing strip (6)

DOWN

1 Done without others (4)
2 Photographic device (6)
3 Illness that comes with red spots (7)
4 Fire at, make movie footage ? (5)
5 Thick oil for smooth running (6)
6 Number (8)
12 Staying with or glueing to (8)
14 Cleared throat, possible with cold ? (7)
16 Not complicated (6)
18 Order the affairs of (6)
19 In the centre of (5)
22 The seat of the faculty of reason (4)

Colossal Book of Crosswords

ACROSS

7 Make one's way by force, strength (6)
8 Unmoving, also type of electricity (6)
9 New when combined , possibly with classical ? (3)
10 Spoken or written system of communication (8)
11 Altered for another use (7)
13 Man made waterway (5)
15 Smell - pleasant ! (5)
16 Ran at a moderately quick pace (7)
18 In a punctual manner (8)
19 Position or relative status (4)
21 Fixed number of lines of verse (6)
22 When made of steel you are courageous (6)

DOWN

1 Destroy by fire (4)
2 Background music - none impact mac ! (13)
3 Sweets made with fruit and gelatin (7)
4 Making use of (5)
5 Makers of something (13)
6 A state of dishonour (8)
12 Embellish, like a Christmas tree ! (8)
14 Coloured wax pencils (7)
17 Take illegally (5)
20 Requirement (4)

Colossal Book of Crosswords

ACROSS

1 Produce of chickens (4)
3 Rain protector (8)
9 Communications with a deity (7)
10 Liquid measure (5)
11 Alternate (5)
12 Line from centre to perimeter of circle (6)
14 Fraction and English Henry ? (6)
16 Not awake (6)
19 Strands that make up materials (6)
21 Country, famous for tea and rubber (5)
24 Possessed (5)
25 The results of a situation or circumstances (7)
26 Element - most abundant one in universe (8)
27 Part of tea service or tennis match ! (3)

DOWN

1 Working for a living (8)
2 Chart, sometimes drawn on squared paper (5)
4 Great unhappiness (6)
5 Decreed or governed (5)
6 Salad vegetable (7)
7 Measured space (4)
8 Acquired knowledge (6)
13 Seemingly (8)
15 Smile or grimace (7)
17 Females lower wear (6)
18 On to land (6)
20 Wireless ? (5)
22 Room entrance covers, often wooden (5)
23 The two of them ! (4)

Colossal Book of Crosswords

ACROSS

1 Food or ground maize (4)
3 Broad range of related ideas (8)
9 Rubbish (7)
10 Organs of smell (5)
11 Law of governmental principles (12)
13 Offensive (6)
15 Small area of standing water, often after rain (6)
17 Accounts that make things comprehensible (12)
20 Appliance that removes moisture - spin ? (5)
21 Condiment used on chips with salt ? (7)
22 All of us - even yore ! (8)
23 Social insects - best kept out of pants ! (4)

DOWN

1 One who practices magic (8)
2 Kitchen clothes cover - with strings ! (5)
4 A full supply of something (6)
5 Making or building (12)
6 React to something (7)
7 Sail support on boat (4)
8 Specifically distinguished from others (12)
12 Steps taken - assure me ! (8)
14 Cloth or material (7)
16 Rough or irregular (6)
18 Body part or church musical instrument (5)
19 Lazy, can be bone ! (4)

Colossal Book of Crosswords

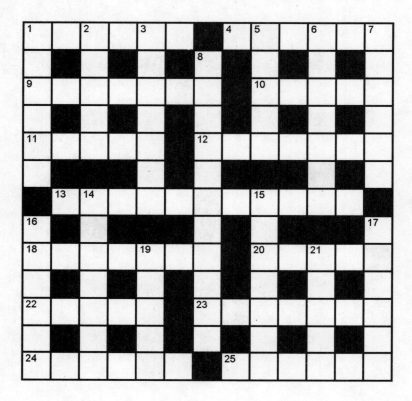

ACROSS

1 Entitlements (6)
4 Increased in temperature or affection (6)
9 Place to catch a train (7)
10 Vulcanised car wheel covers (5)
11 Verbalise, address (5)
12 Pain in the ear (7)
13 Most senior teacher in school (11)
18 Best grade, utmost position (7)
20 Male equivalent to aunt (5)
22 Respond to stimulus (5)
23 Loose woven material used in fishing (7)
24 Taking cover, good thrashing ? (6)
25 Went by bicycle (6)

DOWN

1 Hold off, turn down advances (6)
2 Short prayer before food (5)
3 Swindled, pulled a fast on ? (7)
5 Post, later on (5)
6 Any amazing or wonderful occurrence (7)
7 Taken without delay or made from rushes ? (6)
8 Arousing attention, exciting curiosity - sit entering! (11)
14 Country, part of United Kingdom (7)
15 Area outside of cities and towns (7)
16 Place of worship (6)
17 Price fixed by legislation, tent fixed ? (6)
19 Consumed (5)
21 Uncomfortably cool, sudden dread (5)

ACROSS

1 Take heed of or displayed poster (6)
4 Shuts (6)
9 Country (7)
10 Ship's payload (5)
11 Snap or take tea ! (5)
12 Wife's better half ? (7)
13 Woman whose children have children (11)
18 During the night of the present day (7)
20 Great, ace, first rate ! (5)
22 Sound (5)
23 Smoke stack (7)
24 Things seen (6)
25 United by being of the same opinion (6)

DOWN

1 Close to where we are (6)
2 Location other than here (5)
3 Domestic fowl (7)
5 Secures with a key, waterway feature (5)
6 Come to the top of the water, outer face (7)
7 Weapons, sometimes crossed ? (6)
8 Study of number (11)
14 Standing for office, moving quickly on foot (7)
15 Checking, trying out, difficult time ? (7)
16 Rolling pop group or mineral lumps ? (6)
17 Addressed a deity (6)
19 Large in size or number, more than usual (5)
21 One hundredth part of a pound (5)

Colossal Book of Crosswords

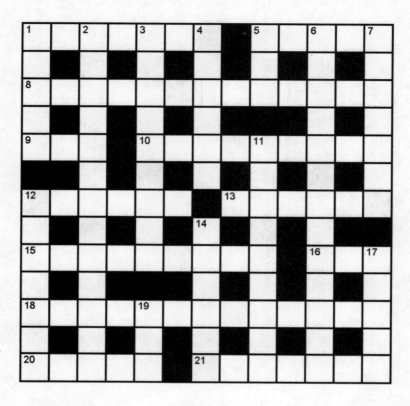

ACROSS

1 Number with a base of 10 (7)
5 Confronted (5)
8 Distance around circle (13)
9 Not me! (3)
10 Youngsters over 12 and under 20 (9)
12 Beetle or bug (6)
13 Fritters away (6)
15 Something said or written - testament (9)
16 Fire remains (3)
18 Books of knowledge (13)
20 Dirty (5)
21 No longer in existence (7)

DOWN

1 Go bad (5)
2 Facts surrounding a situation (13)
3 Facial hair (9)
4 Raised up (6)
5 In favour of (3)
6 Increased density - greater numbers? (13)
7 Female clothes (7)
11 Flat (9)
12 Alternative - in place of (7)
14 Distant - control device? (6)
17 Has not - less O (5)
19 Weep (3)

Colossal Book of Crosswords

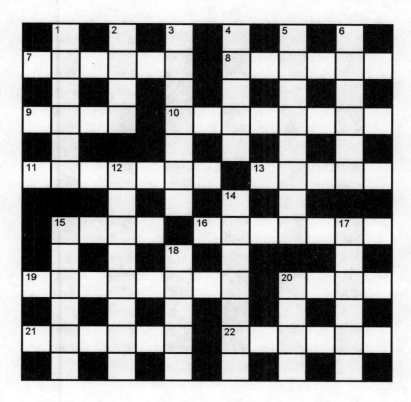

ACROSS

7 Vegetable (6)
8 Fear, type of scary film (6)
9 Capture by stealth (4)
10 With no noise (8)
11 What is left (7)
13 Reveals - public entertainments (5)
15 Electromagnetic radiation travels in these (4)
16 Broken up, shattered (7)
19 Type of church or religion (8)
20 Returning sound - little sir ? (4)
21 Great sadness (6)
22 Less difficult (6)

DOWN

1 Place where something comes from (6)
2 Tented accommodation (4)
3 Children of aunts or uncles (7)
4 Ledge or book support ? (5)
5 Tree parts - bank subdivisions ? (8)
6 To travel behind, go after, come after (6)
12 Unspecified place or destination (8)
14 Slapped or suggestive of something ? (7)
15 Rational motive, sense ? (6)
17 More than one of 20 across ! (6)
18 Reduces speed (5)
20 Relaxation, take your ....! (4)

Colossal Book of Crosswords

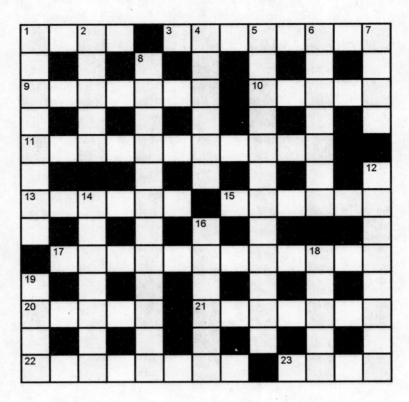

ACROSS

1 Clenched hand (4)
3 Relating to the armed forces (8)
9 Taking it easy (7)
10 Slang - television (5)
11 Garden device for carrying things! (11)
13 Story about mythical or supernatural beings (6)
15 Pointed implement - used in sewing (6)
17 How something is to be done - book ? (12)
20 Ship's payload (5)
21 Essential compounds we get from food - pointer! (7)
22 Spattered or spotted with water or dirt (8)
23 Rear part of aircraft or animal ? (4)

DOWN

1 Goodbye - all fewer! (8)
2 Work out solution to something (5)
4 Redskin - now native american (6)
5 Met at a point - crossed - sit centered! (12)
6 Permitted (7)
7 Toy on a string (2-2)
8 Statements that explain - explains nato! (12)
12 Occurring at or dependent on a particular season (8)
14 Non specific or rank ? (7)
16 Colour from blue and red (6)
18 Sung play? - or ape? (5)
19 Plays at something or parts of a play? (4)

Colossal Book of Crosswords

ACROSS

7 Tropical grass used in cane furniture (6)
8 An indulgence (6)
9 Wake someone or rotate with a spoon (4)
10 Rubbish, meaningless (8)
11 Furnish with, supply (7)
13 Did not, in short! (5)
15 Verbalise, use language (5)
16 Unusually great in size - semi men! (7)
18 Staying temporarily (8)
19 Stop confused spinning toys! (4)
21 Creatures - like human (6)
22 Number (6)

DOWN

1 Open fruit pie (4)
2 Shortenings - via barbitones (13)
3 Violent windstorm (7)
4 Oblique view (5)
5 Looking into by means of tests or trials (13)
6 Gives as a reward - or the rewards themselves! (8)
12 Fixed, mended (8)
14 Just think of it? (7)
17 Before all others (5)
20 Coal mines, the worst! (4)

Colossal Book of Crosswords

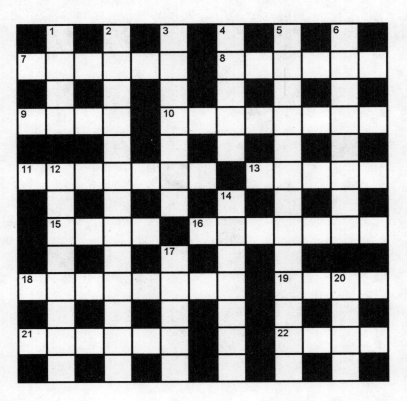

ACROSS

7 Pleasant arrangement of musical notes (6)
8 Robbery on the high seas (6)
9 Small nail and man's name - Pitt! (4)
10 A student's book or booklet containing problems with spaces for solving them (8)
11 One who sees an event - could be legal! (7)
13 With a sudden onset (5)
15 Musical instrument (4)
16 Pleated material or frill used as decoration (7)
18 Write or draw aimlessly or quickly (8)
19 A long narrative poem telling of a hero's deeds (4)
21 An anticipated outcome (6)
22 Eager, enthusiastic, desirous (4)

DOWN

1 Have on, as clothes - abrasion! (4)
2 Anniversary celebration - jug old beeline! (6,7)
3 Cleaning liquid for the eyes (3-4)
4 1960s abstract art form - optical art - in short! (2,3)
5 One of the symbols 1,2,3,4,5,6,7,8,9,0 (6,7)
6 Word square puzzle - so arctic! (8)
12 Offensive to good taste - especially sexual (8)
14 Reaction to exposure - like hay fever (7)
17 Die away, slack off (5)
20 Wading bird in male rib issue! (4)

ACROSS

7 Higher in temperature (6)
8 Less attractive (6)
9 Fruit of broad, green, french and runner plant! (4)
10 Spots of water or paint - less haps! (8)
11 Spectacles or drinking vessels (7)
13 Snatches hold of (5)
15 Dust covered - also Springfield, singer! (5)
17 Grafters, doers, proletarians ? (7)
20 Engrossed in cogitation - ink thing! (8)
21 Plenty of offerings at auction (4)
23 Power plant - nee gin! (6)
24 Outer covers of cartridge or mollusc (6)

DOWN

1 Travelled on horseback (4)
2 Supports for hats or cakes (6)
3 Female clothing items (7)
4 Applies force to move object towards itself (5)
5 Nearer (6)
6 Recall knowledge from memory (8)
12 Showing or feeling mirth or pleasure (8)
14 Having greater length than any other (7)
16 Game with service and advantages (6)
18 Murderer (6)
19 Sorted according to dimensions (5)
22 Not short - lofty! (4)

Colossal Book of Crosswords

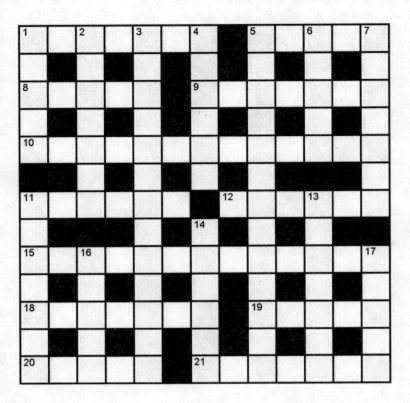

ACROSS

1 Punishment intended as a warning to others (7)
5 A thin crisp slice of potato fried in deep fat (5)
8 Seabirds (5)
9 The real thing (7)
10 Standing above others in character or attainment (13)
11 Excavated reminder of previous age (6)
12 Debate - increased in temperature! (6)
15 Food coolers (13)
18 The first letter of a word (especially a person's name) (7)
19 Copy, of a magazine, or dispute (5)
20 Matter in non solid or liquid form (5)
21 Century (7)

DOWN

1 Moved cautiously along - finished neatly! (5)
2 Books of maps (7)
3 Potential prospects - I spoilt ibises! (13)
4 Affiance, occupy, retain, mesh (6)
5 Thoughtfulness (13)
6 From Ireland (5)
7 Begged - possibly for mercy ? (7)
11 Cultivating the land (7)
13 Half a man's lower garment (7)
14 Riches (6)
16 Two winged insects and fisherman's lures (5)
17 Rapidity (5)

Colossal Book of Crosswords

ACROSS

7 Look for something (6)
8 Not flat or smooth (6)
9 Original thought ? (4)
10 Result or reaction (8)
11 Man's top garment (5)
12 Written work (5)
14 Top of the milk (5)
15 Financial - gained through work (6)
17 People of a town or city (8)
18 Children's playthings (4)
20 Sparkles, as if polished (6)
21 Supermarket shopping carrier (6)

DOWN

1 Unwanted plant, illegal plant ? (4)
2 Group of people who work together (12)
3 Requiring a drink (7)
4 Sudden happening - or pipe breach! (5)
5 Presentation of how to do something (13)
6 Convince by argument (8)
11 In an unwavering line (8)
13 Thickness - destiny rewritten! (7)
16 Can be common or non! (5)
19 Part of an egg (4)

Colossal Book of Crosswords

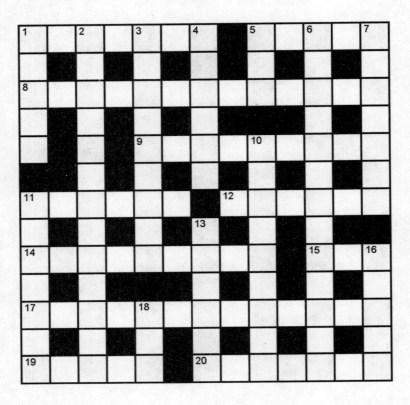

ACROSS

1 Fireworks (7)
5 Woven grain bags (5)
8 Distance round a circle (13)
9 Most attractive (9)
11 An organised structure - yes MST! (6)
12 Missive or part of the alphabet (6)
14 Flat (9)
15 Curve or electrical conduction (3)
17 Books of knowledge (13)
19 In need of a clean - study reorganised! (5)
20 Draws out, lengthens (7)

DOWN

1 Road full of hardship or trials (5)
2 Condition in life (13)
3 Things needed to do a job - men piquet! (9)
4 Undergo or be subjected to (6)
5 Title (3)
6 Complete attention; intense mental effort (13)
7 Having more sugar ? (7)
10 Medical regime for cure of ills - enter matt! (9)
11 Plant from the sea (7)
13 Take away of wash off (6)
16 Boxes of wine or holiday clothes (5)
18 Weep, shout! (3)

Colossal Book of Crosswords

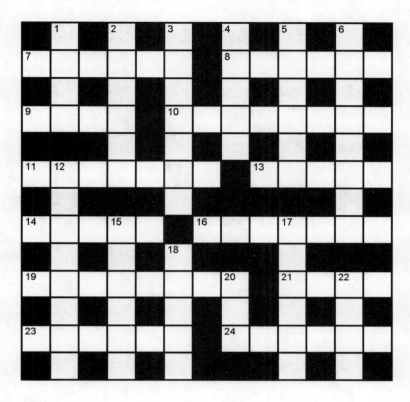

ACROSS

7 Fighting in a ring (6)
8 Fruit and colour (6)
9 Sues confused - makes use of! (4)
10 Putting into sequence - i ssuing command (8)
11 Exhibiting - sometimes off! (7)
13 Partner of gander (5)
14 Finished (5)
16 Largest (7)
19 Snoozing, kipping, like dogs let lie! (8)
21 Enthusiasm, eagerness (4)
23 A state of agitation - confusing tuners! (6)
24 A person of no influence - yon bod! (6)

DOWN

1 Could be top of the .... ? (4)
2 Puzzle with cut out pieces (6)
3 Where a boat might run ? (7)
4 Small lakes (5)
5 Arrangement of hair, coiffure - Ah Dior! (6)
6 Muscles that contract while others relax - to assign! (8)
12 Picking up and touching - stolen property ? (8)
15 Number of legs at a bingo hall ? (6)
17 Garden structure (6)
18 Raises up, elevators (5)
20 Alcoholic spirit with tonic ? (3)
22 Brings together mathematically (4)

ACROSS

7 Associate, member of your class (6)
8 Indicates time. CK LOCO! (6)
9 Weaving machine (4)
10 Machine mender (8)
11 Not acknowledged (7)
13 Book in Bible - monarchs (5)
15 Metal or wood fixing device (5)
17 Biggest (7)
20 Position (8)
21 Infant (4)
22 Were Not, shortly (6)
23 Not unusual (6)

DOWN

1 Feel at home with (6)
2 Fruit (4)
3 Back stroker? (7)
4 Make physical contact with (5)
5 Removing dirt from (8)
6 Playing a part - on stage perhaps (6)
12 Works - as a piece of machinery (8)
14 Ball firing old guns (7)
16 Prepared for eating by applying heat (6)
18 Underground (6)
19 Unclean (5)
21 Tree outer - sounds like a dog! (4)

Colossal Book of Crosswords

ACROSS

7 Go without food (6)
8 Give pleasure to, manners! (6)
9 Short grandmother (4)
10 Devices - me in cash! (8)
11 Groundnuts - not much pay! (7)
13 Doing words (5)
15 Stiff, could be bored (5)
16 Happier, cheerier, the more the better? (7)
18 Cold blooded vertebrate (8)
19 Fishing devices, also used in football! (4)
21 Returning sounds (6)
22 Lags behind, path or track (6)

DOWN

1 Heavenly body, actress ? (4)
2 The way that words are said (13)
3 Crash headgear (7)
4 The final frontier - confused capes? (5)
5 The largest inland sea; between Europe and Africa and Asia (13)
6 Put together, build (8)
12 Proof, presented in court (8)
14 Thickness, number in a given space (7)
17 Damn and ..... explosion ? (5)
20 Speak, chat, converse - maybe small? (4)

Colossal Book of Crosswords

ACROSS

7 Amount broken or cost of something (6)

8 Indulgence, sumptuous (6)

9 Follow, like a private detective (4)

10 Splashing feet in the water at the seaside ? (8)

11 Grazing land (7)

13 Angry, like a hot bun! (5)

15 Ran for office - so tod! (5)

17 More discoloured by impurities - me druid! (7)

20 Carefully thought out in advance - with ruler ? (8)

21 Untruths (4)

22 Knowledge kept from others - see crt! (6)

23 Is equivalent to, comes to, is the sum of (6)

DOWN

1 Country (6)

2 Shout (4)

3 Could be game or goal? (7)

4 Fly an engineless aircraft? (5)

5 Travelled or penetrated into unknown territory, (8)

6 Swimming pants! (6)

12 Normal pants! (8)

14 Pools of water, often left after rain (7)

16 Topics of a discussion or conversation (6)

18 Spread equally, divided fairly (6)

19 What you swear to tell in court (5)

21 Noisy (4)

Colossal Book of Crosswords

ACROSS

1 As well as, in addition to, plus (4)
3 Newspaper and watcher (8)
9 Felt with hand or through emotions (7)
10 Painting support (5)
11 Exterior part of packing, end of router (5)
12 Kind of car - shooting brake (6)
14 Intook air suddenly or noisily - sad peg! (6)
16 Noon (6)
19 Country (6)
21 Carried in ships - go car! (5)
24 Perfect, like an exhibited home? (5)
25 To a great extent or degree (7)
26 Acts like, feigns, shams (8)
27 Dalmations, collies and labradors are all these (4)

DOWN

1 Despite the fact that - hot laugh! (8)
2 Dangerous feat - usually for cinema (5)
4 Emblems worn to show membership or rank (6)
5 Happening - nee TV! (5)
6 Went to see, possibly in hospital? (7)
7 Part in play or film to be played (4)
8 Ask money for, rush impetuously (6)
13 Two words that can be interchanged (8)
15 Tight fit - constrict (7)
17 Measuring units (6)
18 Tatty, untidy, like trousered philanthropist? (6)
20 Work out, as a mystery or crossword clue (5)
22 The number of X to Y (5)
23 Not firm, walking impediment (4)

Colossal Book of Crosswords

ACROSS

7 Good turn, do me one... (6)
8 Not vegetable or mineral - lamina! (6)
9 Cut hair short (4)
10 Observing - gin and tonic mixed (8)
11 Exhausting or having clothes on? (7)
13 In the middle of, amidst (5)
15 Say clearly, part of USA? (5)
16 Maximum lightness - he twist! (7)
18 A territorial possession controlled by a ruling state (8)
19 City in SE France - pleasant or agreeable (4)
21 Go quickly - on a horse (6)
22 Get up and go - gen rye! (6)

DOWN

1 Equitable, reasonable, sometimes with firm? (4)
2 In a relative manner - paralytic move! (13)
3 Pressing clothes (7)
4 Unpleasant (5)
5 State or condition - succint mares! (13)
6 Cautions (8)
12 Outside (8)
14 Robbers (7)
17 Breaks, possibly photographs? (5)
20 Animal restrainer (4)

Colossal Book of Crosswords

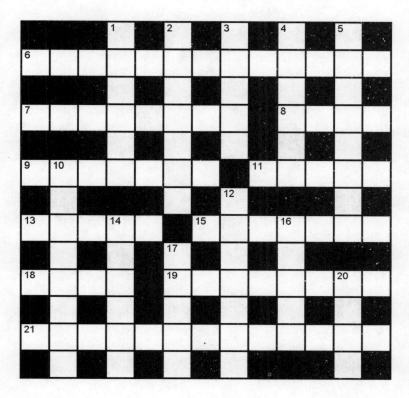

ACROSS

6 Rational thought, agreement, sympathy (13)
7 A molehill blown out of proportion? (8)
8 Keen on something, going is entering! (4)
9 Looks at with great interest (7)
11 Once more, repeat (5)
13 Possibly, perhaps (5)
15 Tunnel - apes sag! (7)
18 Pierced by a bullet or fired from a gun (4)
19 Rain protector, used by Mary Poppins (8)
21 Approval or support - game encounter! (13)

DOWN

1 Wrote or put into cage! (6)
2 Gets away (7)
3 Periods of wet weather ? (5)
4 Combining together mathematically (6)
5 A thing of any kind (8)
10 Passing on knowledge, in the classroom? (8)
12 Vegetable (7)
14 Clothes fastener (6)
16 Gas formed by water boiling (5)
17 Look after, possibly with your life! (5)
20 Rail track (4)

Colossal Book of Crosswords

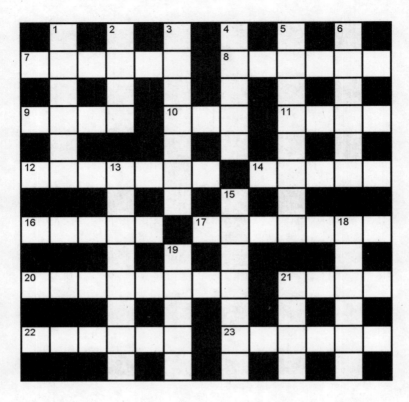

ACROSS

7 Doing your best, difficult (6)
8 Fruits (6)
9 One face (4)
10 Frozen water (3)
11 500 sheets of paper (4)
12 Most wet (7)
14 Cycles (5)
16 Waves left by boat, funeral v igils (5)
17 Having the greatest length (7)
20 How far something is from something else! (8)
21 Set fire to something (4)
22 Solid pressed milk curd (6)
23 Sampled, as food would be (6)

DOWN

1 Get there - via err! (6)
2 Bake in a kiln, sack someone (4)
3 Anti, in opposition to - as giant! (7)
4 Fabricates, builds (5)
5 Giving one a chance - go sprint! (8)
6 Came into existence - mac bee! (6)
13 Places where plays are performed (8)
15 Particular points in time (7)
18 Viewing area for films (6)
19 Beneath (5)
21 Bottom support in rub a serpent game! (4)

Colossal Book of Crosswords

ACROSS

7 In the direction of (6)
8 Directed one's gaze towards something (6)
9 Come together, satisfy condition (4)
10 Arriving at a destination - in charge! (8)
11 Most difficult , most gruelling (7)
13 Stranger than fiction they say! (5)
15 Grows thin, like an old joke (5)
17 Every night (7)
20 Metallic element - atomic number 30 (4)
21 Egg cell (3)
22 Particles that settle on furniture (4)
24 Proper version of can't! (6)
25 Meal (6)

DOWN

1 Tying material, thicker than string (4)
2 Went their separate ways, like curtains! (6)
3 Where you live (7)
4 Free from impurities - lance! (5)
5 Female parent (6)
6 Just after the birth of a child - to anneal! (8)
12 From the USA (8)
14 Sorcerers or magicians (7)
16 Moving quickly, possibly as a contest (6)
18 Concealing oneself, good thrashing! (6)
19 Compass point (5)
23 Wimbledon ranking (4)

Colossal Book of Crosswords

ACROSS

7 The one who comes first in a race (6)
8 Nothing out of the ordinary (6)
9 Not there! (4)
10 Level place where cars and trains pass (8)
11 Cut with or as if with scissors (7)
13 Church ringers (5)
16 Not dirty (5)
17 Royal persons collectively (7)
19 Hugging, holding close affectionately (8)
20 Keen on something or someone (4)
22 Produced a literary work (6)
23 Ammunition or bird's egg cover (6)

DOWN

1 Exhaust someone by confusing rite! (4)
2 Comprehend (10)
3 Farm vehicle (7)
4 Vegetable to make you cry! (5)
5 Greek deity, son of Aphrodite (4)
6 Glove with long sleeve - thrown down? (8)
12 Decorated with pigments (8)
14 Test administrator (8)
15 Something sung! (4)
18 Discovers (5)
21 Speak - use language (4)

Colossal Book of Crosswords

ACROSS

1 Leafy weed or harbour loading area (4)
3 Completes (8)
9 Weather conditions - metical! (7)
10 The courage to carry on (5)
11 Bread or swiss or half of car ? (5)
12 Bigger (6)
15 Cut into three equal parts (6)
17 Having a practical function (6)
20 Reflexive from of "it" - stifle! (6)
22 Top room in house (5)
25 Irritate (5)
26 Impersonate (7)
27 More attractive than... (8)
28 Communists? Under the bed ? (4)

DOWN

1 Adorn with colour or flowers for example (8)
2 Uncomfortably cool (5)
4 Beliefs or models of excellence (6)
5 Located inside, like a cycle tyre tube (5)
6 Of a female (3)
7 Part of plant, stop flow of blood! (4)
8 Was successful in exam or test (6)
13 Fairy that is somewhat mischievous (3)
14 Slowly moving masses of ice (8)
16 Acute, vivid - set nine! (7)
18 Radio noise or electricity (6)
19 Place of work (6)
21 Country (5)
23 Separate the fibers of - provoke (5)
24 Live in a tent (4)

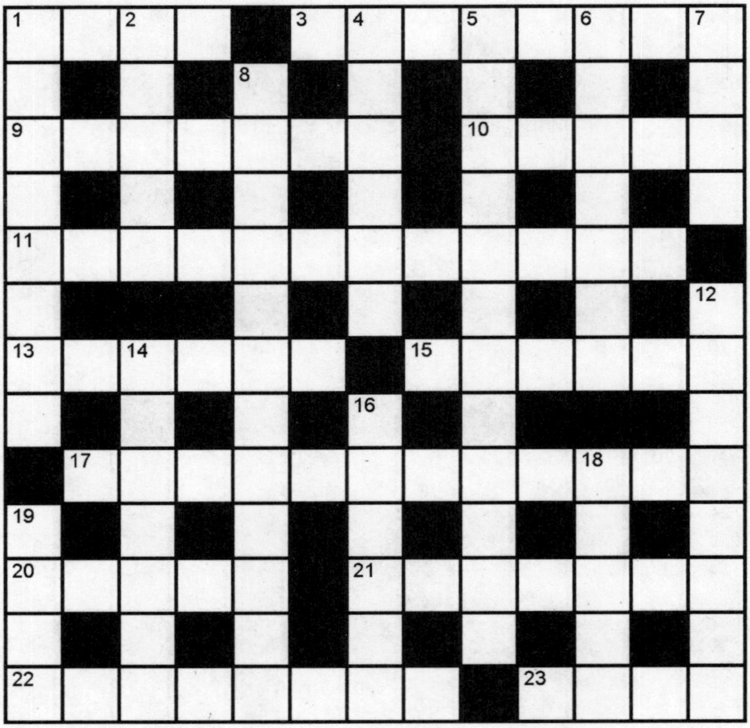

ACROSS

1 Wet thoroughly (4)
3 Went before (8)
9 Landing place (7)
10 having connections with Navy (5)
11 On purpose (12)
13 Not long ago (6)
15 Horse perhaps or woollen garment? (6)
17 Directions (12)
20 Carried goods (5)
21 Male sibling (7)
22 Catastrophe (8)
23 Not a lie (4)

DOWN

1 Criterion (8)
2 Month (5)
4 Send back (6)
5 Building (12)
6 Generate gradually (7)
7 Not shiny (4)
8 Underwear or lock opening numbers! (12)
12 Jam (8)
14 Middles (7)
16 Meek and modest (6)
18 Different - he rot! (5)
19 Chemical that burns (4)

Colossal Book of Crosswords

ACROSS

7 Change for the better (6)
8 What an item costs to purchase (5)
9 Smallest part of an element (4)
10 Place to see a play (7)
11 A personal belief or judgment that is not founded on proof or certainty (7)
13 Door openers (5)
15 Covered entrance (5)
16 Fastened or made firm (7)
18 Toward the East (8)
19 Breathe deeply and heavily (4)
21 Nearly (6)
22 Required or wanted (6)

DOWN

1 Found at the end of the ankles (4)
2 Connection between people or places (13)
3 Feelings (7)
4 Rapidity (5)
5 Standing above others - disguised hint! (13)
6 Look like (8)
12 Without much doubt (8)
14 Deflecting, possibly the rules? (7)
17 Open pastries - possibly custard? (5)
20 Colour - black and white mixed (4)

Colossal Book of Crosswords

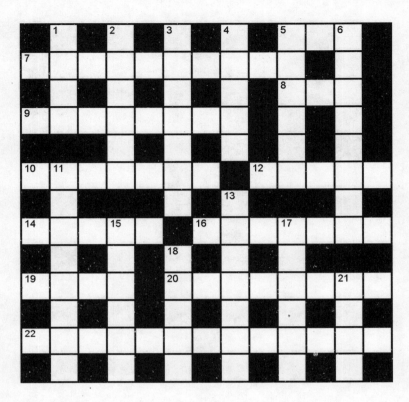

ACROSS

5 Woman's name - gardener? (3)
7 Comprehend (10)
8 Period of time (3)
9 Type of bicycle (8)
10 Flowers (7)
12 Repeat, once more (5)
14 Dull colour (5)
16 Inventor of mechanical computer - beg baba! (7)
19 Cooker (4)
20 Extra hours worked or paid for (8)
22 From or between other countries (13)

DOWN

1 Unfasten (4)
2 Game played at Wimbledon (6)
3 Gets away (7)
4 Place where ghosts hang out? (5)
5 Putting together, possibly numbers (6)
6 A thing of any kind - any night! (8)
11 Getting there (8)
13 Mother and father (7)
15 Season (6)
17 Garment fastener - for pressing? (6)
18 Noise (5)
21 Tight fisted (4)

Colossal Book of Crosswords

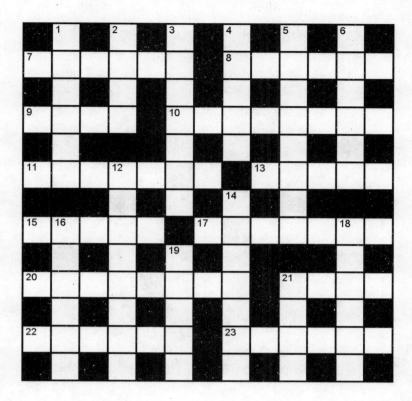

ACROSS

7 A short period caught in time - magic? (6)
8 Something done - a tonic! (6)
9 Gets old, for a long time (4)
10 Written down or taped - red decor! (8)
11 Put down in words (7)
13 Half a century (5)
15 Stands high above, column (5)
17 Largest (7)
20 Was of some import, it counted (8)
21 Sprinkle clouds with silver iodide particles to cause rain (4)
22 Controlling influences - we pros! (6)
23 Begins, jumps in fright? (6)

DOWN

1 Having more length (6)
2 Vegetable plots or sleeping places (4)
3 Began, commenced (7)
4 Month with hares! (5)
5 Beginning, commencing (8)
6 Land that is covered with trees (6)
12 The roaring .... US history! (8)
14 Most wild (7)
16 Speaker (6)
18 Confections (6)
19 Hair, tooth, with the law? (5)
21 Break with a crack (4)

Colossal Book of Crosswords

ACROSS

7 Owning, possessing (6)
8 Permits (6)
9 Little grandmother (4)
10 Putting things in sequences (8)
11 Was suggestive of something - deck sam! (7)
13 Assertion of a right, stake it! (5)
15 Brought together (5)
17 Tube of meat (7)
20 Large grey creature (8)
21 Second hand (4)
23 Bumps or defames (6)
24 Precipitated - cats and dogs? (6)

DOWN

1 Reasonable, travelling show (4)
2 Meal eaten outdoors (6)
3 Pretended not to see - eroding! (7)
4 Girl or boy's name - from a beach? (5)
5 More than one (6)
6 Moving to and fro suspended from above (8)
12 Of no exceptional quality or ability (8)
14 Concerns that should be set straight (7)
16 Anticipate (6)
18 Without much intelligence (6)
19 Be the reason for some event or happening (5)
22 Not at all odd! (4)

Colossal Book of Crosswords

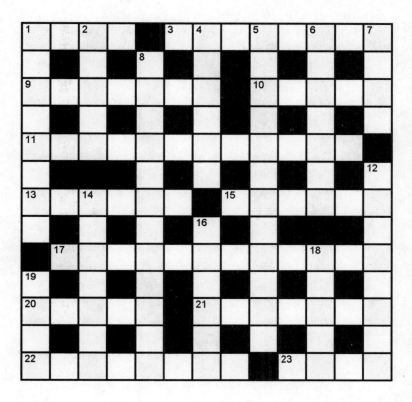

ACROSS

1 Charts - spam returning! (4)
3 Worked or performed surgery (8)
9 Particular branch of knowledge - nice sec! (7)
10 Fast, rapid (5)
11 Musical or written works (12)
13 Giving weapons to (6)
15 Bachelor level qualification (6)
17 Test version of something, model? (12)
20 Entertain with light wit (5)
21 Comes to rest, on long wooden benches? (7)
22 Inhaled and exhaled (8)
23 Make use of (4)

DOWN

1 Instrument player (8)
2 Glass block to bend light (5)
4 Characterised by romantic imagery (6)
5 Needs (12)
6 Diluting agent - with no excess flesh! (7)
7 A British peer of the highest rank (4)
8 A formal public statement - nun men at once! (12)
12 Successfully completed or brought to an end (8)
14 Combination - could be cake (7)
16 Paper product, possibly of lies? (6)
18 Discussions or negotiations (5)
19 Baby sheep (4)

ACROSS

7 Old car or birth sign chart (6)
8 Remove baggage - do luna! (6)
9 Against, maybe blood sports or depressant! (4)
10 Chart or plan out (3)
11 Part of eye and woman's name (4)
12 Hair coil (7)
14 Heron - greet! (5)
17 Normal, not out of the ordinary (5)
18 Someone forced to join up - conscript (7)
20 Atmosphere (8)
21 Roman - 15th of March, May, July, October (4)
23 Surrender, throw in the sponge (4,2)
24 Give pleasure to (6)

DOWN

1 Midday (4)
2 Box, usually metal, with drawers in office (6,7)
3 To move about or proceed hurriedly (7)
4 Short and fat, pudgy, chunky - my pud! (5)
5 Airborne man in uniform? - foreign cliffy! (6,7)
6 Wise men (4)
13 Inability to sleep (8)
15 The organ of sight (3)
16 Stop something before it starts (3-4)
19 Generally incompetent (5)
22 Move gently or carefully - state of leisure (4)

Colossal Book of Crosswords

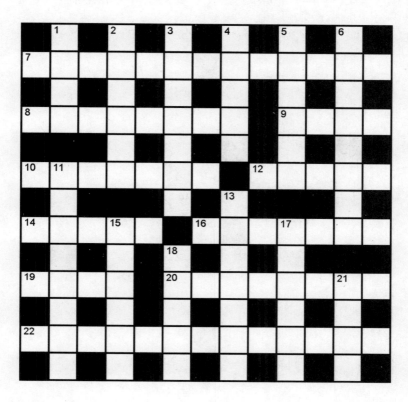

ACROSS

7 Possibilities due to a favourable combination of circumstances (13)
8 Drink or frozen water missile (8)
9 Something that orbits the Earth (4)
10 Accommodation for horses (7)
12 Sea (5)
14 Mad made waterway (5)
16 Lived, or lived at a low level - diet sex! (7)
19 Narrow strip of land that just out to sea (4)
20 Make a strenuous or laboured effort (8)
22 The act of passing information (13)

DOWN

1 Ready for business! (4)
2 Fly catching device produced by spider (6)
3 Cooked by steam - moved ahead hard and fast (7)
4 Went down on knees (5)
5 Nuclear, minute - aim cot! (6)
6 Drink (8)
11 Small kitchen measure (8)
13 Pull out, like a tooth (7)
15 Season (6)
17 Views, often seen on holiday (6)
18 Making use of something or someone (5)
21 Jungle cat (4)

Colossal Book of Crosswords

ACROSS

7 Ruthless, extreme and violent (6)
8 Book consumer? (6)
9 Three of these make a yard (4)
10 Roaring period of American history (8)
11 Kicking football from one player to another (7)
14 Shellfish (5)
16 Listens to what is said (5)
18 Medical people (7)
21 Places where food is prepared (8)
22 Crazy or metal fasteners! (4)
24 Coupled, matched, mated (6)
25 Number (6)

DOWN

1 One face, spin on snooker ball (4)
2 Expresses in writing (6)
3 Bottom or place to put it! (4)
4 Has a go - sometimes at one's patience! (5)
5 More quickly (6)
6 Recall, bring back to mind (8)
12 From the USA (8)
13 Negative (2)
15 Scary creature, very large! (7)
17 Music disc of old - commit sounds to media (6)
19 Underground passage (6)
20 Gives nourishment to (5)
23 Digits of the foot - to stand on the line? (4)

Colossal Book of Crosswords

ACROSS

7 One who operates a boat ? (6)
8 Country (6)
9 Makes hole - cheap lodgings (4)
10 Financial outgoings (8)
11 Clearly apparent or obvious (7)
13 Controlled a motor vehicle (5)
15 Number of degrees at a corner? (5)
17 Male person found in the park! (2)
18 A person considered as a unique individual (4)
20 Breaking free from (8)
21 Weaving device (4)
23 Wrote or put into captivity (6)
24 Revealing names - and possibly shaming? (6)

DOWN

1 Car you pay to travel in (4)
2 Fastened or shut down (6)
3 Gift or maybe current time? (7)
4 Finished or completed (5)
5 Dealer (6)
6 Festival, travelling show, procession (8)
12 Disappeared (8)
14 A solicitation for money or food (7)
16 Acquires knowledge (6)
18 Dignified and sombre - lemons confused! (6)
19 Look after something (5)
22 Possesses (4)

Colossal Book of Crosswords

ACROSS

1 Imperial measure (4)
3 Learned persons (8)
9 Strength, bravery (7)
10 Front of body, also wooden container (5)
11 Keen. Sus it nice hat! (12)
13 Mouse noise, needs oiling? (6)
15 Fruit in salad? (6)
17 Books of words (12)
20 Smell (5)
21 Columns (7)
22 Thoughts from the past (8)
23 In sets of 10 (4)

DOWN

1 Make more or bigger (8)
2 Legal place (5)
4 Type of card - good standing (6)
5 Sometimes (12)
6 USA (7)
7 Tess is confused by tennis word! (4)
8 Maker (12)
12 Is made up of... (8)
14 The same, even, clothes of the group (7)
16 Two of, join together (6)
18 Picture, representation (5)
19 Explosive sound, long arm (4)

Colossal Book of Crosswords

ACROSS

7 Make possible for someone - baleen! (6)
8 Take over - keep busy with (6)
9 Up and down child's toy - with string! (2-2)
10 Awful, like Ivan (8)
11 Large body of frozen water in sea (7)
13 Start (5)
15 Facial expression of displeasure (5)
17 A journey usually by ship (7)
20 Errors (8)
21 Travel on foot (4)
23 Marked by friendly companionship (6)
24 Interior of garments - filling pockets with cash? (6)

DOWN

1 Unfasten (4)
2 Soak up, like a sponge? (6)
3 Correspondence - after your name? (7)
4 Legal or tennis location (5)
5 Busy (6)
6 Forming words with letters in right place! (8)
12 Enclosed passageway in train or house (8)
14 Small container possibly in space (7)
16 Enclosed (6)
18 Working with needle and thread (6)
19 Ability at a task (5)
22 Connection, nexus (4)

Colossal Book of Crosswords

ACROSS

7 Political party - now new? (6)
8 Imperial weights (6)
9 Sounds a cat makes, trendy street? (4)
10 Boney structure (8)
11 An enlisted man or woman who serves in an army (7)
13 Tale (5)
15 Rotates with a spoon (5)
16 Wants, especially sexually? (7)
18 Area (8)
19 Unmarried female (4)
21 Previously (6)
22 Number between one and one hundred (6)

DOWN

1 Contributed to a cause (4)
2 Thoughtfulness, kind regard (13)
3 Artists or cleaners' equipment (7)
4 Offensively curious or inquisitive - parker! (5)
5 Amusement (13)
6 Supply tools or materials for a job (8)
12 Sketched, explained briefly (8)
14 A formally arranged gathering (7)
17 Bee houses - skin problem (5)
20 Take a seat (3)

ACROSS

1 An actor's portrayal of someone in a play (4)
3 Intelligent having been to school? (8)
9 One who studies (7)
10 Requirements (5)
11 Accomplishments (12)
13 Noblemen having rank equal to British earls (6)
15 Suddenly be there - seems to be? (6)
17 All-in-one shops (12)
20 An established line of travel or access (5)
21 Come out of something alive (7)
22 Hilly land (5)
23 Is not without a letter o (4)

DOWN

1 Look into something deeply (8)
2 Express mirth or joy, good fun (5)
4 Work that you are obliged to perform (6)
5 Belonging to the present time (12)
6 Play centre? (7)
7 Just after sunset (4)
8 All the same - in spite of that - yet (12)
12 Possibility - outlook - expectation (8)
14 Strange (7)
16 Made laugh (6)
18 Ways out - sometimes for emergencies (5)
19 Part of larch forest is curved feature (4)

Colossal Book of Crosswords

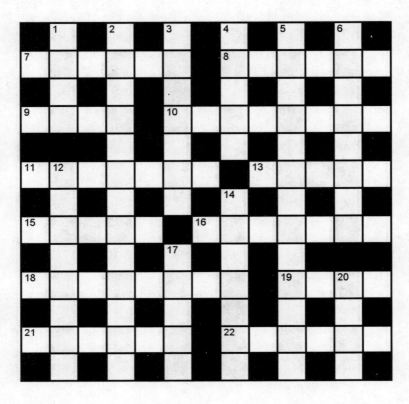

ACROSS

7 The way in which one does something (6)
8 Shuts (6)
9 At this place (4)
10 The very latest, the most up to date (8)
11 The night of the first performance (7)
13 Beneath (5)
15 Footwear (5)
16 Put through chemical change (7)
18 Lacking general education or knowledge (8)
19 Ripped through (4)
21 Discussion, sometimes political (6)
22 Strikingly strange or unusual (6)

DOWN

1 Extreme dislike (4)
2 Concerning many nations (13)
3 Falling out over something, disagreeing (7)
4 Sudden sharp onset - like appendicitis (5)
5 Information sent or received - I cut common ani! (13)
6 Unable to settle (8)
12 Turned over field (8)
14 Put down in words (7)
17 Payments made to support government (5)
20 water falling from the skies! (4)

Colossal Book of Crosswords

ACROSS

1 Italian city (4)
3 Visible light (8)
9 Speak very quietly (7)
10 Knocks against with some force (5)
11 The amount of one thing to another (5)
12 Arm filled part of garment (6)
14 Defence for poor behaviour (6)
16 Country (6)
19 What a mountaineer does - possibly socially? (6)
21 Beat (5)
24 Does as bidden (5)
25 One horned mythical horse (7)
26 Administrative units of government (8)
27 Being nothing more than specified - reem? (4)

DOWN

1 Paid for services - catching bad guys? (8)
2 Damp (5)
4 Expression or musical passage (6)
5 Thick, strong, twisted rope (5)
6 Taken away (7)
7 Thin fog near the ground (4)
8 Kitchen protective wear (6)
13 Make known to the public (8)
15 Place of further or higher education (7)
17 Inside, possibly a space of time (6)
18 Take control of - possibly another's identity (6)
20 Sounds made by instruments (5)
22 Large northern deer - called Elk in Europe (5)
23 Settee (4)

Colossal Book of Crosswords

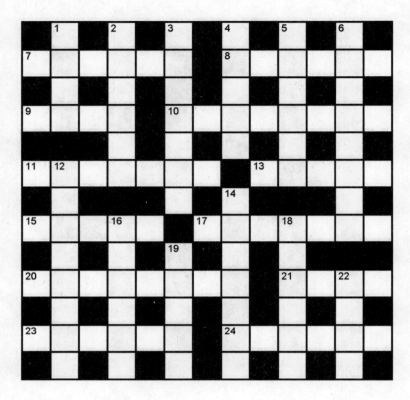

ACROSS

7 Less wealthy than others (6)
8 Said (6)
9 Counting blocks between units and hundreds (4)
10 Gifts (8)
11 Small wild flowers (7)
13 Making use of (5)
15 Appears to be - looks like (5)
17 Making greater sound than others (7)
20 Seven figure numbers (8)
21 Away from home or business (4)
23 Father or mother (6)
24 Baker's dozen less two (6)

DOWN

1 Funny story or remark (4)
2 Fried thin potato slices (6)
3 Removed from the team, slipped from the hands (7)
4 Inquired about (5)
5 Drying cloths found in bathrooms (6)
6 Prison term or spoken set of words (8)
12 From America (8)
14 Scary creature (7)
16 Made runny by application of heat (6)
18 Parts of a whole, with stocks maybe? (6)
19 Days in September plus 10 (5)
22 A long time to wait - historic periods (4)

Colossal Book of Crosswords

ACROSS

7 The air that is inhaled and exhaled in respiration (6)
8 Sung plays (6)
9 Doing word (4)
10 From the states (8)
11 Against; expressing opposition to (7)
13 Own up as guilty of something (5)
15 Undersea skeletons forming reef (5)
17 Someone you have faith or confidence in (7)
20 Natives of a state or nation (8)
21 Possesses (4)
23 Comport oneself properly (6)
24 From a country or area (6)

DOWN

1 A tall perennial woody plant (4)
2 Woody tropical grass (6)
3 Short musical passages - shapers! (7)
4 Loose flowing garments (5)
5 Space of time, american full stop (6)
6 Special interest reading matter, bullet holder (8)
12 Undertook to do, gave commitment (8)
14 Gift or show (7)
16 Creature that is not bird or fish (6)
18 Trousers that end at or above the knee (6)
19 Less (5)
22 Armed force or blue colour (4)

Colossal Book of Crosswords

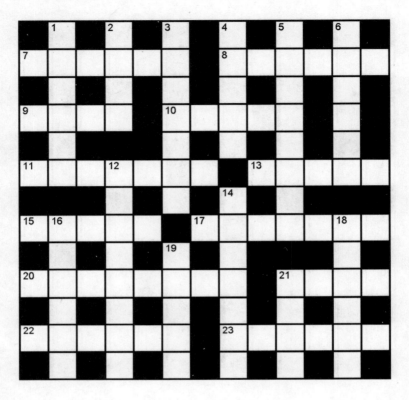

ACROSS

7 Injury, harm or hurt (6)
8 Pictures (6)
9 There's one at the North and another at the South? (4)
10 River in north of England (5)
11 Go ahead, follow course (7)
13 Unwanted flowers (5)
15 A committee appointed to judge a competition (5)
17 Having highest temperature (7)
20 Two persons working together or married (8)
21 Cause to go somewhere, like a letter maybe? (4)
22 Stopped by pulling - horse! (6)
23 Rubber line remover (6)

DOWN

1 Promote over another (6)
2 Friend or marriage partner? (4)
3 Not one nor the other (7)
4 Bird watchers' hidden places (5)
5 Being the greatest distance away (8)
6 Story of supernatural event (6)
12 Making, building (8)
14 Adult male chicken, cock (7)
16 Astonished (6)
18 Through which the external world is experienced (6)
19 Electrical conductors (5)
21 Keep in liquid for a time, wet thoroughly! (4)

Colossal Book of Crosswords

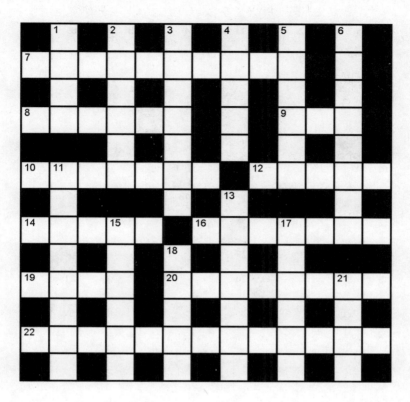

ACROSS

7 Overthrow of government - single rotation (10)
8 Give an assignment (8)
9 Boy's name (3)
10 Compresses (7)
12 Start (5)
14 Tented villages? (5)
16 Persons who perform songs (7)
19 Colliery - buried or floating explosive device (4)
20 Landing places for aircraft (8)
22 The largest inland sea (13)

DOWN

1 Belonging to her (4)
2 Moving pictures seen at the cinema (6)
3 More amusing than another (7)
4 Flying creatures (5)
5 Not the same as (6)
6 Border (8)
11 Came to understand or see the point of (8)
13 Book repository for loaning (7)
15 Attached to the front of a word (6)
17 Crushed to fine powder, like coffee (6)
18 In an unspecified amount of time (5)
21 Device for catching - possibly mouse? (4)

Colossal Book of Crosswords

ACROSS

7 Chances (13)
8 Fit (8)
9 You, part of thousand (4)
10 Flying bomb (7)
12 Singing group (5)
14 Room - to read and write perhaps? (5)
16 Firmament? Good............! (7)
19 Break (4)
20 Took a firm stand (8)
22 Cooling machines (13)

DOWN

1 Rain slightly (4)
2 Negative shapes to produce castings (6)
3 Refined or imposing, regal perhaps! (7)
4 Rap on door (5)
5 Sew - one may save nine? (6)
6 Ardent love (8)
11 Planned - Enid Dent! (8)
13 Pudding (7)
15 Leave (6)
17 Goes to see, usually socially (6)
18 Long, narrow raised strip (5)
21 Listeners on side of head! (4)

Colossal Book of Crosswords

ACROSS

7 Home for car (6)
8 Kind of bomb (6)
9 Dull person, to do with firearms! (4)
10 Stated explicitly or in detail (8)
11 Game played for burnt remains ? (7)
13 Flower holders (5)
15 Consumed (5)
17 Most fat (7)
20 Getting there (8)
21 Go underwater - of fill with water? (4)
22 Upholstered two seater? (6)
23 Distances or cookers (6)

DOWN

1 Political party, now new, hard work! (6)
2 Horse's neck hair (4)
3 Childhood ailment (7)
4 Looked at, possibly longingly (5)
5 Exercising influence or control (8)
6 Coming directly from god (6)
12 One dealing with drugs and prescriptions (7)
14 Black and white striped mammals (7)
16 Went along with, concurred (6)
18 Time of day - nest us! (6)
19 Dug from the earth (5)
21 Musical composition with words (4)

Colossal Book of Crosswords

ACROSS

7 Unusually high waters, lots of tears? (6)
8 Bird, brightly coloured (6)
9 Mirrors of the soul? (4)
10 Lacking in sympathy and kindness (8)
11 For blowing? - ebb slub! (7)
13 Tintin's dog - covered with snow? (5)
15 Tops up - appoints to a job or post (5)
16 Brings to attention a forgotten item, prompts? (7)
18 From the north - rent horn! (8)
19 A journey all the way around a particular place (4)
21 If not - sun els! (6)
22 Supermarket produce carrier (6)

DOWN

1 Take part in game (4)
2 Future prospects or potentials (13)
3 Made a promise or commitment - reads us! (7)
4 Said words - part of cycle wheel (5)
5 The way that words are said (13)
6 Dug out - like a bowl (8)
12 Horned horse of mythology (7)
14 Very little pay - groundnuts (7)
17 Large eating event (5)
20 Unattractive (4)

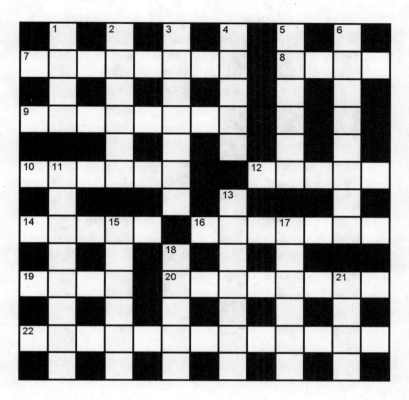

ACROSS

7 Think about something (8)
8 Sound of horn - in go to other side! (4)
9 Nice to look at - angle sip! (8)
10 Atishoo! Exhale when nose is tickled (6)
12 Written piece of work - usually analytical (5)
14 Movies (5)
16 Thickness, denseness (7)
19 Information, often computer based (4)
20 Not inside - roost duo! (8)
22 Piano alongside singer, escort (13)

DOWN

1 Implement, like hammer - reversed loot! (4)
2 Get away, like the great one? (6)
3 Gave information based on consid eration (7)
4 Medications (5)
5 Takes off all clothes or wallpaper! (6)
6 Difference between light and dark - ran scott! (8)
11 Irritation, bothersome (8)
13 Obtaining - tent gig! (7)
15 Field where hay grass is grown - mow ade! (6)
17 Bad weather patterns, take by force (6)
18 Goes round and round - spool reversed! (5)
21 Regular property payment - tear! (4)

Colossal Book of Crosswords

ACROSS

1 Desire for water (6)
4 Ranting, like a madman? (6)
9 Keep back, possibly for special use (7)
10 Cereal, pattern in wood (5)
11 Rest, kip, slumber, snooze (5)
12 Accurate (7)
13 Dimension (11)
18 Circus performer (7)
20 Frothy milk drink, agitate (5)
22 Makes by knitting - stink returns! (5)
23 Come to be aware of - relies a! (7)
24 In the course of (6)
25 Inclined (6)

DOWN

1 Forward force used to propel (6)
2 Give out - children? (5)
3 Pattern of bands of differing colour (7)
5 Dispute, debate, contend (5)
6 From Italy (7)
7 Shot down, with a gun (6)
8 The degree of hotness or coldness (11)
14 Prior to this point, before now (7)
15 Error (7)
16 Shouted orders - like a dog? (6)
17 Mythical story (6)
19 Sink or bowl (5)
21 From another planet? (5)

Colossal Book of Crosswords

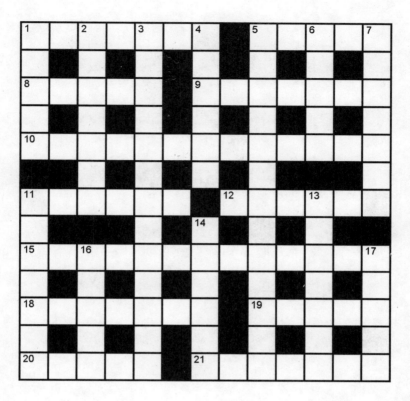

ACROSS

1 Opportunities - possibilities (7)
5 More than asked for, film part actor (5)
8 Consumed by mouth (5)
9 Stimulates, arouses, agitates (7)
10 A straight line at right angles to another line (13)
11 Self effacing, humble opinion (6)
12 Exerted oneself, was employed at (6)
15 Largest inland sea (13)
18 Frugality, reducing cost - possibly drive! (7)
19 Consume liquid (5)
20 Garden stores, casts off skin (5)
21 Pulled, as against a resistance (7)

DOWN

1 Inexpensive (5)
2 Changed (7)
3 Oral communications (13)
4 Not subject to change or variation - say ted! (6)
5 Reference book (13)
6 Complete or whole amount (5)
7 Made certain of, guaranteed (7)
11 Persons composing a group - me be mrs! (7)
13 Retaining (7)
14 Offered up address to deity (6)
16 Operated car, possibly to distraction (5)
17 Bare (5)

Colossal Book of Crosswords

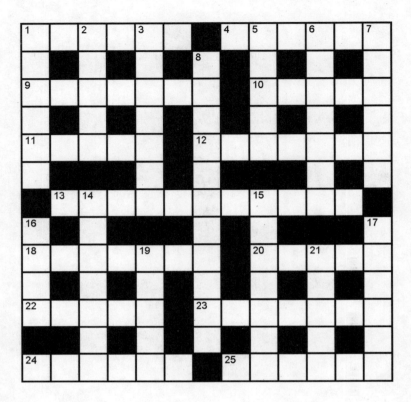

ACROSS

1 Continent (6)
4 A visible mass of water or ice particles suspended at a considerable altitude (6)
9 Freedom to bend the rules - nec lice! (7)
10 Computer input device, rodent (5)
11 Rubbish (5)
12 Skin discoloration obtained on holiday? (7)
13 Seemingly without interruption (11)
18 Numbers based on tens (7)
20 Break out of egg, develop plan or plot (5)
22 Precise amount - ce tax! (5)
23 Given medical care - processed (7)
24 Emblems signifying membership, rank or status (6)
25 Colour (6)

DOWN

1 Permits (6)
2 Unsettles the boat, stones (5)
3 Fasten or put together, link, join (7)
5 Fruit (5)
6 Strange or odd (7)
7 Beholding, going out with (6)
8 A person of considerable prominence, celebrity (11)
14 Fruit tree garden (7)
15 Obtain, reach, accomplish (7)
16 Wood cutting or shaping tool (4)
17 An unilluminated area, to follow (6)
19 Measure (5)
21 Complete amount (5)

Colossal Book of Crosswords

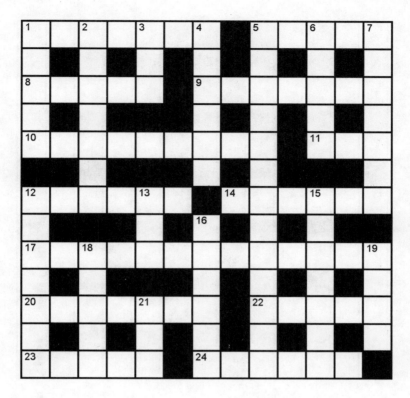

ACROSS

1 Accepted or habitual practices (7)
5 A very strong thick rope made of twisted hemp or steel wire (5)
8 To go stealthily or furtively (5)
9 Not a natural product, manufactured by humans (3-4)
10 Promote, make publicity for (9)
11 Consume solids (3)
12 Place for displaying historical artifacts (6)
14 A person who is not very bright (6)
17 Ice boxes - rag of terriers! (13)
20 Look at in detail, as a physician might (7)
22 Perfect, exactly what is needed (5)
23 Appears to be (5)
24 Distance from one end to the other (6)

DOWN

1 Chocolate drink (5)
2 Garment arm pieces (7)
3 Old age pensioner, initially (3)
4 Top of mountain, meeting (6)
5 Great and constant diligence and attention (13)
6 Great fire - of glory - to go out in? (5)
7 Appointed to office by vote (7)
12 Places to sell goods (7)
13 Geller, spoon bender! (3)
15 Shine on a screen, push forward (7)
16 Show, possibly a secret (6)
18 Component of a fire, e-mail criticism? (5)
19 Worm made fabric (4)
21 It is - in short! (3)

Colossal Book of Crosswords

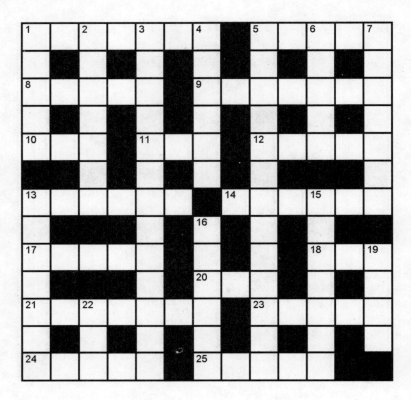

ACROSS

- **1** Risks, involving danger (7)
- **5** Go in or come in (5)
- **8** Consumed as food (5)
- **9** Stirs the feelings or emotions of (7)
- **10** Holing golf ball in stated number of strokes (3)
- **11** Finish (3)
- **12** American colour! (5)
- **13** Self effacing, playing ones achievements down (6)
- **14** Two people, join together (6)
- **17** Any admirable quality, worth (5)
- **18** Mischievous fairy in self propelled car! (3)
- **20** Frozen water (3)
- **21** Airfield for passengers (7)
- **23** Vision seen in sleep (5)
- **24** Faces - contesting groups or teams (5)
- **25** Begin, jump suddenly (5)

DOWN

- **1** Move furtively, unpleasant person (5)
- **2** Changed (7)
- **3** Verbal communications - sec innovators! (13)
- **4** Pass in a specific way; as of time, or money? (6)
- **5** Factual book (13)
- **6** The complete amount (5)
- **7** Keep back to use later (7)
- **13** Any warm-blooded vertebrates (7)
- **15** Gift, show, current time (7)
- **16** Puts pen to paper to communicate (6)
- **19** Favourable public reputation (4)
- **22** Colour (3)

Colossal Book of Crosswords

ACROSS

7 Engines (6)
8 Literature in metrical form (6)
9 Fit together, small slit for coin (4)
10 Clothes worn by armed forces (8)
11 Ruined, sometimes of children (7)
13 A sudden flurry of activity (5)
15 Dreadful, awesome (5)
16 Least difficult (7)
18 Not unusual (8)
19 Tidy, arranged (4)
21 Set fire to, consumed in fire (6)
22 Not often seen (6)

DOWN

1 Swimming hole in ground (4)
2 Monies given to support cause (13)
3 Adopted in order to deceive (7)
4 A lengthwise crack in wood (5)
5 Markedly new or introducing radical change (13)
6 Verbal commitments (8)
12 Strong (8)
14 Legal people (7)
17 Pale yellowish colour - seen on beach? (5)
20 Fit for the task to be done - bodied? (4)

Colossal Book of Crosswords

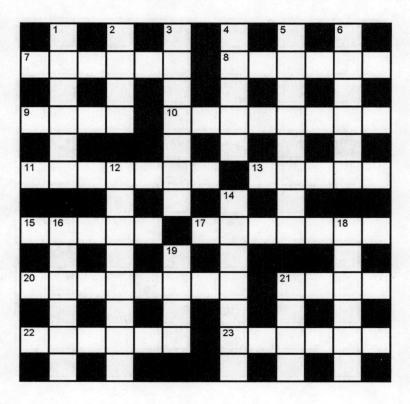

ACROSS

7 Make decision (6)
8 Creature - malian! (6)
9 Shoot or dismiss (4)
10 Prone to being tickled (8)
11 A formally arranged gathering (7)
13 Plenty, cargoes (5)
15 Possessed (5)
17 Creature, very large (7)
20 Least quiet - on site is! (8)
21 Something with a trunk! (4)
22 Information known only to a special group (6)
23 Hair curler or road flattener (6)

DOWN

1 Next to, at the side of - the seaside? (6)
2 Broad in scope or content - like a boy? (4)
3 Subjecting to experiment (7)
4 Timepiece (5)
5 X,000,000s - large numbers! (8)
6 Gave rise to something, made something happen (6)
12 Wealth in the form of money or jewels etc. (8)
14 Medicine men? (7)
16 Made from timber (6)
18 Number (6)
19 Flesh of animals used as food (4)
21 Narrate story, possibly of William? (4)

Colossal Book of Crosswords

ACROSS

7 Add water to - spirits? - end map! (6)
8 More than one (6)
9 Be wide open - like a morning mouth? (4)
10 In a physically or emotionally forceful way (8)
11 Made laugh - possibly pink - with feathers? (7)
13 Two of a kind (4)
15 Country (5)
17 With great emotion (7)
20 One storey house (8)
21 Produced musical tones with the voice (4)
22 Put into words or an expression - sherpa! (6)
23 Dropped off to sleep - back and forth (6)

DOWN

1 Aloha state! (6)
2 Turn quickly - political interpretation? (4)
3 Smelled with nose - or with a cold (7)
4 Rapidity (5)
5 Buy (8)
6 Being the greatest in height (6)
12 Weight (8)
14 Winter weather - on swing! (7)
16 Imparted skills or knowledge to (6)
18 Smell, taste, hearing, touch, sight (6)
19 Having greater age or a tree! (5)
21 Unhappy (3)

Colossal Book of Crosswords

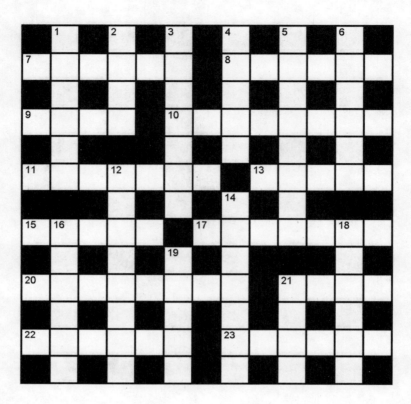

ACROSS

7 Baby cat (6)
8 Country and continent (6)
9 Thing in keeping it empty! (4)
10 Place, location (8)
11 Taught how to do something (7)
13 Limbless reptile - in the grass? (5)
15 Slides - undergarments? (5)
17 A creation of the highest excellence (7)
20 Rain protector (8)
21 Hopeful this thickens in a novel - pilot less I! (4)
22 Reflexive from of "it" - stifle! (6)
23 Number (6)

DOWN

1 Female sibling (6)
2 Small particle, molecule (4)
3 Broke, like nerve? (7)
4 Wetland, fen (5)
5 The work of a writer - grins wit! (8)
6 According to the clock - on the hour (6)
12 Brought in from another country (8)
14 More well defined - re lacer! (7)
16 Boundaries (6)
18 Pressed - possibly with steam (6)
19 Richard singer - steep high face of rock (5)
21 One who writes verse (4)

Colossal Book of Crosswords

ACROSS

7 More active than others - think bees! (6)
8 Tag along behind my leader (6)
9 Sleeping furniture (4)
10 Moving along stealthily - through undergrowth? (8)
11 Got away (7)
13 Support or hold - win election (5)
15 Snowdrop colour (5)
17 Turning to liquid due to heat (7)
20 Rapidest (8)
21 Small mammals - used in cricket? (4)
22 Space visitors? (6)
23 Wobbles, like milk drinks! (6)

DOWN

1 Female kings - borough of New York City (6)
2 Legs, go with needles to make you numb! (4)
3 Fractured or solved (7)
4 Post event - later on (5)
5 Five-toed pachyderm (8)
6 Where lines or streets meet (6)
12 Assaulted, verbally or physically (8)
14 Most moist! (7)
16 Every 60 minutes (6)
18 Scored a goal, caught a fish - tented (6)
19 More than one goose (5)
21 Animal, sounds naked! (4)

Colossal Book of Crosswords

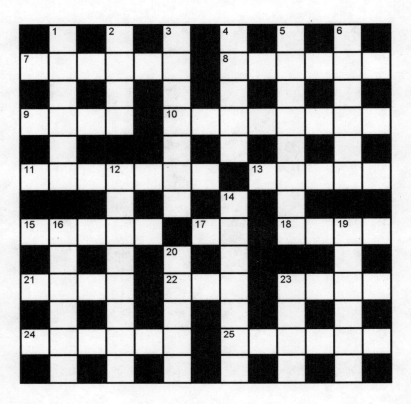

ACROSS

7 Widely different - a diver! (6)
8 Astonished (6)
9 Sometimes comes with fortune? (4)
10 The distinct personality of an individual (8)
11 Sandy holiday spots (7)
13 Blood pump (5)
15 Chips (5)
17 Negative (2)
18 Match for cricket or exam? (4)
21 Worry or cut complex wooden patterns! (4)
22 Inland Revenue Service - initially! (3)
23 Cause to go somewhere (4)
24 Look quickly - nec gal (6)
25 Rubbing out tool (6)

DOWN

1 Cope with - achieve a goal (6)
2 Distance measure (4)
3 Looked up to (7)
4 Stopped goal or put money away (5)
5 Most distant (8)
6 Part of alphabet or envelope full! (6)
12 Making, building (8)
14 Creature like Frankenstein's (7)
16 Not very often (6)
19 At the end of the sun's journey (6)
20 Trees, sometimes scented (5)
23 Regal bird (4)

Colossal Book of Crosswords

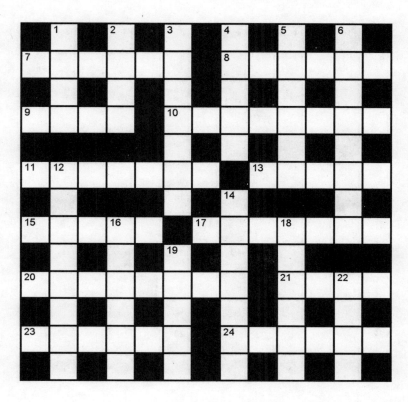

ACROSS

7 Models of excellence or perfection (6)
8 Handy - sue flu! (6)
9 Digital information (4)
10 Having a low probability (8)
11 Work places (7)
13 Medications (5)
15 Goes round - spool comes back! (5)
17 Badly behaved (7)
20 Instructing - asking for food in cafe? (8)
21 Twelve o'clock (4)
23 Marked by dissimilarity (6)
24 Measuring sticks (6)

DOWN

1 Thought, personal view (4)
2 Ms Hari's first name - spy? (4)
3 Characterised by certainty or security (7)
4 Male cattle (5)
5 Less strong (6)
6 The rays of the sun - hustling! (8)
12 Knocking down with force - golf iron! (8)
14 Mammals - annoys persistently (7)
16 Kind of justice relating to poetry (6)
18 Lightly, mildly, softly (6)
19 Gripping and chewing with the teeth - be sit! (5)
22 Belonging to us (4)

Colossal Book of Crosswords

ACROSS

6 Domesticated bovine animals (6)
8 Very unusual - throe (5)
9 Two of, like earrings or trousers? (4)
10 Working out before doing anything (8)
11 Discovering (7)
13 Cycles (5)
15 Any number of members considered as a unit (5)
17 Legendary creature (6)
20 Being of the least size (8)
21 Very well ground (4)
22 Very large people (6)
23 Adds up numbers - noblemen (6)

DOWN

1 Twinkles in sky? (4)
2 Looking furtively, like Tom? (7)
3 Regal (5)
4 Altering (8)
5 European country (6)
7 Woman's name in bad attitude! (3)
12 Multiplying by two (8)
14 Complainers, reviewers (7)
16 Stay behind (6)
18 Number (6)
19 More than one - goose (5)
21 Number of apocolyptic horsemen? (4)

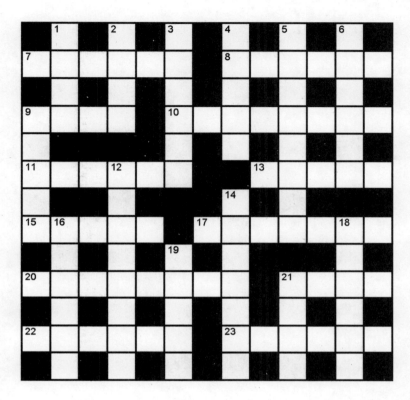

ACROSS

7 Magazine boss (6)
8 Selection, best quality? (6)
9 Sewn edge (4)
10 Cold treat (3-5)
11 Thing, be against! (7)
13 Be about, have to do with (5)
15 Great, to an extreme degree (5)
17 Estimates based on little or no information (7)
20 Naughtiness (8)
21 Ends of - left for waiters? (4)
22 Pops open, explodes, maybe out laughing (6)
23 Seating, controls meeting (6)

DOWN

1 Wood carving tool (4)
2 Thing, part of a list? (4)
3 Painter or sculptor (6)
4 Wood fixing, is driven (5)
5 Travels - nurse joy! (8)
6 Scratch or just get by? (6)
9 What you pull out all of to get job done? (5)
12 Healthy physical activity (8)
14 Outer skin - come to the top of the water (7)
16 One of a kind (6)
18 A person with special knowledge or ability (6)
19 Before everyone else (5)
21 Amphibian who owned a hall? (4)

Colossal Book of Crosswords

ACROSS

7 Meal eaten outdoors (6)
8 Distance from circle centre to edge (6)
9 Cave man's tool - group of people (4)
10 In truth, really... - allay cut! (8)
11 Extension to or beyond the ordinary limit (7)
13 Making use of (5)
15 Rabbit home (5)
17 Closest (7)
20 Be of different opinions (8)
21 Boy at wedding - leaf of book (4)
23 Bad weather or relationship (6)
24 Sliding box in furniture, artist (6)

DOWN

1 Cash register (4)
2 Lacking in power or forcefulness (6)
3 Scrape - cause damage by abrading (7)
4 What you agree to tell in court (5)
5 Models of excellence - ladies! (6)
6 Preliminary plans - tracing of the shapes of (8)
12 Visitors, holidaymakers (8)
14 Fable (6)
16 A seat for one person, (5)
18 Say again (6)
19 Mixture of white and black (4)
22 Clarified butter used in Indian cookery (4)

Colossal Book of Crosswords

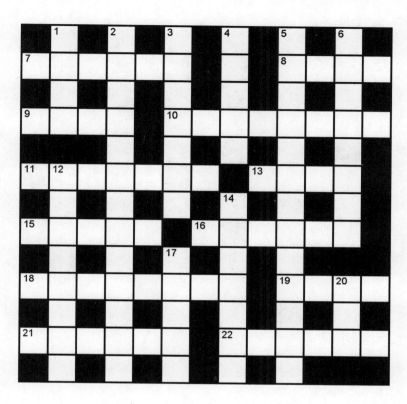

ACROSS

7 Magician (6)
8 Secure door with key (4)
9 American spelling of through (4)
10 Film financier - crude pro! (8)
11 Given medication, given something nice? (7)
13 Part of plant - stop something! (4)
15 Bare, hollow (5)
16 Long bodied reptile (6)
18 From the USA (8)
19 Ferrous metal (4)
21 Closer (6)
22 Unmarried (6)

DOWN

1 Breathe deeply and heavily (4)
2 Makers, producers (13)
3 Taken into one's family (7)
4 Toys that go up and down on a string (2-3)
5 Drawings that help to clarify (13)
6 Made a loud, piercing sound - scared me! (8)
12 Bring back to mind (8)
14 One who gives evidence in a court (7)
17 Number of points gained, get goal! (5)
20 A slippery or viscous liquid or liquefiable substance not miscible with water (3)

Colossal Book of Crosswords

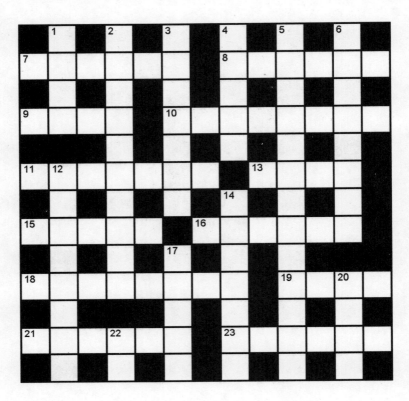

ACROSS

7 Used to change direction of rails for train (6)
8 Gave something, passed something down (6)
9 Colour (4)
10 Responded, replied (8)
11 Small flowers used to make chains (7)
13 Door handle (4)
15 Make words with mouth (5)
16 Season (6)
18 Two slices of bread with a filling between them (8)
19 Golf tournament (4)
21 Game played in court? (6)
23 Remained (6)

DOWN

1 Sheep offcuts - knitting stuff (4)
2 Comprehend (10)
3 Got away! (7)
4 Game played with bishops and knights (5)
5 From or between other countries (13)
6 Month (8)
12 Came into view, seemed to be? (8)
14 At the top (7)
17 At the start (5)
20 Looked at, possibly with bad intent? (4)
22 Nota Bene - in short! (2)

Colossal Book of Crosswords

ACROSS

7 Type of wood (6)
8 Lavatory (6)
9 Other than what is under consideration or implied (4)
10 Form of boating (8)
11 Orifice, way in, opportunity (7)
13 Gastropod mollusk, eaten in france (5)
16 Footwear, start computer system (4)
17 Lowered in price or priority (7)
19 Not having all the facts (8)
21 Slipped along (4)
23 Formal discussion (6)
24 Being able to see - visualising (6)

DOWN

1 High (4)
2 American term for houseman - medical (6)
3 Sticking, standing your ground (7)
4 Glue or twig ? (5)
5 Standing above others in character or attainment (13)
6 Tight fisted (4)
12 Turned soil ready for planting (8)
14 Frozen water (3)
15 Tooth specialist (7)
18 Looked at, stood up to (5)
20 To do with the mouth (4)
22 Travellers hotel (3)

Colossal Book of Crosswords

ACROSS

7 Underground passage (6)
8 Hinged sections of a tables, tree parts! (6)
9 7 days (4)
10 A living organism, possibly from the black lagoon (8)
11 Not able to be found, like a jigsaw piece? (7)
13 Has a go, rugby scores (5)
15 Small coins (5)
17 Woven carrying devices (7)
20 The act of mixing different breeds of animals (8)
22 Shopping reminder (4)
24 Telephoned (6)
25 What witches cast (6)

DOWN

1 Certain (4)
2 Limbless reptiles, with ladders make a game? (6)
3 Positioning (7)
4 Having greater seniority (5)
5 Having greater speed (6)
6 Most merry (8)
12 Belligerence aroused by a real or supposed wrong (3)
14 Biggest (7)
16 Expensive (6)
18 Murderer (6)
19 Warm-blooded egg-laying vertebrates (5)
21 Back end, rise up (4)
23 Condiment - of the earth maybe? (4)

Colossal Book of Crosswords

ACROSS

7 Vegetable (6)
8 Very sad (6)
9 A slight competitive advantage (4)
10 Height above sea level (8)
11 Made a noise like an animal - ted rung! (7)
13 Nominated, mentioned (5)
15 Something you are certain about is this (5)
17 Putting in the post maybe, or signals - sing end! (7)
20 Amounts carried in the hands - dna flush! (8)
21 Decreed or designated beforehand (4)
22 Did as was told, followed orders (6)
23 Narrow furrow, such as in a record (6)

DOWN

1 Edge, possibly between 2 nations (6)
2 Hand gesture found at seaside? (4)
3 Travels (7)
4 Say clearly, condition (5)
5 Away from the West (8)
6 Play violin, dodge taxes (6)
12 In these times - yawn soda! (8)
14 Communication - found in a bottle? (7)
16 Close at hand (4-2)
18 Coming from a country or town (6)
19 Amounts of monies available (5)
21 Idiot (4)

Colossal Book of Crosswords

ACROSS

7 Intense and profound fear - at the movies? (6)
8 Belonging to them (6)
9 Lighting device (4)
10 Passageway - possibly on a train (8)
11 Where sky and earth meet (7)
13 Cowboy roping device (5)
15 Digging implement (5)
17 Place where films are shown (6)
20 Written or spoken communications (8)
21 Underground dwelling favoured by ancestors (4)
22 Violently agitated and turbulent (6)
23 At the bottom (6)

DOWN

1 Red salad fruit eaten as vegetable (6)
2 Device for catching animals (4)
3 Farm machine (7)
4 Famous actors, singers etc (5)
5 Practices that are handed down from the past by tradition (8)
6 Soldiers (6)
12 Hard work, also manufacturing (8)
14 He - flemish! (7)
16 Characterized by romantic imagery (6)
18 Give advice to (6)
19 Be in accord; be in agreement (5)
21 Animal giving milk and meat (3)

Colossal Book of Crosswords

ACROSS

7 Spud (6)
8 Darkness cast by someone in sun (6)
9 Boat propulsion devices (4)
10 Girl's name (3)
11 Consume food (3)
12 Thickness, distribution - dine sty! (7)
14 Where the heart is, where you live (4)
16 Turn round, In the area (5)
18 Attorney (6)
21 Outside (8)
22 Chicken product (3)
23 What you plan to do, purpose (6)
24 Ship flying skull and crossbones (6)

DOWN

1 Find (6)
2 Cooking equipment (4)
3 Short spaces in time, could be magic in song? (7)
4 Demanded of, a question can be this (5)
5 Class, family, group characteristic (8)
6 Liquid container (6)
13 To compress with violence, like a sponge? (7)
15 Horse speed (6)
17 Fighting with gloves (6)
19 Opposite to left, political wing? (5)
20 Ties in rope or string (5)
22 Make money from work (4)

Colossal Book of Crosswords

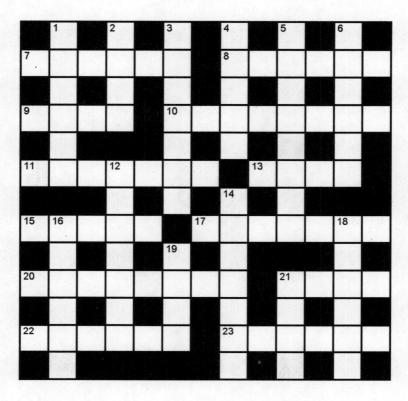

ACROSS

7 Car park next to home? (6)
8 To do with nuclear fission - I to cam (6)
9 Arrive, travel toward (4)
10 Stated explicitly or in detail (8)
11 Fractured, like a joke? (7)
13 Female horse (4)
15 Challenged (5)
17 Most delicate, most lenient (7)
20 Letters containing no lower case (8)
21 Sung musical piece (4)
22 Calm down, long wooden bench (6)
23 See an the end of the day (6)

DOWN

1 Particles suspended in the air (6)
2 Lessen the intensity of, calm (4)
3 Illness usually caught in childhood (7)
4 Removed or made like a photograph (5)
5 Not subordinate, controlling or in charge (8)
6 Split, in order to conquer or rule? (6)
12 Shop dispensing prescriptions (7)
14 Be made up of (7)
16 Astonished (6)
18 One who performs 21 across (6)
19 A person who belongs to the sex that cannot have babies (4)
21 Remitted (4)

Colossal Book of Crosswords

ACROSS

7 Insect having biting mouthparts and front wings (6)
8 Directed one's gaze towards (6)
9 Grass area (4)
10 Who you are, could be mistaken? (8)
11 Make possible for something to happen (6)
13 h2o (5)
15 Sets aside money each week, stop goal (5)
17 Item delivered through the post (6)
20 In reverse (8)
21 The most effort one can make (4)
22 Pulled in, as a horse might be (6)
23 Closer (6)

DOWN

1 Keep, hold on to (6)
2 Hit and make senseless - about nuts! (4)
3 Makes a decision, resolves (7)
4 State of rest (5)
5 The act of distinguishing by comparing (8)
6 Relax - let est! (6)
12 Smashing, reducing to parts (8)
14 Fixing (7)
16 Astonished (6)
18 Hurries about, grasslike plants (6)
19 Comes back to earth (5)
21 Large animal, one of which is a yogi! (4)

118

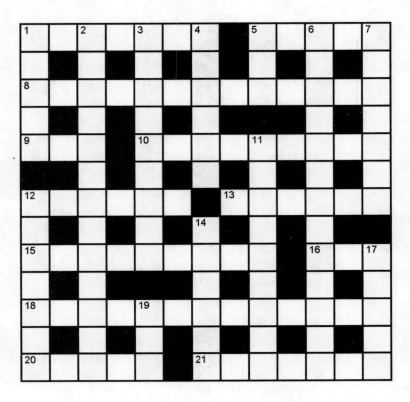

ACROSS

1 Numbers using a base of ten, also UK currency (7)
5 Stood up to, stood in front of (5)
8 Distance round a wheel or other circle (13)
9 Thee - person addressed (3)
10 Youngsters between 13 and 19 (9)
12 Small air-breathing arthropod (6)
13 Spiny succulent plant (6)
15 Written details of banking transactions (9)
16 Left after a fire (3)
18 Books - usually for reference (13)
20 Covered in dust! (5)
21 No longer living, like the dodo (7)

DOWN

1 Rot down, go bad (5)
2 A person's financial situation (good or bad) (13)
3 Facial hair (9)
4 Raised, possibly spirits (6)
5 Animal pelt (3)
6 The strength of a solution, thinking hard! (13)
7 Clothes for women (7)
11 Flat (9)
12 In place of (7)
14 Far away control device (6)
17 Has not, but has lost O (5)
19 Weep, call out (3)

Colossal Book of Crosswords

ACROSS

7 Photographic device (6)
8 Shooting places or kitchen cookers (6)
9 In this place in the red box (4)
10 Persons owing allegiance to a nation (8)
11 Distribute haphazardly (7)
13 Intended (5)
15 Assists (5)
17 Calms down, brings to a close (7)
20 Most foolish (8)
21 Part played by actor (4)
23 Contributory element - of cart? (6)
24 Pointed weapons, lances (6)

DOWN

1 Naked (4)
2 In the near past (6)
3 Small wild flowers (7)
4 People from Arabia (5)
5 What you do when you have a cold? (6)
6 Part of speech or time in jail? (8)
12 Thing used in chemistry! (8)
14 Tooth doctor (7)
16 Having good manners (6)
18 Rotated or made on a lathe (6)
19 Black, blue or rasp! (5)
22 A titled peer of the realm (4)

Colossal Book of Crosswords

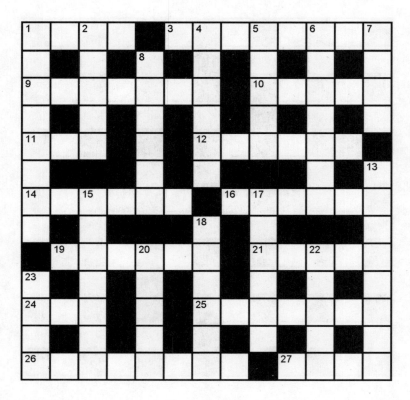

ACROSS

1 Barrel containing wine or spirit (4)
3 A mental or personality disturbance - resinous! (8)
9 River and falls (7)
10 Climb, weighing device (5)
11 Long period of time in the only clock! (3)
12 Nervousness resulting from mental stress (6)
14 Procedure, rules, arrangement (6)
16 Skin disorder (6)
19 Scottish girlie? (6)
21 Hand out parts of something? (5)
24 Little Alison (3)
25 Form a mental image - Lennon record (7)
26 Heraldic left, threatening or scary? (8)
27 Found on front of camera (4)

DOWN

1 Speak with people, reverse order - scorn eve! (8)
2 Killed (5)
4 Pass by, as of time (6)
5 Part of stair - is err! (5)
6 Beach holiday place (7)
7 Rees turns round to find fortune teller! (4)
8 Deep narrow valley (6)
13 Thoughtless, clumsy (8)
15 Large creature in north pacific - on aisle! (3-4)
17 One of two lead actors in film (2-4)
18 Want, lust after (6)
20 Air filled skull cavity (5)
22 Get up, especially after knighting? (5)
23 Girl found in middle of a lasso! (4)

Colossal Book of Crosswords

ACROSS

1 Needing a drink (6)
4 Getting up in the morning (6)
9 Keep back, price below which you will not sell (7)
10 Pattern in wood (5)
11 At a high angle, soak to bring out taste (5)
12 Accurate (7)
13 Built (11)
18 Try (7)
20 Dishonour, disgrace (5)
22 Fish, comes in brown and rainbow (5)
23 Lifting up (7)
24 Rushed quickly - traded! (6)
25 Build something new - nine TV! (6)

DOWN

1 Push forward suddenly (6)
2 Matter of concern - children (5)
3 Pattern of coloured bands - military rank badge (7)
5 Contend, debate, fall out? (5)
6 Just think about it - in image! (7)
7 Shot (down) - end gnu! (6)
8 Ambient heat (11)
14 Taking place in the open air (7)
15 Padded bag, protect from impact (7)
16 Tried a sample of food (6)
17 Elevation above sea level (6)
19 Measure (5)
21 Get up, as a knight might? (5)

ACROSS

1 Opportunity - possibly last? (6)
4 Come in - try competition (5)
8 Consumed (5)
9 Makes excited (7)
10 Straight up! (13)
11 Self effacing (6)
12 Two of something, join carriages together (6)
15 Crazy half of madcap! (3)
16 Goes with firma to make land! (5)
18 Where one goes to fly - part rio! (7)
20 Move in an unhurried fashion - like wood? (5)
21 Opposing groups in a game or match (5)
22 Began (7)

DOWN

1 Unpleasant person, move slowly (5)
2 Changed (7)
3 oral communications - vino ancestors! (13)
4 Book of reference information (13)
5 The whole amount (5)
6 Keep back for later, perhaps a player? (7)
7 Town in North of England (5)
11 Any warm-blooded vertebrates (7)
13 Foretell, weather or future (7)
14 Puts words on paper (6)
17 Cast ballot for a candidate (5)
19 Colour (3)

Colossal Book of Crosswords

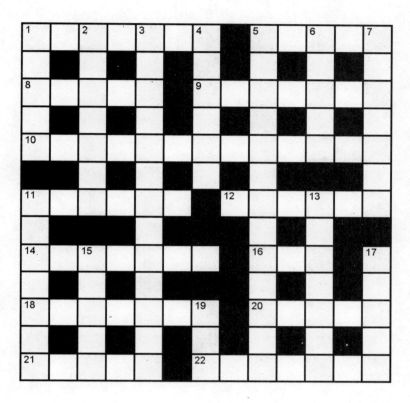

ACROSS

1 Just as you would expect (7)
5 Additional (5)
8 Harvested cereal (5)
9 Try (7)
10 Ice boxes (13)
11 Turned from solid to liquid by heating (6)
12 Families, related groups (6)
14 Look at side by side to make decision (7)
16 What you can make in 10 across? (3)
18 First letter of a word or name (7)
20 Room at top of house, often unused (5)
21 Guzzled, scoffed, consumed by mouth (5)
22 Money required to purchase something (7)

DOWN

1 Animal (5)
2 Full of fun (7)
3 Thoughtfulness or small fee (13)
4 Stood at an angle resting on something (6)
5 Far more than expected - re ordinary tax! (13)
6 Speed in music (5)
7 Creative types - tsarist! (7)
11 Device or mechanical contrivance (7)
13 Take air in and out of the lungs (7)
15 Damp (5)
17 Sailing boat (5)
19 Cut off part, also type of rabbit ear? (3)

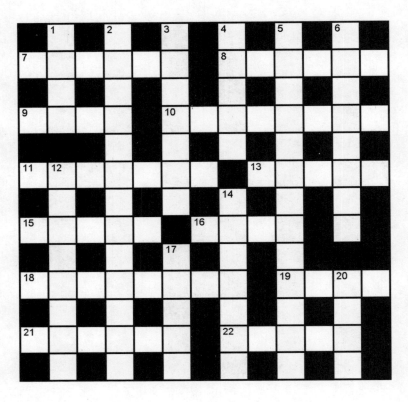

ACROSS

7 Dignified and sombre (6)
8 An indulgence (6)
9 In this place (4)
10 Small fruits (8)
11 Someone travelling through the water? (7)
13 30 day period (5)
15 General direction - of taste or style (5)
16 Dressed in - clothed (4)
18 Different, distinguishable (8)
19 Desire or requirement for something (4)
21 Channel or furrow (6)
22 Mistake (5)

DOWN

1 North and South have one! (4)
2 Certainty that you can do something - I ornamented it (13)
3 Bumped into something or criticised it? (7)
4 Type of music (5)
5 Very different and unexpected (13)
6 Taken into police custody (8)
12 Fighters - sir arrow! (8)
14 Wear, clobber, gear, kit (7)
17 Beneath (5)
20 Sense organ, little jugs have big ones? (4)

Colossal Book of Crosswords

ACROSS

7 Country (6)
8 Quantity (6)
9 Competition to run fastest (4)
10 Accepted as true (8)
11 Gets away (7)
13 Heavy open wagons, pull slowly or heavily (5)
15 Grown up (5)
17 Neither one side nor the other - out of gear! (7)
20 Precipitation (8)
21 Teeth holders (4)
22 Communal activity or event (6)
23 Equal parts of a company (6)

DOWN

1 Man made waterways (6)
2 Be unafraid to do something (4)
3 Glass balls - mad man has lost his? (7)
4 Gather round car race (5)
5 Prediction of weather (8)
6 Make something new, think up weak excuse? (6)
12 Ocean (8)
14 Perceive mentally, as of an idea - las Eire! (7)
16 Mythical fire breathing beast (6)
18 Groups of soldiers (6)
19 Metal rope made of strands, send telegram? (5)
21 Happy, little Gladice! (4)

Colossal Book of Crosswords

ACROSS

7 Country (6)
8 Quantity (6)
9 Competition to run fastest (4)
10 Accepted as true (8)
11 Gets away (7)
13 Heavy open wagons, pull slowly or heavily (5)
15 Grown up (5)
17 Neither one side nor the other - out of gear! (7)
20 Precipitation (8)
21 Teeth holders (4)
22 Communal activity or event (6)
23 Equal parts of a company (6)

DOWN

1 Man made waterways (6)
2 Be unafraid to do something (4)
3 Glass balls - mad man has lost his? (7)
4 Gather round car race (5)
5 Prediction of weather (8)
6 Make something new, think up weak excuse? (6)
12 Ocean (8)
14 Perceive mentally, as of an idea - las Eire! (7)
16 Mythical fire breathing beast (6)
18 Groups of soldiers (6)
19 Metal rope made of strands, send telegram? (5)
21 Happy, little Gladice! (4)

Colossal Book of Crosswords

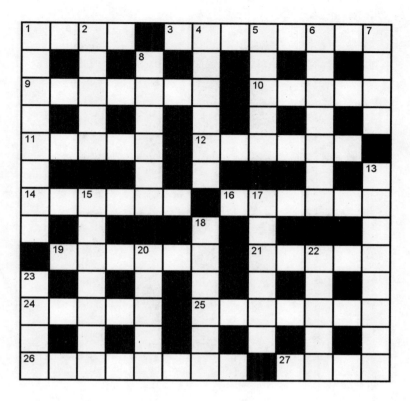

ACROSS

1 Indication - seen on street? (4)
3 Arched railway bridge (8)
9 Counselled (7)
10 Badness, rotting (5)
11 Music and dance nightclub started in the 1960s (5)
12 Amount, distance, level (6)
14 Type of metal, American coin (6)
16 Glass container (6)
19 Suspended water particles seen in sky (6)
21 Have confidence or faith in (5)
24 Requirements (5)
25 Out of the ordinary, unexpected (7)
26 Vegetables (8)
27 In addition to, as well as (4)

DOWN

1 Social status (8)
2 Hands over, as to a charity? (5)
4 In truth - denied! (6)
5 Did not, in short (5)
6 Large hard-shelled thing taken from palm tree (7)
7 Enunciates, articulates (4)
8 Onto land - from the water - come on... (6)
13 Cold-blooded vertebrates (8)
15 Being at the lowest temperature (7)
17 Factory production rate, computer speak (6)
18 Make a promise or commitment (6)
20 Knock over (5)
22 The normal (5)
23 Card game (4)

Colossal Book of Crosswords

ACROSS

7 One who performs magic (6)
8 Old material that is slightly reworked (6)
9 Hire car and driver - cab (4)
10 Under a curse - ace cruds! (8)
11 Small graceful antelope (7)
13 Red breasted bird (5)
15 A sudden forceful flow - paste! (5)
16 A look that can inflict harm! (4,3)
18 Small tree or shrub (8)
19 Castrate or neuter (4)
21 Musical notes - that linger on? (6)
22 Horse sound (5)

DOWN

1 Mineral used in electronics (4)
2 Physical appearance of a ghost (13)
3 In a perfect world it would be like this (7)
4 Dried seaweed, smash something (5)
5 Special plastic material - romp athletics! (13)
6 Something hard to endure - repays it! (8)
12 Collection of letters (8)
14 Time of day (7)
17 Relating to religion (5)
20 Remnants of fire (3)

129

ACROSS

7 Deprive somebody of something by deceit (3-3)
8 Book writer (6)
9 Tablet (4)
10 Metal rod or place to have drink (3)
11 Green fruit (4)
12 Pull back from a battle (7)
13 Put on a production, or the place you do it? (5)
15 Similar (5)
17 City in Northern Italy (7)
19 A receptacle for spit (usually in a public place) (8)
20 Where two surfaces meet, slight advantage (4)
22 A man who is engaged to be married (6)
24 The power to entice or attract (6)

DOWN

1 Hi fidelity music system, only smaller! (2-2)
2 Travel on shoes with steel or rubber rollers attached to their soles (6-7)
3 A little unusual, informal (7)
4 Have about one's person (5)
5 Shoes with pointed supports at back (8,5)
6 A .45-caliber submachine gun (5-3)
9 Average score on a golf course? (3)
14 The middle of the day (7)
16 Edge of vase or cup, watch for many a slip! (3)
18 Drying cloth (5)
21 Wound by piercing (4)
23 Not out! (2)

Colossal Book of Crosswords

ACROSS

7 A system of principles (6)
8 Movie icon seen in night sky? (4)
9 French city - pleasant (4)
10 Morally reprehensible (8)
11 Consider obligatory; request and expect (7)
13 A powerful stroke, exhale hard (4)
15 Cooking liquid (5)
17 Enclosure in courtroom for jury (4-3)
20 Dishonest scheme - pub up jot! (3-2,3)
21 Adhesive (4)
22 Sloping letter form (6)
23 Indicate or indicator (6)

DOWN

1 Hit, withdraw labour (6)
2 A small but appreciable amount (4)
3 Attendant and shield bearer to a knight (7)
4 Face of dislike (5)
5 To do with the stars (6)
6 Type of nut (6)
12 Unfasten - possibly railway carriages (8)
14 Polish and make shiny (7)
16 Worthy of trust or belief (6)
18 Relating to or resembling the eye (6)
19 Throw out (5)
21 Garbage in - garbage out - initially! (4)

Colossal Book of Crosswords

ACROSS

7 Sex drive (6)
8 Ornamental shrub (6)
9 Smoking device (4)
10 Like or being a phantom - crest lap (8)
11 Colourful swirled pattern of curved shapes (7)
13 Dog's favourite - mostly ebony? (4)
15 A fleshy underground stem or root (5)
16 Wimbledon player - goes in the garden? (4)
19 An escape from jail (5-3)
21 Pals turn and hit across face is result! (4)
22 Make your mind up (6)
23 One set aside to use if needed - as a tyre (5)

DOWN

1 Silicon dioxide - sic Ali! (6)
2 Large freshwater fish (4)
3 Olympic racing sled (7)
4 Determined by tragic fate (5)
5 Dissenting - cut Sofia! (8)
6 Vandalise, draw on, mess up (6)
11 Plant container or drug (3)
12 An outline or synopsis of a play - is cornea! (8)
14 Christen - bit apse! (7)
17 A coloured glassy compound - on baths or pots (6)
18 Column (5)
20 Fishing line holder (4)
21 Unforseen problem (4)

Colossal Book of Crosswords

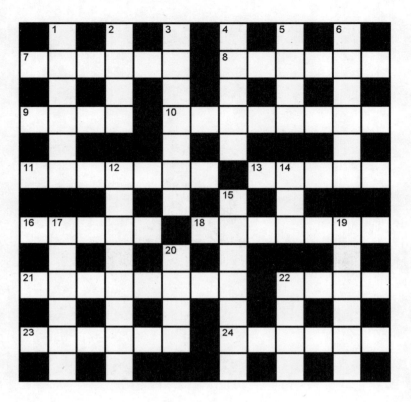

ACROSS

7 Make a decision about something (6)
8 Shouted loudly, like a lion (6)
9 The ends of something, like fingers (4)
10 Most delightful, sugariest! (8)
11 Agricultural class of old (7)
13 Stiff paper rectangles used to play snap (5)
16 Made a hole by prodding with finger (5)
18 Most inhuman - set clod! (7)
21 Huge (8)
22 Card game (4)
23 Monkey nut (6)
24 Looked at unblinkingly (6)

DOWN

1 Sexual wanting - is deer! (6)
2 Smacks, slaps, records in the top 10! (4)
3 Making fun of by harassing (7)
4 Carrying a weapon (5)
5 Compass point (4)
6 Created disorder, could be about? (6)
12 Committee - gentries! (8)
14 Put together to make a total in maths (3)
15 Made up of (7)
17 Weight - 16 of these make a pound (6)
19 Keeps the sun off, sunglasses (6)
20 Defended and strengthened hill top (4)
22 Washing material (4)

Colossal Book of Crosswords

ACROSS

7 Not at all the same as - in luke! (6)
8 Pressed clothes with a hot device (6)
9 Metal conductor, send telegram, chicken? (4)
10 Visible light for example - range (8)
11 The 4 parts of the year (7)
13 Flying devices made with sticks and string (5)
15 Cycles, to put it another way (5)
17 Adult male chicken (7)
20 Could be hot air - rubber inflatables! (8)
21 Arrange into groups (4)
22 Game played in court! (6)
23 Configurations, figures - phases! (6)

DOWN

1 All of, complete (6)
2 Place where building takes place - for sore eyes! (4)
3 Fooling, playing - sings me! (7)
4 Shoots gun, sacks! (5)
5 Holds, includes - sanction! (8)
6 Rubbish - I won't do it! (6)
12 Thieving, nicking, robbing from (8)
14 Own (7)
16 Pictures (6)
18 Merited through behavior (6)
19 Female mate of gander (5)
21 Place to sit! (4)

Colossal Book of Crosswords

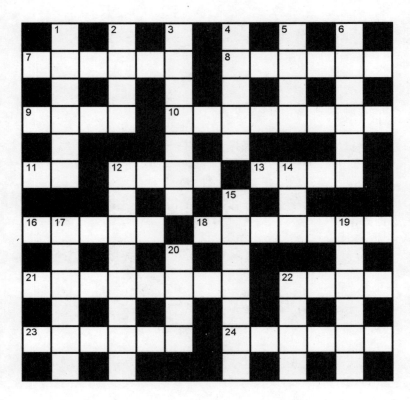

ACROSS

7 Having good manners (6)
8 Relied on for support - leaden! (6)
9 Sudden, uncontrollable urges - and starts! (4)
10 The act of perceiving the odour of something (8)
11 I (2)
12 Give musical voice to - two make a US prison! (4)
13 Shakespeare? (4)
16 Was bothered about - cedar! (5)
18 Made up of (7)
21 Related groups of people (8)
22 Remain (4)
23 Intensely or extremely bad - see rev! (6)
24 Handed out fairly (6)

DOWN

1 Constabulary (6)
2 Bony cage enclosing heart, lungs, etc (4)
3 Periods of learning that will teach you! (7)
4 From another planet (5)
5 Dance or plaything (4)
6 Pulled in as a horse (6)
12 Example possibly for diagnosis (8)
14 Small advertisements (3)
15 Own, have control of (7)
17 Filled with the emotional impact of overwhelming surprise or shock (6)
19 Says clearly, parts of USA (6)
20 Grab with teeth, chomp (4)
22 Mark left after tissue heals (4)

Colossal Book of Crosswords

ACROSS

7 Magnitude, level, degree - text ne! (6)
8 Stop vehicle, roadside cafe - socks? (4-2)
9 Turn sharply; change direction abruptly (4)
10 (law) a party to a lawsuit - lit giant! (8)
11 Contrary to your interests - vas deer! (7)
13 Seal with caulking, as a boat (5)
15 In days or times past - part of bold ending! (5)
17 Floor covering (7)
20 Vegetable - red (8)
21 Resist the force of, manage with no help (4)
22 Lunatic (6)
23 Downbeat, unpleasant - got try! (6)

DOWN

1 Pull out further, give hand of friendship (6)
2 A low dam (4)
3 Make use of, put to good use (7)
4 Feeling a need to see others suffer (5)
5 Outrageous disregard (8)
6 Smoke stack on ship, cone for liquid pouring (6)
12 Thrilling atmosphere - from the main circuit? (8)
14 Favourable or superior viewing position (7)
16 Margin of error, tolerance (6)
18 Number (6)
19 Time being - no NEC! (5)
21 12 inch measure (4)

Colossal Book of Crosswords

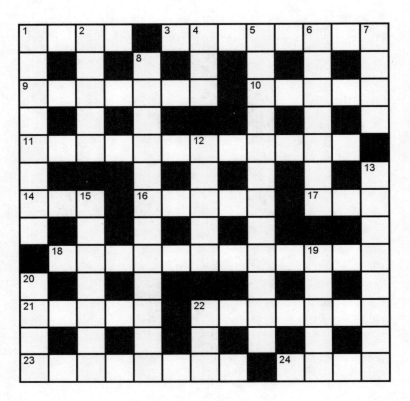

ACROSS

1 That which is sung - also snog messed up! (4)
3 Holiday homes towed by cars (8)
9 At ease, unwound (7)
10 Rushed to get somewhere (5)
11 The outcomes of action - queen sconces! (12)
14 Edge or rim, possibly of mouth (3)
16 One of a series published periodically (5)
17 As well, also, excessively (3)
18 Notwithstanding, even so - even shelters! (12)
21 Go and see someone or something (5)
22 Painters and sculptors (7)
23 Sorted out, decided (8)
24 Mathematical symbol (4)

DOWN

1 In a rigorous manner - cry stilt! (8)
2 Man made stocking material (5)
4 Used to connect words, clauses or sentences (3)
5 Orderly groupings (of things or persons) (12)
6 Very old - cane tin! (7)
7 Face (4)
8 Try out model or test version - pelt examiner! (12)
12 Knocked over, unhappy or worried state (5)
13 Is made up of (8)
15 Gives pleasure to (7)
19 Art support (5)
20 At all times; all the time and on every occasion (4)
22 Emulator or primate (3)

Colossal Book of Crosswords

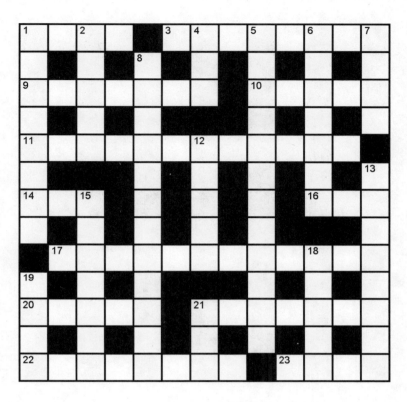

ACROSS

1 Torture instrument, display f rame (4)
3 Type of saw - Scots cur! (8)
9 Plant growing in the sea, (7)
10 Indian coin (5)
11 Thesis - disorients at! (12)
14 Small, long-eared horse like animal (3)
16 Body of water (3)
17 From door to door, as in a search (5-2-5)
20 Declare as sacred and forbidden (5)
21 A moulding at the corner between the ceiling and the top of a wall (7)
22 Seep through (8)
23 Shut up, confined - could be emotions? (4)

DOWN

1 Remainder - derail us! (8)
2 Blokes, leather riding leggings (5)
4 Colour (3)
5 Between the troposphere and the mesosphere (12)
6 Plenty of (7)
7 Type of diagram or woody plant (4)
8 Trading post, shop that sells a little of everything (7,5)
12 Harass with persistent criticism or carping (5)
13 Lower ground floor (8)
15 Drool - or blebs! (7)
18 Bring together (5)
19 A short distance sees pets turn round! (4)
21 Slice, the first being the deepest? (3)

Colossal Book of Crosswords

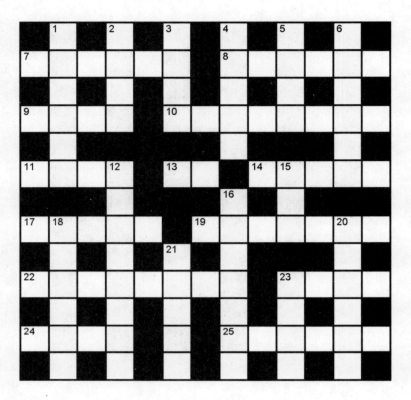

ACROSS

7 Coating on metal from aging process (6)

8 Without moral standards or principles - a molar! (6)

9 Leaning to one side or the other (4)

10 Situation - re casino! (8)

11 Shopping carriers, loads of something (4)

13 For example, to cut it short! (2)

14 Sword (5)

17 Moved gently or carefully (5)

19 Wailing spirit from Ireland (7)

22 Extend, drag out (8)

23 Mal's about to become a - close violently (4)

24 Running competition (4)

25 Join two pieces of metal - with metal (6)

DOWN

1 Posh dock? (6)

2 Unmarried Mrs? (4)

3 Settles account or bill (4)

4 Black bird (5)

5 Sort of star, or small vauxhall? (4)

6 Belonging to a country (6)

12 Climbing garden plant - we peseta! (8)

15 Small advertisements (3)

16 A Christian sacrament (7)

18 Aircraft person, male! (6)

20 Hard white tooth covering (6)

21 Gentleman's gentleman (5)

23 Material (4)

Colossal Book of Crosswords

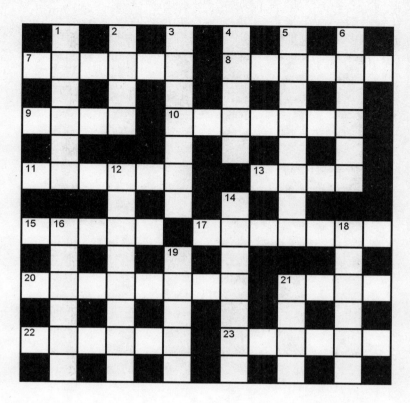

ACROSS

7 Still, not moving type of electricity (6)
8 Goes up, as a mountain (6)
9 Do as one is told (4)
10 Day of the week (7)
11 Folks, inhabit (6)
13 Burning liquid (4)
15 Map book (5)
17 Period of time, sitting (7)
20 Loudest (8)
21 Grain used as food, or Sir Tim? (4)
22 Started meeting, made available (6)
23 List of ingredients to make food dish (6)

DOWN

1 Horse home - reliable (6)
2 Remain where you are (4)
3 Run away in different directions (7)
4 Metal fastening used to fix wood (5)
5 Arched bridges (8)
6 Followed orders (6)
12 Lauding - pairings! (8)
14 100 years (7)
16 Soldiers (6)
18 Take over an area (6)
19 Give sustenance to (5)
21 Group of related peoples (4)

ACROSS

1 Wood fixings (6)
4 Caresses with the lips - ski SSE! (6)
9 Go round like a door? (7)
10 A dramatic work intended for performance by actors on a stage (5)
11 Heartbeat, as felt in writs or neck? (5)
12 Unable to escape (7)
13 Message describing how something is to be done (11)
18 Gloomiest, most depressing, blackest (7)
20 Make (somebody) laugh (5)
22 Happening (5)
23 A member of a police force (7)
24 Further than something, the pale? (6)
25 Plot or plan, strategy or dodge (6)

DOWN

1 Takes wallpaper off wall, or clothes? (6)
2 The contestant you hope to defeat (5)
3 Craziest, most untamed, like the West! (7)
5 Country (5)
6 Hair cleaner (7)
7 Football tiered seats (6)
8 Smashing up of something - tinctures do! (11)
14 Where babies or baby plants grow (7)
15 Motor vehicles deal illegally (7)
16 Verb modifier - braved! (6)
17 Qualification - in centigrade? (6)
19 Consumed as food (5)
21 Relative (5)

Colossal Book of Crosswords

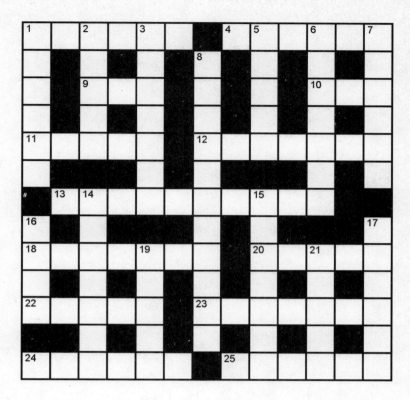

ACROSS

1 Indoors, within (6)
4 Travelling through the air (6)
9 Electrical measure (3)
10 Small creature found in man's pants! (3)
11 Local taxes, ranks (5)
12 Start of tennis game - with a smile? (7)
13 Ground shaking natural disaster (10)
18 Holiday cases (7)
20 After fifth (5)
22 Beam with brightness after polishing (5)
23 Sure (7)
24 Difficulty that causes worry or emotional tension (6)
25 Made happen, gave rise to - sauced! (6)

DOWN

1 Make certain of (6)
2 Intelligent or well turned out (5)
3 Small amount paid to reserve something (7)
5 Unsuccessful person, failure (5)
6 Form a mental image of something (7)
7 Bring together (6)
8 As a result of something (11)
14 More cross - earring! (7)
15 Country (7)
16 Mathematical symbol (4)
17 Called on the telephone (6)
19 Calculated spaces - domains - regions (5)
21 Roentgen rays - used in hospitals (1-4)

Colossal Book of Crosswords

ACROSS

1 Two wheeled transportation device (7)
5 Flyer (5)
8 Once more (5)
9 Hand movement to show feeling (7)
10 Set apart from other such things - disguised hint! (13)
11 Organisation - methods or rules governing behavior (6)
12 Plainly, merely (6)
15 Highly unusual or exceptional (13)
18 Traveller in foreign parts (7)
19 Perfect! (5)
20 Small bird with red breast (5)
21 Saves from (7)

DOWN

1 Game playing surface (5)
2 Taught groups in schools - sec lass! (7)
3 Thoughtfulness (13)
4 Betroth, or hire someone to work for you (6)
5 Future potential - bites oils sip I! (13)
6 Express mirth out loud (and the world joins in!) (5)
7 Day of the week (7)
11 Nicer, more sugary (7)
13 Flat top, of mountains? (7)
14 Novellist, author (6)
16 Digit (5)
17 Egg yellows! (5)

Colossal Book of Crosswords

ACROSS

1 Secret sexual relationships (7)
5 Failed to do something - did not, shorter (5)
8 Large person, beanstalk dweller? (5)
9 Put together, like a song (7)
10 Amusement - nine treatment! (13)
11 To do with race (6)
12 Hit someone, or knock down all tenpins! (6)
15 Swindle someone (3)
17 President Eisenhower - nickname (3)
19 No longer in existence - think Dodo! (7)
20 Picture, could be mental (5)
21 Large waves could be this - at lid! (5)
22 Seaside riding beasts - (Equus asinus) (7)

DOWN

1 Fish with a baited hook (5)
2 Excessively agitated (7)
3 Concerning more than one nation (13)
4 To do with people - get together! (6)
5 Public show of support or anger - DIY show? (13)
6 Went in motor vehicle (5)
7 Entertainment or place of same (7)
11 Most wealthy (7)
13 Reproduce someone's behavior or looks (7)
14 Changed from a solid to a liquid state (6)
16 Made a note of something said - toned! (5)
18 Wants, requirements (5)

Colossal Book of Crosswords

ACROSS

1 Specific practices of long standing - Scots um! (7)
5 Meeting controller, seating furniture item (5)
8 Inexpensive (5)
9 Locating, outcome of enquiry (7)
10 Large ad in paper or on TV (13)
11 Save from difficult situation (6)
12 Gluey - could be a difficult situation! (6)
15 Thoughtfulness (13)
18 Amount - often controlled (7)
19 Things - possibly in a list (5)
20 Garden storage units - often wooden (5)
21 Underground passageways (7)

DOWN

1 Chocolate bean (5)
2 Book holders fixed to walls (7)
3 Possibilities - do they sometimes knock? (13)
4 Something on the end of a word (6)
5 Complete attention; intense mental effort (13)
6 Full of life, and sometimes kicking? (5)
7 Quite so! Justifiedly (7)
11 Instructions for cookery, often in books (7)
13 Inhabitants of China (7)
14 Monkey nut (6)
16 Hospital carer (5)
17 Birds' homes (5)

Colossal Book of Crosswords

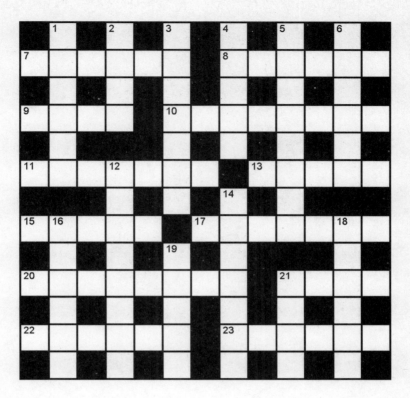

ACROSS

7 Place to buy and sell (6)
8 Covers up with soil - fox's home (6)
9 Device to capture something, part returns! (4)
10 Furnished with - pod diver! (8)
11 Took pleasure from (7)
13 Applying the mind to learning - or the room you use to do it in? (5)
15 More tan once, less than three times (5)
17 Rabbit houses (7)
20 Hatched frogspawn (8)
21 Torn clothes sometimes lead to riches? (4)
22 Go to, be at, listen to (6)
23 Rely upon, have faith in (6)

DOWN

1 No use for cultivation (6)
2 Bypass, rubbish container, small jump (4)
3 Came to a complete halt (7)
4 Fruit (5)
5 Creative - attic sir? (8)
6 Defence device, protect (6)
12 Having a tenant, being in use (8)
14 Exterior, having a small chance of success (7)
16 An abundance of material possessions (6)
18 Walking cautiously - end gig! (6)
19 Move smoothly and effortlessly (5)
21 Thick string? Open pore to see! (4)

Colossal Book of Crosswords

ACROSS

7 Narrow channel found on record (6)
8 Great fear (6)
9 Bitter tasting, bad milk? (4)
10 Decade, after twenties! (8)
11 Fruit tree plantation (7)
13 Before all others (5)
15 Whisky making device - static (5)
17 Highly educated - Leander! (7)
20 More than millions! (8)
21 Title (4)
22 A human being (6)
23 Gas - O! (6)

DOWN

1 Military protective covering (6)
2 Having little money (4)
3 Go out, into possible uncertainty (7)
4 Top room, found among cat ticklers! (5)
5 More pretty! (8)
6 Holiday lodgings - not hostel! (6)
12 Unable to manage independently (8)
14 Period of time devoted to specific activity (7)
16 Related groups - bestir! (6)
18 Obtained through work (6)
19 Urban areas smaller than cities (5)
21 Produce egg (3)

Colossal Book of Crosswords

ACROSS

7 Sticks tied together (6)
8 Sounds returning after reflecting from surfaces (6)
9 Particular services (4)
10 Approximate the cost of something (8)
11 Vegetables, usually orange (7)
13 Stand above someone, tall thin building (5)
15 Country (5)
17 Small wild flowers (7)
20 Creates or manufactures a man-made product (8)
21 Submachine gun, gas powered (4)
22 Lightproof box used in photography (6)
23 Almost (6)

DOWN

1 A former communist country (6)
2 Make a sum by combining numbers (4)
3 Rest day - TV sheen! (7)
4 Monies owed (5)
5 Washes hair - hoops sam! (8)
6 Middle (6)
12 Rudolph is one (8)
14 Giving rise to something - saucing! (7)
16 Country (6)
18 To an equal depth or amount (6)
19 Large sea (5)
21 Wooden support, smile brightly (4)

Colossal Book of Crosswords

ACROSS

1 Ballot (4)
3 Counted by slimmers? (8)
9 More finely honed - harpers! (7)
10 Survive - sex it! (5)
11 Subject matter - film music? (5)
12 Acquired by using sight - aids? (6)
14 Motorcyclists or jockeys for example? (6)
16 Harsh (6)
19 Play violin - like Nero? (6)
21 Stout-bodied amphibians - from the Hall? (5)
24 Country and type of pottery (5)
25 Stress in thing pulled taught? (7)
26 Attendance list used in school (8)
27 Not pretend - actually happening! (4)

DOWN

1 Guests (8)
2 Track down, through thin paper? (5)
4 Get there (6)
5 Cooking chambers (5)
6 Pretend to be someone else, copy (7)
7 Land where something is put (4)
8 Go before a magistrate - re papa! (6)
13 Dependent on a particular season (8)
15 Controlling car, or sending me mad! (7)
17 Pull or push out, offer friendship (6)
18 Insect or Volkswagen? (6)
20 Shares out cards in a game (5)
22 Similar (5)
23 mark left by healed cut (4)

ACROSS

1 Half a pair of mens leg coverings? (7)
5 Goes up, like hot air (5)
8 In general, being non specific (9)
9 Period of time in true rail history (3)
10 Have faith in someone (5)
12 Highest structure or tale? (7)
13 Place where people live - huge Robin Hood! (13)
15 Having no function (7)
17 Computer data storage devices (5)
19 Belonging to him (3)
20 A basic truth or law or assumption (9)
22 From the sea? (5)
23 Unhappiness, sorrowfulness (7)

DOWN

1 Well fitting, not loose (5)
2 Possess (3)
3 Pull out to full length or further? (7)
4 Kinships - nip horsetails! (13)
5 Regal, of ruling family (5)
6 Bones, sometimes found in cupboards? (9)
7 At an angle - ants led! (7)
11 Of worldwide scope or applicability (9)
13 Zeros (7)
14 Made smaller or lowered in price (7)
16 Depleted, void (5)
18 Garden stores (5)
21 Apple, blueberry, meat and potato? (3)

Colossal Book of Crosswords

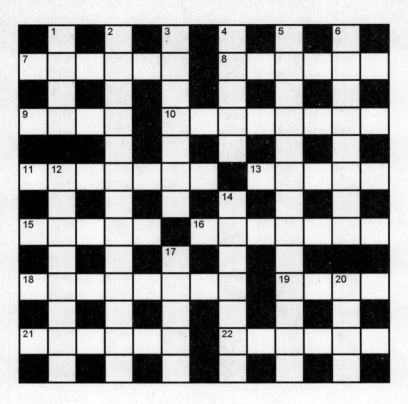

ACROSS

7 Chases, romantically, or places of justice (6)
8 Kerchief (6)
9 Computer information (4)
10 Given permission for a loan, or building project? (8)
11 Puts one in mind of (7)
13 Grey matter! (5)
15 Book of maps (5)
16 Languages - no guest! (7)
18 Time spent learning a job or craft (8)
19 Sail holder on ship (4)
21 Notified of danger or risk (6)
22 Mess, of hair or wool or weeds maybe? (6)

DOWN

1 Comfy two seater (4)
2 Groups of people who work together (13)
3 Small land masses surrounded by sea (7)
4 Places to buy things (5)
5 The expression of approval and support (13)
6 In like or similar manner, the same (8)
12 Outside (8)
14 Does not remember (7)
17 Comes across something previously lost (5)
20 Condiment found in water (4)

Colossal Book of Crosswords

ACROSS

7 Salad item (6)
8 Any part of the rainbow will be one! (6)
9 Implements (4)
10 Move from one team to another (8)
11 Country (7)
13 Animal parasites and garden helpers (5)
15 Unclear about something (5)
17 Time for relaxation (7)
20 Paint a word picture (8)
21 Domesticated bovine animals (4)
22 Distinguishing speech sound, maybe local? (6)
23 Electorate (6)

DOWN

1 Slacken off (6)
2 Beams of light (4)
3 Arranging into piles, like letters (7)
4 Sea (5)
5 Fruit tree flowers (8)
6 Place of antiquities (6)
12 Sets off - clues han! (8)
14 Be worthy of or have a certain rating (7)
16 Organisation that arranges work (6)
18 Money given for criminal capture? (6)
19 Retirement age for some (5)
21 Felines, also musical play (4)

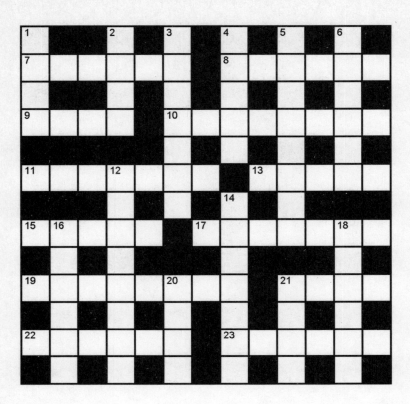

ACROSS

7 Lower in temperature (6)
8 Lavatory (6)
9 Friend or sex partner (4)
10 Clumsy (8)
11 Change from one religion to another (7)
13 Have a feeling about something (5)
15 Tablets (5)
17 Persons who are tricked or swindled (7)
19 Moves forward, in technology perhaps? (8)
21 This waits for no man (4)
22 A cream broken makes photo gear! (6)
23 Cleans with soap and water (6)

DOWN

1 A fraudulent business scheme - macs inside out! (4)
2 The boundary of a surface (4)
3 Shopping - various items - some green? (7)
4 Wakes up - with a spoon? (5)
5 Daftest, most foolish (8)
6 Parts of poems or hymns (6)
12 Small settlements (8)
14 Puzzles made with cut out pieces (7)
16 From India (6)
18 Someone who belongs to a certain group (6)
20 Scots family group with tartan (4)
21 Try out - cricket match? (4)

Colossal Book of Crosswords

ACROSS

7 Native american dwelling (6)
8 Sea thief with black and white flag (6)
9 Small insects that thrive in colonies (4)
10 Nonstick, slithery, slimy (8)
11 Wandered or sailed aimlessly (7)
13 What is left after fires (5)
15 Get a goal (5)
17 Areas of water left after rain (7)
20 Be of a different opinion (8)
21 Goes about on one leg - beer plant? (4)
22 Cutting weapons, leaves of grass (6)
23 Cognitive processes whereby past is remembered (6)

DOWN

1 Mealtime (6)
2 Night birds or people? (4)
3 Broken, like a record? (7)
4 Snapped or broken in two (5)
5 Asked for hand in marriage (8)
6 Do without food (6)
12 Towards the front (8)
14 Buildings housing historical artefacts (7)
16 Cold (6)
18 Someone with great knowledge (6)
19 Have faith in (5)
21 Where you live, where the heart is? (4)

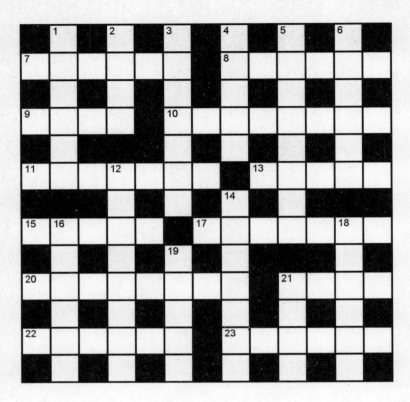

ACROSS

7 Country (6)
8 Frightens (6)
9 Previously priced at .... (4)
10 Unswerving following of someone or something (8)
11 Learner (7)
13 Vision, for sore eyes? (5)
15 Yellow fruit (5)
17 Groups in a school (7)
20 Attribute shared by a group or class (8)
21 Trees when cut for fires (4)
22 Clothes boxes and elephant's noses! (6)
23 Not so long ago (6)

DOWN

1 Have an impact on (6)
2 Travel by walking (4)
3 Places where flowers and vegetables are grown (7)
4 One way device (5)
5 Leads the team, team leaders (8)
6 Lacking obstructions or difficulties (6)
12 Leaving player out of team - pop grind! (8)
14 Theatrical performers or sports people (7)
16 Mistakes (6)
18 Making one's way with care (6)
19 An alloy of copper and zinc (5)
21 The state of needing something that is absent (4)

155

Colossal Book of Crosswords

ACROSS

7 Wild and menacing (6)
8 Surprised or shocked (6)
9 Scented flower (4)
10 Keeps under cover (8)
11 Go forward (7)
13 Animals (5)
15 Cooks in fat (5)
17 Tooth and gum doctor (7)
20 Seats of government (8)
21 Bad things that you do in life, could be cardinal! (4)
22 Insect or overhanging brows (6)
23 Closer (6)

DOWN

1 Good turn, done for a friend (6)
2 Arriving after the start (4)
3 Childhood illness, usually (7)
4 Assigns a rank or position to something (5)
5 Most distant (8)
6 Great fear (6)
12 Shops dispensing drugs (8)
14 Fooling around, untidying something (7)
16 One who reads a book (6)
18 One who sings (6)
19 Amusements or pastimes (5)
21 Pals return to find face hit! (4)

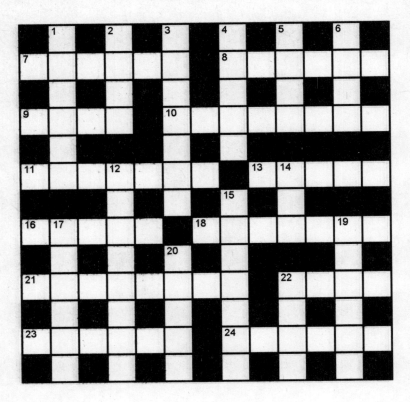

ACROSS

7 Short trip to deliver message (6)
8 Build up, usually money (6)
9 An ancient city in Asia Minor (4)
10 Volcanic glass - bin adios! (8)
11 Method of cooking usually in a wok (4-3)
13 Particular number of magazine of paper (5)
16 Pop open like pricked balloon (5)
18 Engage in boisterous, drunken merry-making - rioters! (7)
21 Reach the highest point of (8)
22 Precious stone (4)
23 Qualification at Bachelor or Master level (6)
24 First in order of birth (6)

DOWN

1 A crumbling and drying of timber (3,3)
2 A bit naughty (4)
3 Break from a meeting or gathering (7)
4 Wild flower (5)
5 Liquid that burns or corrodes (4)
6 Girl's name - Lenska, actress for example (4)
12 Girl's name and herb (8)
14 Little sister found in insistent noise! (3)
15 Items of neck wear for formal gatherings (3,4)
17 Loan shark - re urus! (6)
19 Raise in a relief - stamp (6)
20 A fleshy underground stem or root (5)
22 Naughty, unrefined (4)

Colossal Book of Crosswords

ACROSS

7 Book writer (6)
8 A rational motive for a belief or action (6)
9 Walk with a damaged leg (4)
10 From Egypt (8)
11 Type of stone (7)
13 Girl or beach type (5)
15 From Switzerland (5)
17 Edges of a country maybe (7)
20 Envelop completely (8)
21 Tax paid on imported goods (4)
22 Grown ups (6)
23 Is the same as, is the sum of two numbers (6)

DOWN

1 More fully engaged or occupied (6)
2 Boat for passengers or cargo carriage (4)
3 Holy men (7)
4 Colours made up of black and white only (5)
5 Towards the east! (8)
6 A person who shows fear or timidity (6)
12 Nose openings, may be flared (8)
14 Military man (7)
16 Cuts or other damage to body (6)
18 Baby's toy that makes noise when shaken (6)
19 Estimate based on little or no information (5)
21 Instrument and part of ear (4)

Colossal Book of Crosswords

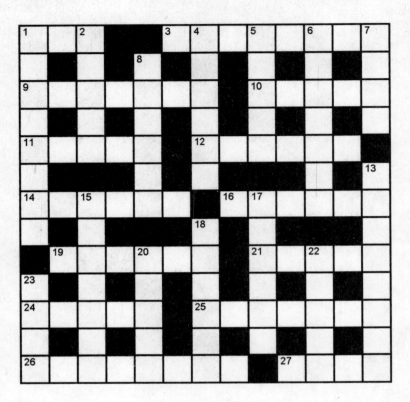

ACROSS

1 A slippery or viscous liquid (3)
3 Given the go ahead (8)
9 Think that someone is involved in a crime (7)
10 Cast away by hand, gave a party (5)
11 Building tops - for so! (5)
12 From foreign parts - cox tie! (6)
14 Consuming food (6)
16 Pushes in like canal boats (6)
19 Sound of something falling in water (6)
21 The contestant you hope to defeat (5)
24 Country producing pottery (5)
25 Bright red (7)
26 Set up, bring order to (8)
27 Look at something that is written or printed (4)

DOWN

1 Watched, seen (8)
2 Cowboy rope for catching animals (5)
4 Tapped gently in affectionate manner (6)
5 Relative amounts of one to another - a riot! (5)
6 Never the same, changing (7)
7 Soft fine feathers (4)
8 Period of learning (6)
13 On its own, cut off or left behind (8)
15 Giving extra payment to a waiter or driver (7)
17 Away from home in a foreign land (6)
18 Spectres of the dead (6)
20 Once more (5)
22 One way device, in car engine sometimes (5)
23 Returning sound, bounced back (4)

Colossal Book of Crosswords

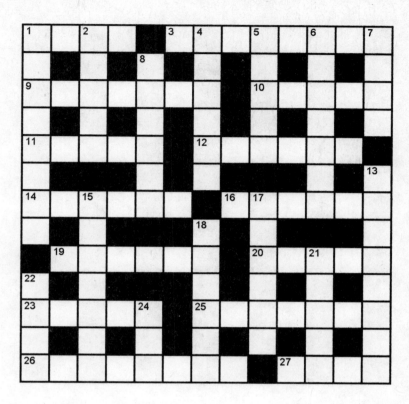

ACROSS

1 Let go, allow to fall (4)
3 Strictly correct (8)
9 Having no function (7)
10 Grabs with teeth and jaws (5)
11 Makes hotter, selection races (5)
12 Capital of England (6)
14 Finishing (6)
16 Country, once in USSR (6)
19 Special sets of circumstances (6)
20 Minimal in magnitude (5)
23 Number of one thing to another, 1:3 for example (5)
25 Unprofessional, unpaid (7)
26 All at once, without warning (8)
27 Brings together (4)

DOWN

1 Female child (8)
2 Sung play (5)
4 Fortified dwelling and chess move (6)
5 Densely populated area (5)
6 Military engagements, things done (7)
7 Compass point (4)
8 Reduce in intensity (6)
13 Grazing areas, sometimes we head for new ones (8)
15 Zealous in affection (7)
17 Take out luggage (6)
18 Country (6)
21 Forwards - at the front (5)
22 Star turn to reveal creative pastimes (4)
24 Singular (3)

Colossal Book of Crosswords

ACROSS

7 Pass in a specific way; as of time, pays out cash (6)
8 Any substance that causes injury or illness (6)
9 Joint in leg (4)
10 Things, written in newspapers (8)
11 Cast about, plough the fields and do this to seed (7)
13 Void, having no content (5)
15 Sudden loud noises (5)
16 Salad bowl content (7)
18 On the upper floor (8)
19 Short instruction or musical sound (4)
21 Takes pleasure from something (6)
22 Having been unsealed - nee pod! (6)

DOWN

1 Unseal! (4)
2 Criminal enquiry to find the guilty (13)
3 Feeling guilt or embarrassment or remorse (7)
4 Blemishes, catches sight of (5)
5 Situation, possibly financial, possibly reduced! (13)
6 To do with the home, servant (8)
12 Bringing hands together in applause (8)
14 Stress or latent hostility (7)
17 In the middle of (5)
20 Swarm is meet in retreat! (4)

Colossal Book of Crosswords

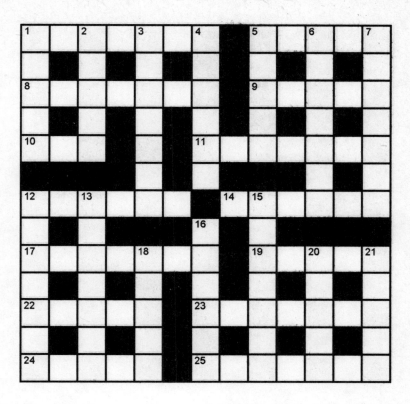

ACROSS

1 Road, belonging to the crown? (7)
5 Skill in an occupation or trade (5)
8 Odd, different (7)
9 Unfasten, release from bondage (5)
10 Fasten, take into bondage (3)
11 Fought against (7)
12 Discussion, sometimes followed by a vote (6)
14 Covered in grass, like a knoll? (6)
17 Place where things can be kept (7)
19 True information (5)
22 Not tight (5)
23 Removing skins, prior to cooking sometimes (7)
24 Up and down toys - on string! (2-3)
25 Take out, remove, like a tooth (7)

DOWN

1 Favourite place where people gather (5)
2 Measure amount, instrument to do this (5)
3 Would not - less o! (7)
4 Colour of custard (6)
5 A compact mass, cluster, flock (5)
6 Painters and sculptors (7)
7 Day of the week (7)
12 Show off, show characteristics (7)
13 Science of living things (7)
15 Bounce light from a surface (7)
16 Persons, citizens of a state or country (6)
18 Places, subjects of study (5)
20 A communist nation (5)
21 Ability to see (5)

Colossal Book of Crosswords

ACROSS

7 Take the trouble to do something (6)
8 Being of use or service (6)
9 Complete collection, part of tennis match (3)
10 A feeling of envy, green-eyed monster! (8)
11 Sloping letters (7)
13 Could be common, feel something is right (5)
15 More than once (5)
17 Two wheeled man powered transport (7)
20 One who does tricks (8)
21 Come up, like yeast bread? (4)
22 Homes, dwellings (6)
23 Suit maker (6)

DOWN

1 Part of UK, in the south (6)
2 Fired from a gun, type of gun? (4)
3 Show slides, push forward (7)
4 Sweet substance used in cakes, etc (5)
5 Getting back to normal, gradual healing (8)
6 Visitors to whom hospitality is extended (6)
12 Most fortunate - tickle us! (8)
14 Formality in bearing and appearance (7)
16 Device used in armed fighting (6)
18 Punishment intended as a warning to others (6)
19 Before all others (5)
21 Horizontal bar (4)

Colossal Book of Crosswords

ACROSS

1 Shout or telephone someone (4)
3 Digestive organs, puts up with (8)
9 Times of the year (7)
10 Large rodent (3)
11 Your personal views or intentions (5)
12 Remove cargo (6)
14 Almost (6)
16 At rest, slumbering (6)
19 A plant cultivated for its blooms (6)
21 A restraint used to slow or stop a vehicle (5)
24 Stitched together with needle and thread (5)
25 Tanned animal skin (7)
26 Toward one side (8)
27 Second hand (4)

DOWN

1 Soft bag filled with padding, damper (7)
2 Holiday, go out from a place (5)
4 Thin layer, of lies or paper? (6)
5 The significance of a story or event (5)
6 Small house, sometimes in countryside (7)
7 Come to a halt (4)
8 Impression of something very old (6)
13 Came into view, seemed (8)
15 Permitted (7)
17 Underground railway, underground pass (6)
18 Umbrella, informally (6)
20 Deceased man's wife (5)
22 Residue following burning (5)
23 Makes use of something (4)

ACROSS

1 Murdering, possibly time? (7)
5 Preliminary design or document (5)
8 Large trucks (7)
9 Poem (3)
10 What a witch will cast (5)
11 Awarded office by ballot (7)
12 Make shine by cleaning and rubbing (6)
14 Crazily (6)
17 Announce officially - cleared! (7)
19 Perfect, like a partner? (5)
22 Language of ancient Rome (5)
23 Decorator or artist (7)
24 Father, papa (5)
25 US currency (7)

DOWN

1 Murders (5)
2 Very big (5)
3 Frozen water drips (7)
4 Breathed noisily and exhaustedly (6)
5 Trip the light fantastic, terpsichore (5)
6 Take into one's family (7)
7 Day of the week (7)
12 Walked in water up to ankle deep (7)
13 Discovered, determined, found (7)
15 Letter replacing first name, first (7)
16 Assisted, aided (6)
18 Irritate (5)
20 Additional (5)
21 Accompany ladies - titled persons (5)

ACROSS

7 Secret sexual relationship (6)
8 Destroyed (6)
9 Caustic substance, green fruit (4)
10 Projecting land mass - in amount! (8)
11 Most idle (7)
13 Grab hold of, understand (5)
15 Electric current passed through body (5)
17 Hoodwinked (7)
20 Suddenly, without warning (8)
21 No longer in captivity (4)
22 Natural body of running water (6)
23 Number (6)

DOWN

1 Country and continent (6)
2 Make easier, make less difficult (4)
3 Verbal commitment, undertaking (7)
4 Having or displaying great dignity or nobility (5)
5 Belonging to the past (8)
6 Exceptional creative ability (6)
12 Consider as part of something (8)
14 Colouring sticks (7)
16 Established customs (6)
18 Happenings (6)
19 Individual instances of a type of symbol (5)
21 Having or displaying warmth or affection (4)

Colossal Book of Crosswords

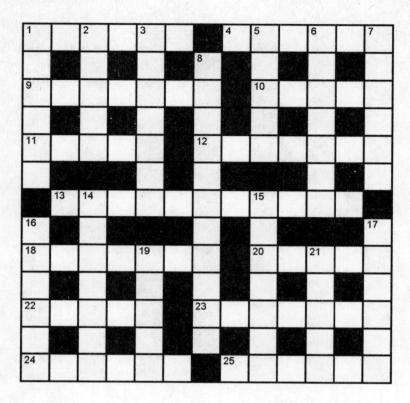

ACROSS

1 Take over land, fill time with activity (6)
4 Made laugh, entertained (6)
9 Country (7)
10 Cover worn in kitchen (5)
11 Medical attendant (5)
12 Goes out from, the hand of friendship? (7)
13 Complete with pictures or diagrams (11)
18 Taste or atmosphere (7)
20 Lighting device for carrying (5)
22 Be extant (5)
23 Make visible (7)
24 Large felines of forests in Asia; endangered (6)
25 A unit of temperature on a specified scale (6)

DOWN

1 Large bodies of sea water (6)
2 A roll of tobacco for smoking (5)
3 Eat paul - confused for high flat land area (7)
5 Have in mind as a purpose (5)
6 Odd, unusual (7)
7 From Denmark (6)
8 Seeking out new and daring enterprises (11)
14 An inclination, to do something (7)
15 Newspaper piece, part of training contract (7)
16 A symptom caused by an illness or a drug (6)
17 Run towards, pay by credit card (6)
19 Being on the outside or further from a centre (5)
21 A large natural stream of water (5)

ACROSS

1 Belonging to us (4)
3 On or of upper floors of a building (8)
9 Breed of hunting dog (7)
10 Sung play, can be grand (5)
11 Fine, see through, straight drop! (5)
12 Playground toy (6)
14 Names of works of art or books (6)
16 Boat propulsion device (6)
19 Early radio components - pre transistors (6)
21 Allow entrance, own up (5)
24 Horse controls (5)
25 Of no exceptional quality or ability (7)
26 Number (8)
27 Demands of, requires question answering (4)

DOWN

1 Being directly across from each other; facing (8)
2 Increasing the size of a bet (as in poker) (5)
4 Put into words or an expression (6)
5 Plural of that (5)
6 Country (7)
7 Smack across face (4)
8 Die of food deprivation (6)
13 Bird coverings (8)
15 Ripping, travelling very quickly along (7)
17 Astonished, astounded (6)
18 Break free of imprisonment (6)
20 Go and see someone (5)
22 Food servings (5)
23 Not false, proper alignment (4)

Colossal Book of Crosswords

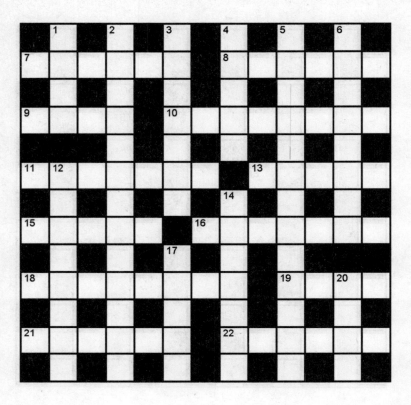

ACROSS

7 Place to see films (6)
8 Unmoving, source of electricity? (6)
9 Building block for children - ogle transformed! (4)
10 Worthy of honour - dueHonourr! (8)
11 Learning periods (7)
13 Sample by mouth (5)
15 Worries (5)
16 All that is remembered of the past - shy riot! (7)
18 In a resentful manner - by litter! (8)
19 Fishing poles (4)
21 Pretend not to see (6)
22 Yearned for (6)

DOWN

1 (Ca(OH)2) (4)
2 Presentation or protest (13)
3 Getting clean with soap and water (7)
4 Utilising (5)
5 Making something (13)
6 Film supervisor - record it! (8)
12 The latter parts of the days (8)
14 Pedal powered transport (7)
17 Had a go at - put into court (5)
20 Antlered creature (sounds expensive!) (4)

Colossal Book of Crosswords

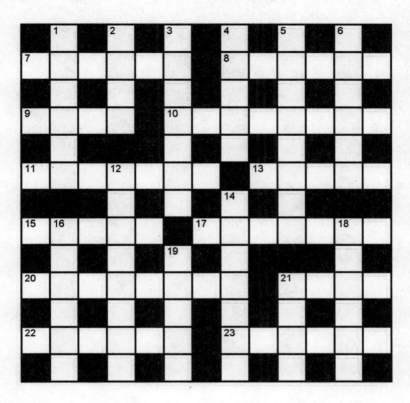

ACROSS

7 Disappear (6)
8 Frozen water, suspended (6)
9 Not different (4)
10 Stops from happening (8)
11 Provided with a worthy adversary or competitor (7)
13 Aquatic bird, pinch bottom! (5)
15 Being derived from (5)
17 Tooth doctor (7)
20 A wheeled vehicle drawn by horses (8)
21 Canvas holiday accommodation (4)
22 Very strong or vigorous, grave, strict (6)
23 Open toed footwear (6)

DOWN

1 Country (6)
2 Mile, confused, fruit (4)
3 Transport commercially, possibly over water (7)
4 Garment with covered interior (5)
5 Coastguard rescue vessel (8)
6 Dishes on which food is served and eaten (6)
12 Fruits with a single hard stone (8)
14 Go backwards (7)
16 Taken aback (6)
18 Day of the week, for resting? (6)
19 Removed (5)
21 The quality of a person's voice (4)

Colossal Book of Crosswords

ACROSS

1 Money (4)
3 Laughed quietly or with restraint (8)
9 Closest (7)
10 Child minder (5)
11 Problems (12)
14 Gone by; or in the past (3)
16 Support oneself (5)
17 As well, in addition, plus (3)
18 Put (things or places) in order (12)
21 Not securely fixed (5)
22 An oxide containing two atoms of oxygen in the molecule (7)
23 Cause for concern (8)
24 Particular services, employments (4)

DOWN

1 From Canada (8)
2 Employed personnel in a business, stick (5)
4 Small crude shelter used as a dwelling (3)
5 The way in which someone or something is composed - coot tinnitus! (12)
6 Being the greatest in length - lo gents! (7)
7 Period of time (3)
8 On purpose (12)
12 Making use of (5)
13 Moral excellence (8)
15 In the garden perhaps, not indoor! (7)
19 Finger ends or wood joiners (5)
20 Propel with breath, like football, strike (4)
22 Secret hideaway hidden in Dennis Smith! (3)

Colossal Book of Crosswords

ACROSS

6 Not private; open to or concerning the people (6)
7 A general conscious awareness, common? (5)
8 Ruminant with horns (4)
9 Large outdoor fire, traditional on November 5th (7)
10 Wine store (6)
12 Here is without an i (5)
14 Cutting device (5)
16 Load bearing trucks (7)
19 Work of poet or author - twin rigs! (8)
20 Slender (4)
21 Head covering for motor cyclist (6)
22 Thin - escape? (6)

DOWN

1 Continent (6)
2 Plan against someone, or the plan itself (4)
3 Large floating mass of frozen water (7)
4 Train driver or applied scientist (8)
5 Harsh (6)
7 Fall to bottom of sea - kitchen pot wash area! (4)
11 Period between birth and death (8)
13 Living accommodation - lodgings (7)
15 Cared for when ill, brought back to health (6)
17 Magazine or newspaper controller (6)
18 Make with needles and wool (4)
20 Certain (4)

Colossal Book of Crosswords

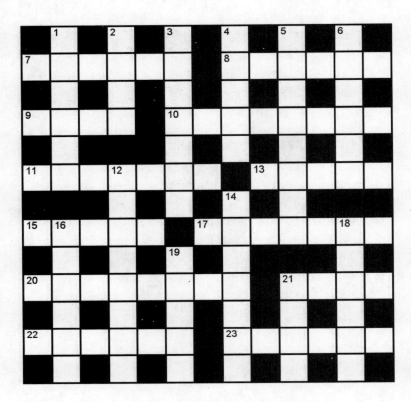

ACROSS

7 Find - cat Leo! (6)
8 Putting down in a layer, producing eggs (6)
9 Drivers' compartments (4)
10 Flat areas - comes to the top of the sea (8)
11 Line where sky and earth meet (7)
13 Top prize, level of best degree (5)
15 Group of lions, self respect (5)
17 Adult male chicken (7)
20 Arguments, crossbow arrows (8)
21 Portable container, look at with view to robbery (4)
22 Writing or drawing implement (6)
23 Make it possible for someone to do something (6)

DOWN

1 Love apple (6)
2 Felines (4)
3 Stress as in taut pulled material (7)
4 Fear or fire bell (5)
5 Egyptian structures (8)
6 Heavenly persons (6)
12 By a circuitous route (8)
14 Cooked in a hot oven (7)
16 Established lines of travel or access (6)
18 With little difficulty (6)
19 Expresses an idea in words (5)
21 Fuel from mines (4)

Colossal Book of Crosswords

ACROSS

7 Place where there is no air, cleaner? (6)
8 On a ship or train (6)
9 Halt (4)
10 Sent back, possibly to sender (8)
11 Take something to be true (7)
13 Make an addition by combining numbers (5)
15 Ice crystals forming a white deposit - Jack? (5)
17 Right, put right (7)
20 Spattered a liquid around (8)
21 Present (4)
22 Difficult, not straightforward (6)
23 Closer (6)

DOWN

1 Hostile meeting, conflict, fight against (6)
2 Drop somewhere unceremoniously (4)
3 Make better (7)
4 Rubbish left out for disposal (5)
5 Linking room in offices or trains (8)
6 Drop below point where water becomes solid (6)
12 Example or occurence (8)
14 Keeping hold of, retaining (7)
16 Sound of gun, written findings (6)
18 Hot drink (6)
19 They would! (5)
21 Creature kept for milk - butter! (4)

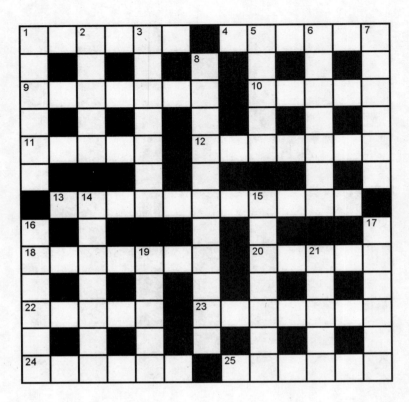

ACROSS

1 Receive willingly something given or offered (6)
4 Jail (6)
9 Picture giving instructions (7)
10 Yellow fruit (5)
11 Impudent aggressiveness (5)
12 Aeroplane take off and landing place (7)
13 Added to, gave to (11)
18 Mythical horned horse (7)
20 Jockey (5)
22 Small fruit source of oil (5)
23 cases taken on trip or holiday (7)
24 Fight back, hold off opposition (6)
25 Takes without permission, robs (6)

DOWN

1 Bringing something to meeting, joining numbers (6)
2 Controller of meeting (5)
3 One part in a hundred (7)
5 Measuring stick (5)
6 A human being, an individual (7)
7 Number (6)
8 Tin playtime - reorder, waiting with impatience (11)
14 Where things comes from, like species (7)
15 Vertical, model citizen? (7)
16 Jokes, laughter, fun all contribute to this (6)
17 Unpleasant people, moves furtively (6)
19 Does as ordered (5)
21 Theatre production (5)

Colossal Book of Crosswords

ACROSS

1 Admit into a group or community (6)
4 Box used for burial (6)
9 Plant leaf used for smoking and chewing (7)
10 Tossed through the air (5)
11 Platform for books, etc (5)
12 Flaps of material under the laces of a shoe (7)
13 A lavishly produced performance (11)
18 Most blanched - twist he! (7)
20 Send or direct for treatment (5)
22 Mean or intend to express or convey (5)
23 Every night (7)
24 Speaking, old sore (6)
25 Remained in one place (6)

DOWN

1 Creative person (6)
2 Thick wire, often twisted from many strands (5)
3 Ocean (7)
5 Frequently, many times (5)
6 Standard procedure, liquid food for infants (7)
7 Latest, most recent (6)
8 Strikingly different - snorting cat! (11)
14 First, as school (7)
15 Vertical (7)
16 Marshy lands, fills quickly (6)
17 Offered up to god (6)
19 Consumed by mouth (5)
21 Insult aimed at overweight person (5)

Colossal Book of Crosswords

ACROSS

1 Hits (6)
4 Cut with uneven or ragged edge (6)
9 Detonate, burst open (7)
10 Special winning card, get the better of (5)
11 Trio (5)
12 Pull out of shape (7)
13 Rural areas (11)
18 Sleeping quarters (7)
20 Country (5)
22 Kitchen protective wear (5)
23 Nought, nil, zilch (7)
24 Lowered and raised head to show agreement (6)
25 Grown ups (6)

DOWN

1 Number (6)
2 Topmost one in two - possibly hand? (5)
3 Found in food - pointer! (7)
5 Post, later on, subsequently (5)
6 Made a sound, like a pig! (7)
7 Extent downward or inward - tes phd! (6)
8 Dimension (11)
14 Told what to do, asked for food from menu (7)
15 Moved very slightly, like sand? (7)
16 Get hold of (6)
17 Flat bottomed boats (6)
19 Sixteenth part of a pound in weight (5)
21 Make soldiers perform, or make hole (5)

Colossal Book of Crosswords

ACROSS

1 Going out with, seeing someone (6)
4 Distribute evenly in many directions (6)
9 Used to make cigarettes (7)
10 Small lakes, brings together resources or skills (5)
11 The immediate descendants of a person (5)
12 The act of narration (7)
13 Coming near to - chapping oar! (11)
18 Try - matt pet! (7)
20 Larger than average person (5)
22 Something considered choice to eat (5)
23 An insignificant place - here now! (7)
24 Beat, of a song, poem or heartbeat (6)
25 Operating software in computer - sets my! (6)

DOWN

1 Small part or isolated fact (6)
2 Long hollow conduits (5)
3 Weapons using atomic energy (7)
5 Learner in school (5)
6 Wearing away by water, wind, etc (7)
7 The creation of something in the mind - signed! (6)
8 Strikingly different when compared (11)
14 A workshop where clayware is made (7)
15 Main road - hay whig! (7)
16 Beat up badly, or coat like fish for frying (6)
17 Small river or exodus of people (6)
19 Cigarette lighter or football contest (5)
21 Are not! (5)

ACROSS

1 An arrangement scheme (6)
4 Tremble convulsively - shrive! (6)
9 Large North American Bison (7)
10 Prize for cricket match - sea sh! (5)
11 Fatigued (5)
12 Sees something - announcements (7)
13 Feeling uneasy and self-conscious (11)
18 Sets of items wrapped or tied together (7)
21 Coat with a thin layer of gold or silver (5)
23 Be, live (5)
24 Cover completely or make imperceptible (7)
25 Type of vision or passageway (6)
26 Playground toy (6)

DOWN

1 Discuss the pros and cons of an issue (6)
2 Freer from risk or danger - fears! (5)
3 The mother of your father or mother (7)
5 Blood pump in animals (5)
6 Conveyance - he Clive! (7)
7 Hold back, fight back, refuse to comply (6)
8 Thick skin on foot (4)
14 An official recognition of merit - in Monet! (7)
15 Imagine, speculate, reckon - us popes! (7)
16 A real thing, or express

179

Colossal Book of Crosswords

ACROSS

7 Type of tree and wood (6)
8 An indulgence, elegant and sumptuous (6)
9 The left or the right (4)
10 Eavesdropper or radio fan - enlist re! (8)
11 Odd, out of the ordinary (7)
13 Set a maximum threshold (5)
15 Take without asking (5)
16 From abroad, alien (7)
18 So raided, confused, forms verge (8)
19 Ceramic wall decoration (4)
21 Set off, possibly sky rocket (6)
22 Number (6)

DOWN

1 Hire car with driver (4)
2 A promise, capacity for rational thought (13)
3 From Italy (7)
4 People having the same social or economic status (5)
5 Trying something out, looking into something (13)
6 Very cold, change to ice (8)
12 Belonging to the nation (8)
14 A person - see moon! (7)
17 Dark part of diurnal cycle (5)
20 Plenty on offer at auction room (4)

ACROSS

7 Umbrella (6)
8 Required, be in want of (6)
9 Thyself ;(archaic) (4)
10 The main things you are thinking about (8)
11 Medical man or woman (6)
13 Higher than, beyond reproach? (5)
15 Original thoughts (5)
16 With pride (7)
18 Going on forever, having no end (8)
19 Precipitation of ice pellets (4)
21 Fruit (6)
22 Unfasten to some degree, slacken (6)

DOWN

1 Curved opening span (4)
2 Pictures, may be used to instruct (13)
3 Something baffling, sometimes a crime (7)
4 Organisation of workers (5)
5 People living near one another, area they live in (13)
6 Celebration (8)
12 Not at all unusual, not out of it! (8)
14 In an organised fashion, under control (7)
17 Anointed to stop squeaking! (5)
20 Frozen water (3)

Colossal Book of Crosswords

ACROSS

7 The one who comes first in a race (6)
8 Caught - as a fish (6)
9 (psychoanalysis) the conscious mind (3)
10 Quick drawings or comedy skits (8)
11 Part of something (7)
13 Door handles (5)
15 Urban areas with a fixed boundary - smaller than cities (5)
16 Places where things come from or begin (7)
18 Written or spoken agreement (8)
19 Notes forming a sequence in music (4)
21 Large whale (6)
22 The lands along the edge of a body of water (6)

DOWN

1 Headlong plunge into water (4)
2 Sadly, by bad luck (13)
3 Wearing away (7)
4 Footwear (5)
5 The strength of a solution (13)
6 Look like, have similar features (8)
12 To do with money - comic one! (8)
14 Of tests - becomes most delicate when ruffled! (7)
17 Body covering (4)
20 Be in want of (4)

Colossal Book of Crosswords

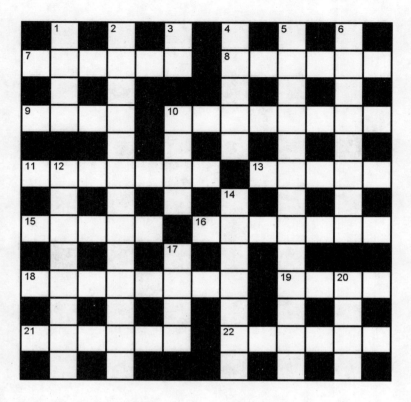

ACROSS

7 Wood of trees, move clumsily (6)
8 Middle (6)
9 Animal (4)
10 Belonging to the nation (8)
11 Taste (7)
13 At a subsequent time (5)
15 To go stealthily or furtively (5)
16 Write differently; alter the writing of (7)
18 Penalised for a crime (8)
19 Wheel bearing shaft in a vehicle (4)
21 An administrative unit of government (6)
22 Measuring sticks or kings (6)

DOWN

1 Crude or naughty (4)
2 Shortenings like this for e.g. (13)
3 Public relations - initially! (2)
4 Sharp or intense (5)
5 Cub of Montreal - anag - ill at ease (13)
6 Something used to beautify (8)
10 Type of word, can be proper or common (4)
12 Spoken or written communication (8)
14 Literate persons - reds are! (7)
17 People in general found in the yard of ale contest! (4)
20 Peer of the realm, of the manor? (4)

Colossal Book of Crosswords

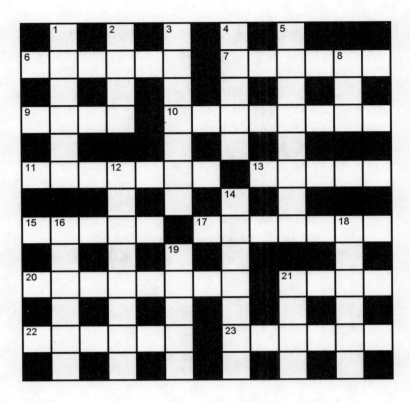

ACROSS

6 Postal communication, part of alphabet (6)
7 Sufficient (6)
9 Wake up, with a spoon (4)
10 Often, hang around regularly (8)
11 Closed door violently (7)
13 Does as he is told (5)
15 Say (5)
17 Knitted garment (7)
20 Short break or period of time between events (8)
21 Tool for digging or guitar playing (4)
22 Hidden (6)
23 Too much, like baggage (6)

DOWN

1 To do with teeth (6)
2 Celestial body, actor playing lead role (4)
3 Wandered about aimlessly (7)
4 Less than before (5)
5 Town and river in US (8)
8 Alcoholic drink, called in card game (3)
12 Mumbled under breath - deter tum! (8)
14 Distended, like a flooded river (7)
16 Calibrating instrument with a fork perhaps? (6)
18 Poor reason for not doing something (6)
19 Something that happens at a given time and place (5)
21 The speed at which someone runs (4)

Colossal Book of Crosswords

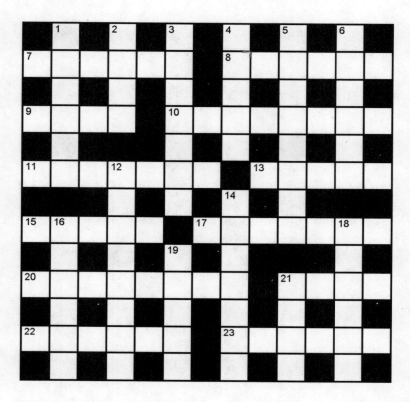

ACROSS

7 Puzzle needing to be solved, sieve (6)
8 Sent in two different ways like hair (6)
9 At this place, sister and wife of Zeus (4)
10 Packaging, around a gift maybe (8)
11 Wax lighting units, with wick (7)
13 Do business, exchange goods (5)
15 Competitor (5)
17 Remaining in a place - gain sty! (7)
20 Unofficial (8)
21 Part of larch tree is curved opening (4)
22 Every year (6)
23 Response to question (6)

DOWN

1 Place where movies are seen (6)
2 Lazy (4)
3 Betwixt, with things on either side (7)
4 Weapon (5)
5 Done in the correct way (8)
6 Canted over, for support? (6)
12 The lines spoken by characters in drama (8)
14 From Italy (7)
16 Time a cricket team is in to bat (6)
18 Metal (6)
19 Extract metal from rocks by heating (5)
21 As well as, plus, too, in addition (4)

ACROSS

7 Place where artist works (6)
8 Literature in metrical form, sometimes rhyming (6)
9 Place or measured space (4)
10 Touching, a crime with stolen goods! (8)
11 Puzzle, crime story presented in novel form (7)
13 Beneath (the weather?) (5)
15 Approximately (5)
17 Exterior (7)
20 Tubes of meat, served with mash! (8)
21 Unwell, vomiting (4)
22 Stress on a component, filter tea (6)
23 Movement (6)

DOWN

1 Bad weather (6)
2 Thought found in my ideal lifestyle! (4)
3 Female parents (7)
4 Becomes available, shop starts trading (5)
5 Emotions (8)
6 Country famous for croissant (6)
12 Day of the week (8)
14 Day of the week (7)
16 Handsomeness in the eye of the beholder? (6)
18 Medical person (6)
19 Growing old (5)
21 Takes a seat for artistic portrait? (4)

Colossal Book of Crosswords

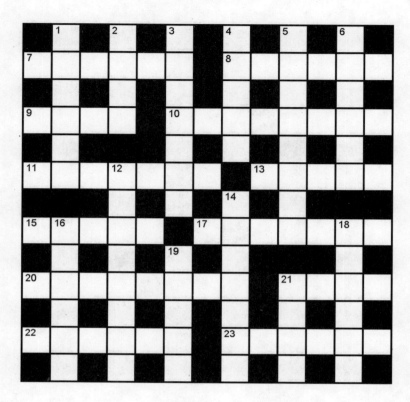

ACROSS

7 Prior to, earlier in time (6)
8 Taking place in reality; not pretended or imitated (6)
9 Bottom of geometric figure, support (4)
10 Roaring period in American history (8)
11 The meteorological conditions (7)
13 Small rodent, found on computer? (5)
15 Footwear (5)
17 Imaginary creature (7)
20 Where road and rail meet (8)
21 Spray clouds to make rain, planted thing (4)
22 Information known to only a select few (6)
23 Frothy milk drinks (6)

DOWN

1 Came into existence (6)
2 Relatively many but unspecified in number (4)
3 Concentrated on the middle of something (7)
4 Hoards money, stops a goal (5)
5 Stops on a railway line for embarkation (8)
6 Written documents - sapper! (6)
12 Wealth, possibly buried? (8)
14 having the greatest length (7)
16 Tougher, more difficult (6)
18 Number in soccer team (6)
19 Number of additional sense (5)
21 Sea creature or wax fastener on letter (4)

Colossal Book of Crosswords

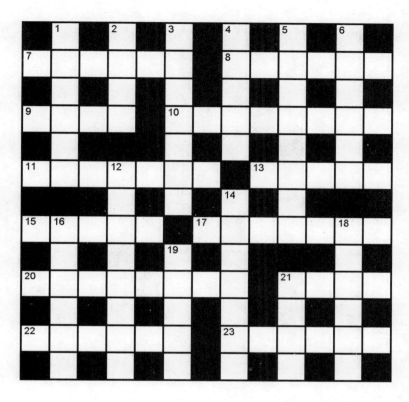

ACROSS

7 Male parent (6)
8 To do with nuclear energy - tom CIA! (6)
9 Plant with fronds (4)
10 Trusted that something was true (8)
11 Bent down - to dishonorable depths? (7)
13 Farm storehouses (5)
15 Having a foundation - beads! (5)
17 Highest temperature (7)
20 Enjoyable - an petals! (8)
21 Place to sit or thing placed on it! (4)
22 Beat in battle or game (6)
23 Pencil, blackboard or ink rubber! (6)

DOWN

1 Least dangerous place - feasts! (6)
2 Skinny (4)
3 Took hold of roughly, snatched at (7)
4 Done without skill or in an unpleasant way (5)
5 Prediction (8)
6 Bird, message carrier? (6)
12 Worked, like a surgeon maybe? (8)
14 Decade when the 2nd world war ended (7)
16 Not awake (6)
18 Says, clearly and categorically (6)
19 Floating makeshift boats (5)
21 Mark left after trauma has healed (4)

188

Colossal Book of Crosswords

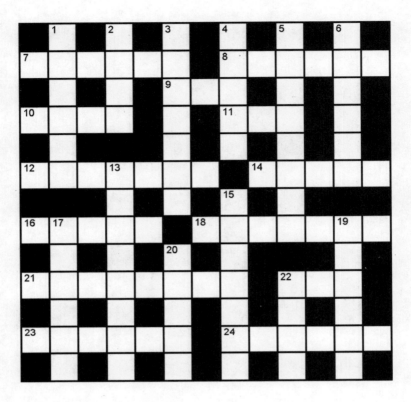

ACROSS

7 Sign, pay attention (6)
8 Almost (6)
9 Very small amount in last advance! (3)
10 Leave out (4)
11 Consume food (3)
12 Putting something in a particular location (7)
14 In the middle of (5)
16 Woolly creatures (5)
18 Going by, as time? (7)
21 A thing of any kind - tinny hag! (8)
22 Perceive by sight (3)
23 Facial hair growths (6)
24 Frothy milk drinks (6)

DOWN

1 Nothing out of the ordinary (6)
2 Raise, transport device in tall buildings (4)
3 Gambling - big tent! (7)
4 Beneath (5)
5 Boat bosses (8)
6 Rests during the night (6)
13 Living thing - rue carte! (8)
15 Biggest (7)
17 Passed to someone by hand, over (6)
19 In want of (6)
20 Primary, before all others (5)
22 Place to sit (4)

Colossal Book of Crosswords

ACROSS

7 Person serving meal in restaurant (6)
8 Group of singers, sound of disapproval? (6)
9 Appear to be (4)
10 Hour of ending of war (8)
11 Falls down suddenly and violently (7)
13 Having a foundation, in reality? - be sad! (5)
15 Dwellings in rocks (5)
17 Quickest, most rapid (7)
20 Not unusual (8)
21 Incline, meat with little fat (4)
22 Upper body clothing item - can be bet! (5)
23 Borrowed on payment of fee (6)

DOWN

1 Progression of your working life (6)
2 Part of plant (4)
3 Told to do something (by superior) (7)
4 Measures of land (5)
5 Prediction, esp of weather (8)
6 Difficult to detect, faint - bustle! (6)
12 Stated explicitly or in detail, not general (8)
14 Legal representative (6)
16 Transversely - so cars! (6)
18 Parts of a company, hands out evenly (6)
19 One of the four basic taste sensations, from the sea? (5)
21 Connection, sometimes thought missing? (4)

Colossal Book of Crosswords

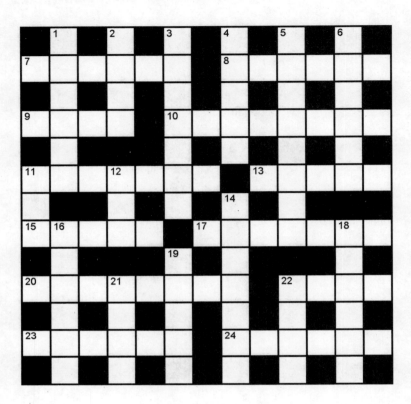

ACROSS

7 Attack brutally and fiercely (6)
8 One who is literate? (6)
9 Ripped, moved violently (4)
10 Not man made - alchemic! (8)
11 Duped (7)
13 Shoe ties (5)
15 Of short duration or distance (5)
17 Own (7)
20 Had import, was of concern (8)
22 Beach material, rub wood smooth (4)
23 Measure of angle or temperature, qualification (6)
24 Small paddle boats (6)

DOWN

1 Act of kindness, approve above others (6)
2 Lack of clarity, was purple in the 70s! (4)
3 Person at front of class (7)
4 Colour, environmentally safe (5)
5 Not lower case letters, column tops (8)
6 Comport oneself in a proper manner - eve bah! (6)
11 Restaurant bill, also small flap tucked in (3)
12 Snooker implement, actor's prompt (3)
14 Lead orchestra or take fares on bus (7)
16 Make a loud noise like a lion? (6)
18 Smell, taste, touch, sight, hearing (6)
19 Has a go at - especially in rugby! (5)
21 Ripped (4)
22 Slide beneath the sea, in the kitchen! (4)

Colossal Book of Crosswords

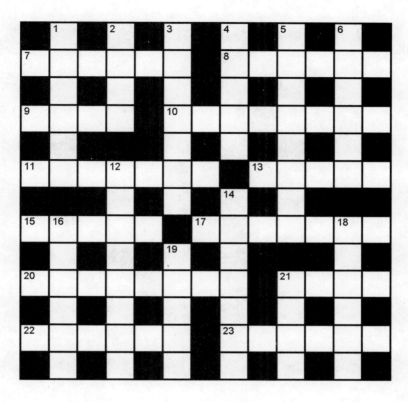

ACROSS

7 John Lennon was one (6)
8 Torn or pulled up violently (6)
9 Weaving machine (4)
10 Low level country, opposite highlands? (8)
11 Having received information or counsel (7)
13 Jewel found in oyster (5)
15 Speech made to audience (5)
17 Country (7)
20 Worked or controlled (8)
21 With dashes makes morse code! (4)
22 Enclosed - fought with swords (6)
23 Giving a name to (6)

DOWN

1 Assistant in a duel, comes after first (6)
2 Any thing, confused mite! (4)
3 Responds to question (7)
4 Animal noise (5)
5 Seemingly - ant paper! (8)
6 One who buys books? (6)
12 Not as a direct effect or consequence (8)
14 Sweet course, also club informally! (7)
16 Late meal (6)
18 Have in mind as a purpose - tinned! (6)
19 Read a subject at college, room for thought? (5)
21 A hemispherical roof (4)

Colossal Book of Crosswords

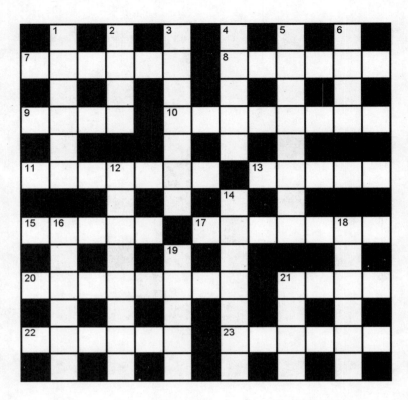

ACROSS

7 Military type, relating to the sea (6)
8 Head cover used in war on on motorcycles (6)
9 Type of weather (4)
10 Salve, unguent (8)
11 Furnish with - do viper! (7)
13 Conscious awareness - can be common! (5)
15 Fish cover, climb, weighing device (5)
17 Reflexive form of "her" (7)
20 Living entity - is Morgan! (8)
21 Little granny! (4)
22 Dull and uninteresting - making holes! (6)
23 They are part of the human body - Severn! (6)

DOWN

1 The way in which something is done (6)
2 The range of the eye (4)
3 Makes a recording of, discs that contain recordings! (7)
4 Call on the telephone (5)
5 Mountaineers or social status seekers (8)
6 Butter, runner or broad (4)
12 Igneous rock produced by eruption (8)
14 One of the parts that something divides into (7)
16 Vegetable (6)
18 The person at the front, editor's column (6)
19 Calls on the phone, finger jewellry (5)
21 Bacteria - start of an idea (4)

Colossal Book of Crosswords

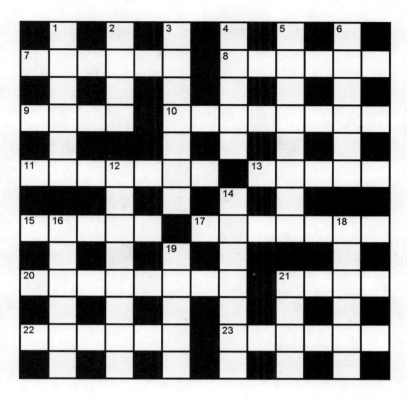

ACROSS

7 Home for motor vehicle (6)
8 Colouring stick (6)
9 Smack across face (4)
10 Distribute loosely (8)
11 Type of rock (7)
13 The quality of being united (5)
15 Incorrect (5)
17 Made a short time ago (7)
20 Made a loud cry - scared me! (8)
21 Pile (4)
22 Impression of antique creature - if loss! (6)
23 Closer (6)

DOWN

1 Suit maker (6)
2 A prison for forced labourers (4)
3 Distribution of things in an area - concentration (7)
4 Frighten, cause fear in (5)
5 Written or spoken cautions (8)
6 Lavatory (6)
12 Having no intelligible meaning (8)
14 Do business by exchanging goods (7)
16 Make a mathematical calculation (6)
18 Filled with a great quantity, of money? (6)
19 Stink, stench, pong (5)
21 Teacher in charge of school (4)

Colossal Book of Crosswords

ACROSS

4 Raise and lower head in agreement (3)
7 Vicious, brutal and cruel (6)
8 Flower and girl's name (4)
9 Definite, not general (8)
10 Broken into small pieces before use, like herbs (7)
12 Manufactures, constructs (5)
14 Amusements or pastimes (5)
16 Most rotund or overweight (7)
19 Coming via a circuitous route - in credit! (8)
20 Source of all light on earth? (3)
21 Drive headlong at high speed (6)
22 Going down of the sun (6)

DOWN

1 Particles suspended in the air (6)
2 High wind (4)
3 Illness with rash (7)
4 Reputations, what children call each other? (5)
5 On top, in control (8)
6 Coming from god (6)
11 Example - imp scene! (8)
13 Quickest, most rapid (7)
15 Happens every year (6)
17 By which we perceive the world - nesses! (6)
18 Facial hair (5)
20 Fell to the bottom of the sea (4)

ACROSS

1 Person in charge, circular ornament (4)
3 Accented, emphasised (8)
9 Louder - ironies! (7)
10 Wood pattern (5)
11 Computer storage devices (5)
12 Tired (6)
14 What a quiver contains (6)
16 Place of learning or thought (6)
19 More unattractive (6)
21 From Rome (5)
24 Got up (5)
25 Main film in a movie theatre - rue feat! (7)
26 Total and complete (8)
27 The other one from that! (4)

DOWN

1 Prohibit esp. by legal means or social pressure (3)
2 Rotates (5)
4 Forward power - truths! (6)
5 Bird (5)
6 Hair cleaning liquid (7)
7 Depression made by collision (4)
8 Puzzle made up of many pieces (6)
11 Unable to hear (4)
13 Bedding, covers (8)
15 Areas (7)
17 Breakfast food (6)
18 Money left after all expenses are paid (6)
20 Perfect (5)
22 Oral opening (5)
23 Information in digital form (4)

Colossal Book of Crosswords

ACROSS

1 Propels a boat with oars (4)
2 Member of family (8)
8 Error (7)
10 Throws out, as a fishing line (5)
11 To do with number and calculation (12)
14 Consume (3)
16 One time period in a sequence (5)
17 As well (3)
18 Accounts, statements that tell of reasons (12)
21 Country (5)
22 Land upon which crops grow readily (7)
23 Putting on clothes or salad mixture? (8)
24 Pigmented liquids used in writing or printing (4)

DOWN

1 Call to mind an event passed (8)
3 Organ of sight (3)
4 Design and construction of buildings or computers (12)
5 In no time, could be coffee! (7)
6 Freedom from difficulty or hardship or effort (4)
7 Butterfly or moth larvae (12)
9 Group in maths, or part of tennis match (3)
12 Once more (5)
13 Gun holders (8)
15 Relating to fabric (7)
19 Vegetable that can make you cry! (5)
20 Turns litmus paper red (4)
22 Enjoyment, pleasure (3)

Colossal Book of Crosswords

ACROSS

1 Small house or potato topped meat pie (7)
5 Parts of plants, comes from (5)
8 Type of music (9)
9 Baby bed (3)
10 Crossness! (5)
12 Unwinds, unfurls (7)
13 In a relative manner; by comparison to something else (13)
15 Consider in detail, dissect (7)
17 Being on the outside or further from a centre (5)
19 Plastic runner used for gliding over snow (3)
20 People from USA (9)
22 Arrives (5)
23 In a constricted manner (7)

DOWN

1 Chocolate drink (5)
2 Drink made from dried leaves (3)
3 European republic (7)
4 The act of giving hope or support to someone (13)
5 Related to the sun, like an eclipse (5)
6 Very, very good - of the highest quality (9)
7 Fulfil the requirements or expectations of (7)
11 Big gym! (9)
13 Adhering to established standards and principles (7)
14 Pressing clothes with heat and steam (7)
16 Periods of time (5)
18 Corroded ferrous metal (5)
21 Small social insect (3)

Colossal Book of Crosswords

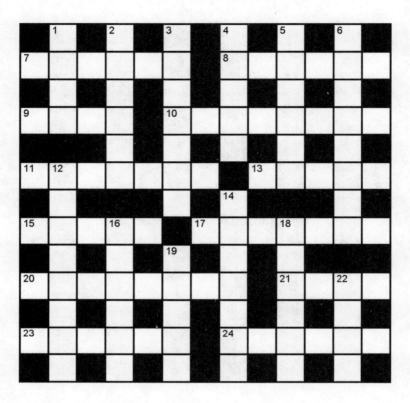

ACROSS

7 Fruit from tropics, kind of republic? (6)
8 Use of physical or mental energy; hard work (6)
9 Device for ringing (4)
10 Easy to perceive; especially clearly outlined (8)
11 Removes contents, used bottles (7)
13 Monks' clothes (5)
15 Explosion, swear word? (5)
17 Made, brought into existence (7)
20 Emphasised (8)
21 Aircraft or their engines (4)
23 Exchanged some goods for others (6)
24 Grassy plants growing near rivers (6)

DOWN

1 A challenge, perhaps for Dan? (4)
2 Form of dance (6)
3 Touched something (7)
4 Awareness - hopefully common to all! (5)
5 Country (6)
6 A customary way of operation or behavior (8)
12 To do with the armed forces (8)
14 Dealers - retards! (7)
16 Passes in a specific way; as of time (6)
18 Alter, perhaps for a better fit (6)
19 Words spoken to audience - ideas! (5)
22 Not now but earlier (4)

Colossal Book of Crosswords

ACROSS

6 Mild wind (6)
8 Animate being - manila! (6)
9 Write with mechanical device (4)
10 Compressed with violence, out of natural shape (8)
11 Propelled by means of engine of some sort (7)
13 Containers for bottles of wine (5)
15 Fight with sword, around garden! (5)
17 Able to grow crops easily (7)
20 Fighters (8)
21 Job that has to be done (4)
23 Area thick with trees (6)
24 Sewing device (6)

DOWN

1 Harsh (6)
2 Viral disease (7)
3 Uncertain, loose (5)
4 Movie theatre (6)
5 Goodbye, adios, cheerio (8)
7 Man's name and electromagnetic output (3)
12 Controller of machine or telephone (8)
14 Learning periods in school or college (7)
16 Floor covering, sometimes fitted (6)
18 Ranks in society (6)
19 Of imposing height (5)
22 Material made by worms! (4)

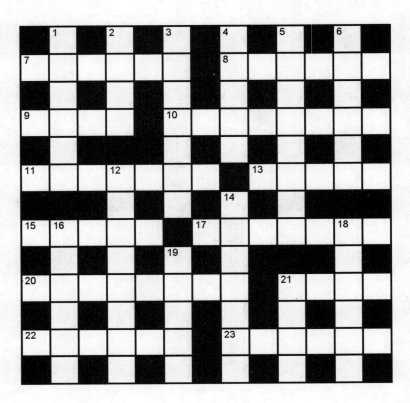

ACROSS

7 Belonging to or coming from a place or area (6)

8 Horses feet! (6)

9 Leave out (4)

10 Exact sameness - nit deity! (8)

11 A room used primarily for sleeping, with pot? (7)

13 Taxes paid or scales of fees (5)

15 Sudden and sharp (5)

17 Tanned animal hide (7)

20 Supermarket purchase carriers, with wheels (8)

21 Clean (4)

22 The act of manufacture (6)

23 Brought back to health (6)

DOWN

1 The sensation caused by heat energy (6)

2 Eating habit, possibly to lose weight (4)

3 Brought to an end; settled conclusively (7)

4 Footwear (5)

5 Written or verbal agreement (8)

6 Mild, kindly (6)

12 Made of or resembling metal (8)

14 Fooling around, not being serious - signs me! (7)

16 Breakfast food (6)

18 Less difficult (6)

19 A projecting ridge on a mountain (5)

21 A unit of language, promise (4)

Colossal Book of Crosswords

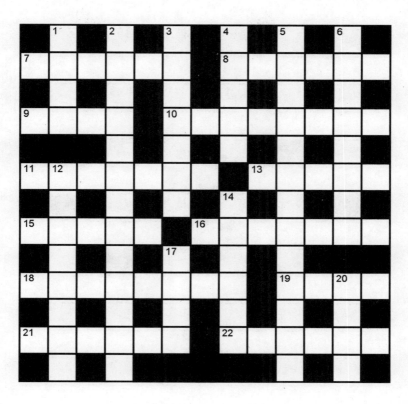

ACROSS

7 Be expected to - hold us! (6)
8 Strip of fine material used in hair (6)
9 Someone who fights for a cause (4)
10 Paid or honoured for efforts (8)
11 The reason why - ease cub! (7)
13 Cooking machines (5)
15 Learner at school, part of eye (5)
16 Requests urgently and forcefully (7)
18 Cooking by suspending above boiling water (8)
19 A tiny or scarcely detectable amount (4)
21 Cooked in boiling liquid (6)
22 Twisted, jumbled or confused mass (6)

DOWN

1 Footwear (4)
2 In a mechanical manner; by a mechanism (13)
3 Location, shown on letter, speak to (7)
4 Royal headgear (5)
5 Shortened forms of words (13)
6 Exercised authority over, ruled (8)
12 Mathematical statement - eat quoin! (8)
14 Elevation especially above sea level (6)
17 Rediscover something once lost (4)
20 Kind of story - improbable! (4)

Colossal Book of Crosswords

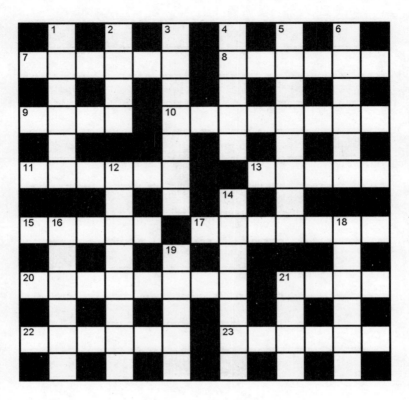

ACROSS

7 Vegetable (6)
8 Motorboat (6)
9 Grape plant (4)
10 Position in the community - nag dints! (8)
11 Why someone does something (7)
13 Before all others (5)
15 Digit (5)
17 Heavy loads used in physical training (7)
20 Snow pressed into a ball for throwing (playfully) (8)
21 A slipper that has no fitting around the heel (4)
22 A thick fatty oil used to lubricate machinery (6)
23 Treat carefully (6)

DOWN

1 Take note of, be aware (6)
2 Disappear gradually (4)
3 Protective structure for machine - sin Hugo! (7)
4 Free from impurities - like a bill of health? (5)
5 Hugging romantically (8)
6 Parts of a drama - censes! (6)
12 To a small degree or extent - me so what! (8)
14 Taking away outre skin (7)
16 In need of food (6)
18 Higher than others (6)
19 Was bothered about, concerned for (5)
21 Not much, a small pond! (4)

Colossal Book of Crosswords

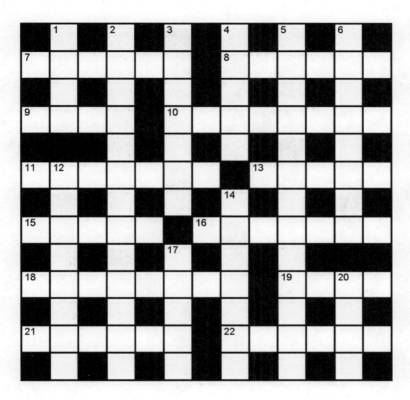

ACROSS

7 In less time than thought - on Eros! (6)
8 Slacken off (6)
9 Nought, nil (4)
10 Quick drawings (8)
11 Spread about at random (7)
13 Door handles (5)
15 Type of piano (5)
16 Givers of information - sucrose! (7)
18 Take away (8)
19 An indefinite period (4)
21 Sent to prison (6)
22 Expected to - hold us! (6)

DOWN

1 Had children, size of gun barrel? (4)
2 Sadly, due to ill luck (13)
3 In clothes, food decorated with herbs, etc (7)
4 From another planet! (5)
5 Great mental effort - not concertina! (13)
6 Look like something else (8)
12 Round (8)
14 Least hard or harsh - of setts! (7)
17 Abounding in sand (5)
20 Reduce to liquid by applying heat (4)

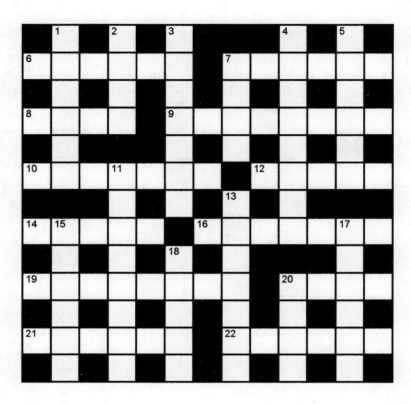

ACROSS

6 Any epidemic disease (6)
7 Not private (6)
8 Determines the sum of numbers (4)
9 Freed from a burden, evil, or distress (8)
10 The opposite of 8? (7)
12 A special set of circumstances (5)
14 Climb mountain, climb by ladder (5)
16 Physical device prohibiting passage, or cream! (7)
19 Made of metal or resembling metal (8)
20 Arriving after the agreed time or dead! (4)
21 Most important (6)
22 Strain, work required to do something (6)

DOWN

1 Engineless aircraft (6)
2 Historic periods (4)
3 Things known only to a special group (7)
4 Someone who watches (8)
5 Message bird (6)
7 Throw stones at, animal skin (4)
11 Denizen of a village (8)
13 Duplicates, sporting contests (7)
15 Small fruit with one stone (6)
17 All, complete (6)
18 Material (5)
20 Course of existence of an individual - broken file! (4)

Colossal Book of Crosswords

ACROSS

1 Groups, scenes used in drama production (4)
3 Begged persistently and urgently (8)
9 Aerodrome (7)
10 Amphibians, could be natterjacks? (5)
11 Quickly going away and passing out of sight (12)
13 Automata (6)
15 Boss, person in charge (6)
17 Written details of how something works (12)
20 Greeting (5)
21 Establish the validity of something (5)
22 An event resulting in great loss and misfortune (8)
23 Questions, seeks an answer to (4)

DOWN

1 Normal quality, flag (8)
2 Rotates, changes sides (5)
4 Caught in a mesh, like a fish (6)
5 Where two or more roads meet (12)
6 Having acquired necessary skills (7)
7 Suspended powder, clean this from furniture etc (4)
8 Contests that offer a prize - composite nit! (12)
12 Gifts (8)
14 Things wrapped together and secured (7)
16 Colour (6)
18 Warning signs of something about to happen (5)
19 Garden structure, slough off skin (4)

Colossal Book of Crosswords

ACROSS

7 What we breathe (3)
8 Fires gun, new growth (6)
9 Fifty percent (4)
10 Feeling or showing gratitude (8)
11 Year books, personal records (7)
13 Where actors perform (5)
15 Put question to (5)
17 Responded to 15 (7)
20 Part of history - Irish cot! (8)
21 Drinking vessel, hold in hands (3)
23 Frightens (6)
24 Area of land belonging to large house (6)

DOWN

1 Computer information (4)
2 Pick over another, like better (6)
3 Spread out all over the place, run off in haste (7)
4 Normal (5)
5 Firework or severe telling off! (6)
6 To exert strenuous effort against opposition (8)
12 Inborn pattern of behavior (8)
14 Saved from something (7)
16 Comes in (6)
18 Find (6)
19 Not canned or otherwise preserved (5)
22 Lots of - things to go with pans in kitchen! (4)

ACROSS

1 Indicate something with finger (rude!) (5)
5 Conveyances that carries skiers up a hill (5)
8 Designed for a particular use - icy lapels! (9)
9 Gone by; or in the past, found in sago pudding! (3)
10 Boiling water turns to this (5)
12 Highest (7)
13 People living near one another (13)
15 Slight movements of the air (7)
17 Bare, with no clothes on! (5)
19 Allow, permit, rent out flat (3)
20 Remove opposition (9)
22 The popular taste at a given time (5)
23 Spotted, seen - the digs! (7)

DOWN

1 Positions or garden fence supports (5)
2 Frozen water (3)
3 Prove superior, be victorious (7)
4 States of connectedness between peoples (13)
5 Unwavering in devotion to friend (5)
6 The underlying structure - wok farmer! (9)
7 Caught sight of, like Dick the pudding? (7)
11 It would seem to be - end levity! (9)
13 Small food items before meal or with drinks (7)
14 Sound of telephone or bell (7)
16 A unifying idea, like a park? (5)
18 Great fear confused adder! (5)
21 Back end of ship (3)

ACROSS

7 Show, bring out, make known (6)
8 Three legged camera stand (6)
9 Sea bird (4)
10 Being two identical items - mac thing! (8)
11 Country (7)
13 In the middle of (5)
15 Unconfined, clear, public (4)
17 Imprecise but fairly close to correct (7)
20 Folding rain cover - rum label! (8)
21 Make a low continuous sound (4)
22 Removed outer skin prior to cooking or eating (6)
23 At a greater volume, more audibly (6)

DOWN

1 Make fast, lock up (6)
2 Back of shoe, can sometimes get high! (4)
3 Known substance - teen elm! (7)
4 Say clearly - part of USA (5)
5 Engaged in war (8)
6 Things that can be heard - sun dos! (6)
12 Solid homogeneous inorganic substances - in realms! (8)
14 Completely, without reservation (7)
16 Questioned persistently - mud pep! (6)
18 Wood, move in an ungainly fashion (6)
19 Playground toy, photo transparency (5)
21 60 minutes (4)

ACROSS

7 Game played on lawn (6)
8 Padded gymnastic apparatus on legs (6)
9 By oneself, unassisted (4)
10 Went to, an event (8)
11 Run off in all directions (7)
13 A person who thinks they are better than the rest (4)
15 Bird or dockside lifting device (5)
16 Restricted quantity, possibly edition (7)
18 Holiday clothes carrier (4-4)
19 Magnetic, adhesive or red! (4)
21 Measure of liquid, containing 8 pints (6)
22 Cutlery item for eating soup (5)

DOWN

1 The principal character in a play (4)
2 Sadly (13)
3 Break free, get away (6)
4 Small photograph (5)
5 The way that words are spoken - puritanic noon! (13)
6 Be similar to - mere bels! (8)
12 Advertisement - sent round? (8)
14 Health impairment, sickness (7)
17 Acquire more, increase in (4)
20 Writing implements, female swans (4)

ACROSS

7 Woody tropical grass having hollow stems (6)
8 Concrete supports - pig nil! (6)
9 Armed service - in boats (4)
10 An investigation, case study - as inlays! (8)
11 Characterised by certainty or security (7)
13 Good natured, helpful, considerate (4)
15 Cloudy liquid, opaque (5)
17 Parts of jackets or shirts (7)
20 Measure of water depth (8)
21 Headwear once thought common (3)
22 Fastened shut, with a kiss? (6)
23 In the direction of (6)

DOWN

1 Mixtures of foods, usually lettuce and tomato (6)
2 Follow order or instruction (4)
3 Situated in a particular spot or position (7)
4 Situated in a particular spot or position (5)
5 Period in school for fun or games out of lessons (8)
6 Unfastened, unbound (6)
12 Lacking in sympathy - inky Lund (8)
14 Air trips - of fantasy? (7)
16 Pressed clothes with heat to make flat (6)
18 One who has great knowledge (6)
19 Discover, ascertain (4)
21 Females of domestic cattle (4)

Colossal Book of Crosswords

ACROSS

7 Bird that lays eggs in another's nest (6)
8 Tall structures, columns - sort we! (6)
9 Travel through water (4)
10 The gymnastic moves of an acrobat (8)
11 Riding a bicycle (7)
13 Go along with, be in accord (5)
15 Sturdy kind of beer (5)
17 Flat top of hilly area (7)
20 Blood taken for diagnostic purposes (8)
21 King of the jungle (4)
22 Show, make visible, divulge (6)
23 Final part of something, conclusion (6)

DOWN

1 Underground rail or foot passage (6)
2 Take a thin layer from the surface (4)
3 Putting into letter box - it pongs! (7)
4 Small particles - moats! (5)
5 The time of day immediately following sunset (8)
6 Member of royal family (6)
12 Sends off on a maiden voyage with champagne (8)
14 At an angle - ten dals! (7)
16 Struck lightly repeatedly (6)
18 Quantity (6)
19 Aroma (5)
21 Pan tops (4)

212

ACROSS

7 Serviceman, confused airmen! (6)
8 Has a changeable quality - is rave! (6)
9 Measure of land size (4)
10 Leaning in one direction or another (8)
11 Bigger than another (7)
13 In the middle of (5)
15 Say clearly (5)
17 Considered - wedge hi! (7)
20 The one before (8)
21 Meat cooked with vegetables in oven (4)
22 Ran quickly, dashed (6)
23 Pencil line remover, usually rubber (6)

DOWN

1 Disease (6)
2 Ready to pick or eat (4)
3 Climatic conditions (7)
4 A special set of circumstances (5)
5 Change to ice (8)
6 Barriers that serve to enclose an area (6)
12 The state of being active (8)
14 An acute and highly contagious viral disease (7)
16 The raised helical rib going around a screw (6)
18 A small hole for the passage of a cord (6)
19 A blue dyestuff used by Ancient Britons (4)
21 Submerge in a liquid (4)

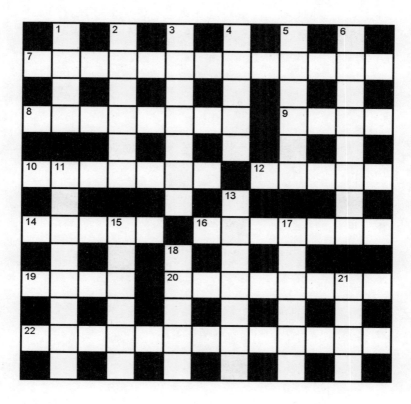

ACROSS

7 Markedly new or introducing radical change (13)
8 Urgently needed; absolutely necessary (8)
9 Lessen the intensity of; calm (4)
10 Adult male chicken (7)
12 Christ (5)
14 Light springing movements upwards or forwards (5)
16 Produced from an egg (7)
19 Denuded of leaves (4)
20 Having no intelligible meaning (8)
22 The act of making up your mind about something (13)

DOWN

1 Having a high price (4)
2 Openings through which food is taken in (6)
3 A retailer of meat (7)
4 The name of a work of art or literary composition (5)
5 Exhale spasmodically (6)
6 Exert this on someone through threats (8)
11 Performed surgery on (8)
13 A message informing of danger (7)
15 Put together from parts, assembled - dip EEC! (6)
17 Boxes with lids; used for storage (6)
18 An opposing military force (5)
21 A public entertainment or exhibition (4)

Colossal Book of Crosswords

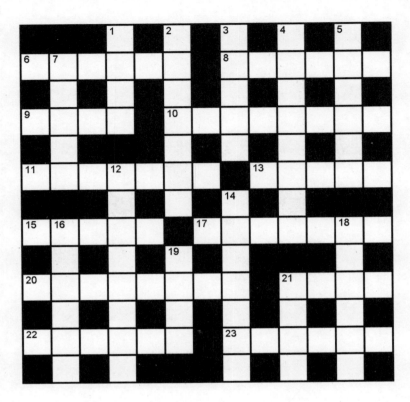

ACROSS

6 Fasten to (6)
8 Filled with fear or apprehension (6)
9 Joint consisting of a line formed by joining two pieces (4)
10 An applicant likely to be chosen (8)
11 Taken on a certain form, attribute, or aspect (7)
13 One skilled in caring for the sick (5)
15 Periods of seven consecutive days (5)
17 Protected by insurance (7)
20 Having a deeply disquieting or disturbing effect (8)
21 A body of matter without definite shape (4)
22 Being associated as a companion or associate (6)
23 Almost (6)

DOWN

1 Come to like someone (4)
2 Gave away information about somebody (7)
3 Edge tool used in shaving (5)
4 A collection of precious things - trove? (8)
5 Areas of land cleared of trees and usually enclosed (6)
7 A hairdo formed by braiding or twisting the hair (5)
12 Lacking in sympathy and kindness (8)
14 Prolonged unfulfilled desire or need (7)
16 An implement used to erase something (6)
18 With ease (6)
19 The range of the eye (4)
21 Indicate pain, discomfort, or displeasure (4)

Colossal Book of Crosswords

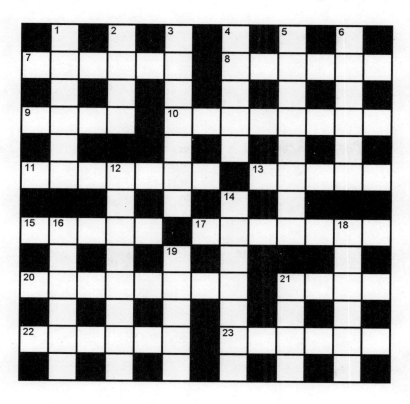

ACROSS

7 A seat for the rider of a horse (6)
8 Not often (6)
9 Having a strong healthy body (4)
10 (of a person) possessing physical strength and weight; rugged and powerful (8)
11 Take something away by force (7)
13 Evidence that helps to solve a problem (5)
15 A message that departs from the main subject (5)
17 Thrown from side to side (7)
20 Two words that can be interchanged in a context (8)
21 Burrowing marine mollusk living on sand or mud (4)
22 A living organism (6)
23 Brief descriptions given for identification (6)

DOWN

1 Woody tropical grass, used in furniture (6)
2 Lazy (4)
3 Part of a whole (7)
4 Faith in someone or something (5)
5 Difficulties (8)
6 Give pleasure to; be pleasing to (6)
12 Places in a house to sleep (8)
14 Visit a doctor or other professional for opinion (7)
16 Ancient proverb or sore ? (6)
18 Almost (6)
19 A periodically repeated sequence of events (5)
21 Taxis (4)

Colossal Book of Crosswords

ACROSS

7 Not in black and white (6)
8 Someone who robs at sea (6)
9 Proper alignment, correct, right (4)
10 The decade from 1920 to 1929 (8)
11 Put down into words (7)
13 A weapon with a handle and blade (5)
15 Once more (5)
17 A protective cover (7)
20 Sport (8)
21 A small amount of solid food; a mouthful (4)
22 A thoroughfare that is lined with buildings (6)
23 Thin coats of water colour paint, cleans (6)

DOWN

1 Having little money or few possessions (4)
2 Cooked until ready to serve (4)
3 A male with the same parents as someone else (7)
4 Distance travelled per unit time (5)
5 Makes believe (8)
6 Reflexive from of "it" (6)
12 The decade from 1930 to 1939 (8)
14 Travels behind, goes after, comes after (7)
16 The visible disembodied souls of dead people! (6)
18 Caught with a net (6)
19 The loose soft material that makes up a large part of the land surface (5)
21 The supreme effort one can make (4)

Colossal Book of Crosswords

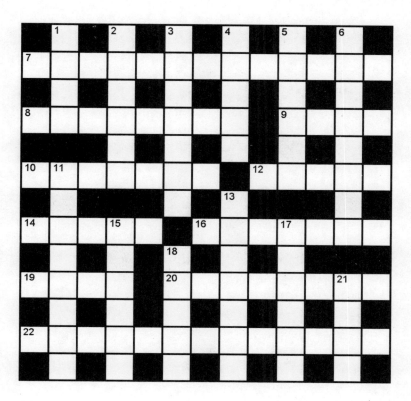

ACROSS

7 The statement of an exchange of promises (13)
8 Make more attractive by adding colour, etc. (8)
9 Keen on something (4)
10 Without much difficulty (7)
12 Growing old (5)
14 Fruit (5)
16 Moved around, maybe like sand? (7)
19 Number (4)
20 A systematic means of communicating (8)
22 The act of making up your mind about something (13)

DOWN

1 On one occasion (4)
2 1/60 of a minute (6)
3 Normally (7)
4 Swallowed, as a drug or tablet (5)
5 Determining the sum of (6)
6 An occurrence of something (8)
11 Someone who travels into little known regions (8)
13 Making something shine by polishing it (7)
15 Bigger (6)
17 Following the third position (6)
18 Go up or advance (5)
21 Become larger, greater, or bigger (4)

ACROSS

7 Season (6)
8 A hired hand who tends cattle (6)
9 Of meat, in order to get a gamey taste (4)
10 (of waves) curling over and crashing into surf (8)
11 Has faith or relies on someone (7)
13 Furious (5)
15 Annual or biennial grass (5)
17 Subject to an imposed burden (7)
20 The pursuit (of a person or animal) by following (8)
21 What birds do with their wings (4)
22 Land that is covered with trees and shrubs (6)
23 Someone who expresses in language (6)

DOWN

1 The time yet to come (6)
2 Either of two saclike respiratory organs in the chest (4)
3 Any person (7)
4 Someone who guards prisoners, fastener (5)
5 Aroused or activated (8)
6 Earlier, rather than later? (6)
12 Considered in detail (8)
14 Badly behaved (7)
16 Intense and profound fear (6)
18 Pencil rubber (6)
19 The musical interval between one note and another five notes away from it (5)
21 A fabric made of compressed matted fibers (4)

Colossal Book of Crosswords

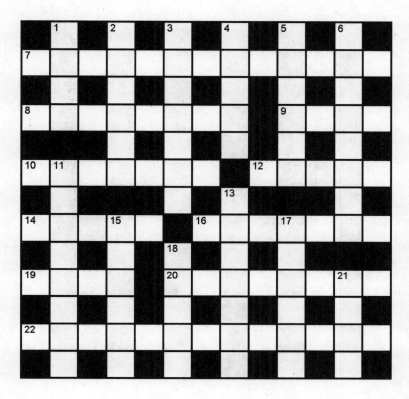

ACROSS

7 Detected with the senses - disguised hint! (13)
8 Mended, fixed (8)
9 Affirming the truth of a statement (4)
10 American biscuits (7)
12 Food taken at different times of the day (5)
14 Grown up (5)
16 Own (7)
19 Smile, grimace, or snarl (4)
20 The content of cognition (8)
22 Feeling ill at ease - bar of Uncle Tom! (13)

DOWN

1 A collection of objects laid on top of each other (4)
2 An offensive against and enemy (using weapons) (6)
3 Items inserted in a written record (7)
4 Assets in the form of money (5)
5 Towards the land from the water (6)
6 Cold-blooded vertebrates (8)
11 Issuing commands (8)
13 A flag that shows its nationality, can be trooped (7)
15 The capital and largest city of England (6)
17 Communicate silently and non-verbally (6)
18 A rod carried as a symbol (5)
21 Let something be known (4)

Colossal Book of Crosswords

ACROSS

1 Removes unwanted substances from (6)
4 A natural body of running water (6)
9 Nonfictional prose in magazine (7)
10 A theatrical performer (5)
11 Make fun of - at see! (5)
12 Lying in or toward the east (7)
13 Shortened, as of words (11)
18 An athlete who performs acts requiring skill (7)
20 Overly eager speed (and possible carelessness) (5)
22 Reduce to small pieces or particles by pounding (5)
23 Perform surgery on (7)
24 Number (5)
25 Positions on a scale of intensity, in computer games? (6)

DOWN

1 Freewheels (6)
2 Additional, bit part actor (5)
3 Weapons using atomic energy (7)
5 Rips up, things that are cried when sad! (5)
6 Beyond a norm in views or actions (7)
7 To do with the sea and life therein (6)
8 Native American living area (11)
14 A structure that impedes free movement (7)
15 A person trained to compete in sports (7)
16 What you aim for (6)
17 Break, especially in an American courtroom (6)
19 An emblem (5)
21 Coach for travelling pre motor car (5)

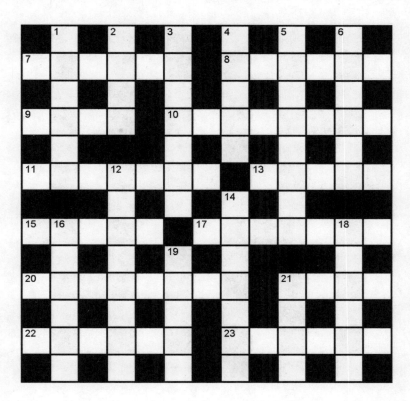

ACROSS

7 Attack brutally and fiercely (6)
8 Sets of limits - roams - angers! (6)
9 A strong cord (4)
10 Responded to a question - we sander! (8)
11 Hoodwinked, fooled (7)
13 Groups of cattle (5)
15 Let loose, from bondage? (5)
17 Having largest diameter (7)
20 Coated in flour and water mix before frying (8)
21 Went under, like a sad person's heart? (4)
22 A game played with rackets (6)
23 United States inventor of an improved chain-stitch sewing machine (1811-1875) (6)

DOWN

1 A political party formed in Great Britain in 1900 (6)
2 Garden tool or dissolute man (4)
3 Taking it easy (7)
4 Glass object used to deviate light (5)
5 A fixed charge for borrowing money (8)
6 Rely upon (6)
12 Making, manufacturing (8)
14 Toughest, most difficult (7)
16 Made a loud noise, as of animal (6)
18 The daily event of the sun sinking below the horizon (6)
19 A joint (5)
21 Any stars around which planetary systems evolve (4)

Colossal Book of Crosswords

ACROSS

1 Chamber for smelting ore (7)
5 Express one's choice or preference by ballot (5)
8 Existing in fancy only - it caftans! (9)
9 (folklore) fairies that are somewhat mischievous (3)
10 Weighty (5)
12 Accept something as true (7)
13 Shortened forms of words (13)
15 Caring only about oneself (7)
17 On guard, on the lookout, ready for action! (5)
19 An adult male person (as opposed to a woman) (3)
20 Elementary particles with negative charge (9)
22 Frock (5)
23 Flesh of large domesticated fowl usually roasted (7)

DOWN

1 Position five in a countable series of things (5)
2 An unbroken series of events (3)
3 Consider in detail (7)
4 The act of forming something - melt absinthes! (13)
5 Given to expressing yourself freely or insistently (5)
6 As a consequence - re thereof! (9)
7 Disagrees, dissents (7)
11 A vehicle that takes people to and from hospitals (9)
13 Accepted without verification or proof (7)
14 A truck that has a cab but no body (7)
16 Thing from a list (5)
18 Long pointed teeth specialized for fighting (5)
21 Metal-bearing mineral valuable enough to be mined (3)

Colossal Book of Crosswords

ACROSS

1 A small cut of meat including part of a rib (4)
3 An imaginary creature represented as a white horse with a long horn growing from its forehead (8)
9 Gases ejected from an engine as waste products (7)
10 Offensively curious or inquisitive (5)
11 Salty fluid secreted by sweat glands (12)
13 Hissing noise cause by electrical interference (6)
15 Workplace for the teaching or practice of an art (6)
17 Relating to or used in farming (12)
20 The deliberate act of deviating from the truth (5)
21 A source of difficulty (7)
22 The act of harassing someone (8)
23 Extremities of something that has length (4)

DOWN

1 Least expensive (8)
2 Not the same one or ones already mentioned (5)
4 The natural world (6)
5 Law determining the fundamental political principles of a government (12)
6 Reply (7)
7 Expresses an idea, etc. in words (4)
8 In an amazing manner (12)
12 Large smooth masses of rock (8)
14 More angry! (7)
16 A round fastener sewn to shirts (6)
18 Songbird with a reddish breast (5)
19 Travelled through the air (4)

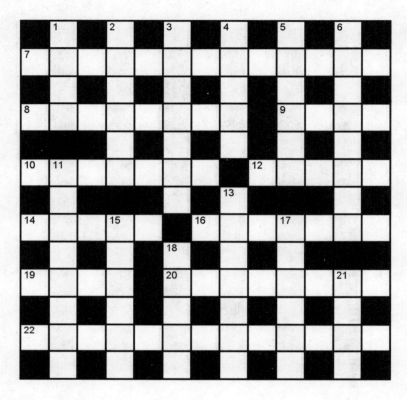

ACROSS

7 Your state with regard to wealth - scarcest cumin! (13)
8 Generally agreed upon; not subject to dispute (8)
9 Any of several small graceful hawks (4)
10 A heavy toxic silvery-white radioactive metallic element (7)
12 Inquired about (5)
14 Commonly encountered (5)
16 Most distant in time or space (7)
19 A cleansing agent made from fats (4)
20 Feelings (8)
22 Purpose and strength to succeed (13)

DOWN

1 A bluish-white lustrous metallic element (4)
2 A covering that serves to conceal or shelter (6)
3 Does not play for pay (7)
4 A state of deep mental absorption (5)
5 Limbless scaly elongate reptiles (6)
6 Turns the paddle; in canoeing (8)
11 Brought back to good health or condition (8)
13 Female hero (7)
15 Fruits with red or yellow or green skin (6)
17 The results of the printing process (6)
18 Appears to be (5)
21 The middle of the day (4)

ACROSS

7 Of the appetites and passions of the body (6)
8 The single one of its kind (6)
9 Unusually great in size (4)
10 Served as the inciting cause of (8)
11 The longest horizontal dimensions of something (7)
13 Movies, flicks (5)
15 Transport vehicle usually towed - a gown! (5)
17 Alight, on fire, great ambition or desire! (7)
20 Visiting a house as a ghost and scaring people! (8)
21 Part of bird (4)
22 Pleasantly occupied - medusa! (6)
23 Reply (6)

DOWN

1 Engage or hire for work, promise to marry? (6)
2 Leave out part (4)
3 In a satisfactory manner, on the night! (7)
4 A woman who is the custodian of children (5)
5 An army unit large enough to sustain combat (8)
6 A depository for displaying objects having historical value (6)
12 Moral excellence or admirableness (8)
14 A thief who enters a building with intent to steal (7)
16 Scares, frightens, clocks? (6)
18 Closer (6)
19 Helpful to other people (4)
21 Actively or fully engaged or occupied (4)

Colossal Book of Crosswords

ACROSS

1 An enclosure that is set back or indented (6)
4 Unmoving (6)
9 Examine and note the similarities or differences (7)
10 In a less successful or desirable manner (5)
11 A disreputable vagrant (5)
12 Declarations of intentions to inflict harm (7)
13 Knowledge acquired through study or experience (11)
18 Direct toward itself or oneself (7)
20 Applying to ordinary citizens (5)
22 An expensive vessel propelled by sail or power (5)
23 Opposing military forces (7)
24 A frequently visited place - roster! (6)
25 A distinct feature or element in a problem - at spec! (6)

DOWN

1 Repeat aloud from memory (6)
2 A punctuation mark (5)
3 The act of washing your hair (7)
5 Anything tall and thin - wrote! (5)
6 A localized and violently destructive windstorm (7)
7 A solid food prepared from pressed curd (6)
8 Metric unit of length equal to one hundredth of a meter (11)
14 Signs posted in a public place as an advertisement (7)
15 A summons issued to a parking offender (7)
16 A professional person authorized to practice law (6)
17 A toilet in England (6)
19 Located farther aft (5)
21 Express in coherent verbal form (5)

Colossal Book of Crosswords

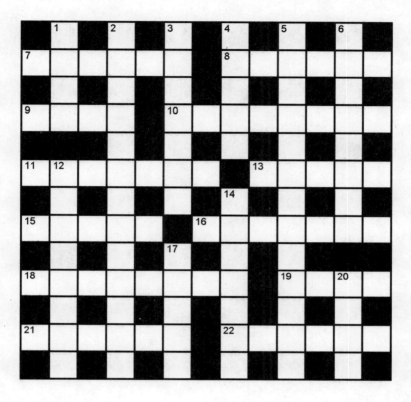

ACROSS

7 The chair of state of a monarch (6)
8 Involving the joint activity of two or more (6)
9 Travelled through water (4)
10 Without deviation - lyric ted! (8)
11 A natural inclination - in angle! (7)
13 A blow from a flat object (as an open hand) (5)
15 Caught or fixed (5)
16 An impairment of health - seaside! (7)
18 Makes believe - pet nerds! (8)
19 Acquire or deserve by one's efforts or actions (4)
21 Reverse the winding or twisting of (6)
22 The food and drink of the gods - trance! (6)

DOWN

1 A public entertainment or exhibition (4)
2 A connection allowing access between persons or places - mountain comic! (13)
3 The act of supplying food and nourishment (7)
4 Covered with a dense coat of fine silky hairs (5)
5 The length of the closed curve of a circle (13)
6 Substitute a person or thing (8)
12 A movement into or inward (8)
14 Touching with the lips - snogging? (7)
17 Rested one's weight on one's knees (5)
20 A deep prolonged loud noise (4)

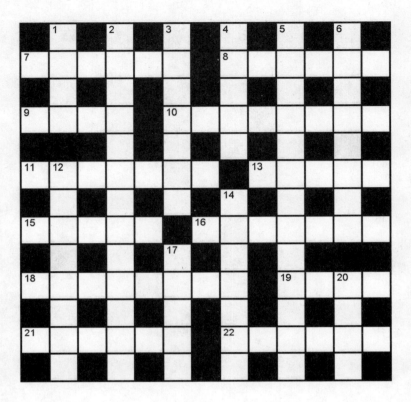

ACROSS

7 The contestant who wins the contest (6)
8 Narrow strip of fine material (6)
9 A man distinguished by exceptional courage (4)
10 Of imposing height - winter go! (8)
11 A large outdoor fire - November 5th? (7)
13 Stay clear from (5)
15 Not living together as man and wife (5)
16 Plan, organize, and carry out (an event) (7)
18 Any entry into an area not previously occupied - so in vain! (8)
19 A small part that can be considered separately (4)
21 The brothers of your father (6)
22 Had a yen for - dongle! (6)

DOWN

1 Number (4)
2 Experiencing physical discomfort - countable form! (13)
3 A person who is able to write (7)
4 A facial expression of dislike or displeasure (5)
5 Shortened forms of a word or phrase (13)
6 Repairing the joints of bricks (8)
12 A contestant - pop tenon! (8)
14 Incorrectly (7)
17 In the centre of - St Dim! (5)
20 Looked at, possibly greedily? (4)

Colossal Book of Crosswords

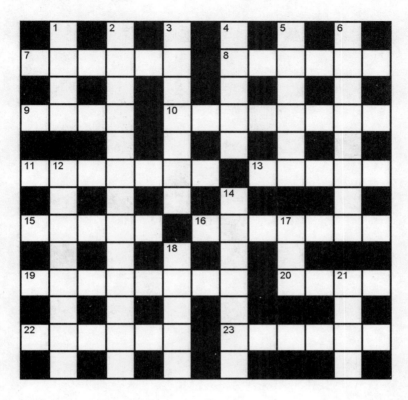

ACROSS

7 A protruding abdomen (6)
8 The place where something begins (6)
9 Roman Emperor (4)
10 Systematic training by multiple repetitions (8)
11 Extremely hungry (7)
13 Signal pleasure with facial expression (5)
15 Sudden expulsion of air from the lungs (5)
16 Provided for - ever cod! (7)
19 Very hard native crystalline carbon (8)
20 Other than what is under consideration or implied (4)
22 Hard dark-brown wood (6)
23 A US coin worth one twentieth of a dollar (6)

DOWN

1 Overcome the wildness of an animal (4)
2 The expression of approval and support - game encounter! (13)
3 Having wheels (7)
4 Bedding that keeps a person warm in bed (5)
5 A situation comedy, in short! (6)
6 Pass into a solution, Terminate (legally) (8)
12 Of weather or climate; hot and humid (8)
14 Throwing carelessly (7)
17 Adam's wife in Judeo-Christian mythology (3)
18 A unit of length used in navigation (5)
21 A mature fertilised plant ovule (4)

Colossal Book of Crosswords

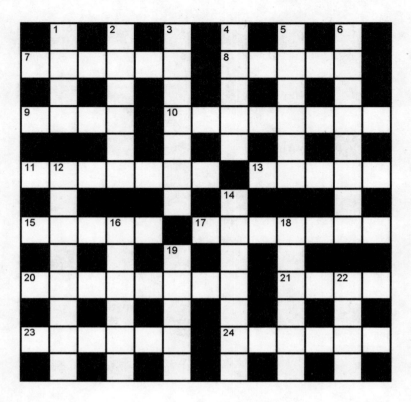

ACROSS

7 Strikes repeatedly with a heavy impact (6)

8 An implement used for catching fish (5)

9 Colour of sky? (4)

10 Latter part of days - seven gin! (8)

11 Under - below - nee bath! (7)

13 Portable shelters usually of canvas (5)

15 Challenges (5)

17 Tenting, confused, catching fish (7)

20 Move towards (8)

21 Certain to occur; destined or inevitable (4)

23 Sadness associated with some wrong done (6)

24 An affix that added in front of the word (6)

DOWN

1 Resources that can be shared (4)

2 A symptom consisting of the involuntary expulsion of air from the nose (6)

3 Distinct features or elements in a problem (7)

4 Required as useful, just, or proper - a desk! (5)

5 Bring to an end; settle conclusively (6)

6 Cause fear in - ref night! (8)

12 Punishments intended as a warning to others (8)

14 Maybe, possibly (7)

16 Mistakes made by accident (6)

18 Move or stir about violently - sets do! (6)

19 Travels by raft in water (5)

22 Complain bitterly - liar! (4)

Colossal Book of Crosswords

ACROSS

7 List in numerical order (6)
8 Not the same as ones already mentioned - throes! (6)
9 Nil, nought, nothing (4)
10 Easiest - misspelt! (8)
11 Rendered capable or able for some task (7)
13 Securing with rope (5)
15 Present (4)
17 A usually secretive or illicit sexual relationship (6)
20 A container that holds a magnetic tape (8)
21 Leg joint (4)
23 Keep busy with - coy cup! (6)
24 Game played with net, balls and rackets (6)

DOWN

1 A succession of notes (4)
2 Suck or take up or in (6)
3 An implement that has hairs or bristles firmly set into a handle (7)
4 Compositions - mopes! (5)
5 To a complete degree, entirely (6)
6 Cell inhabitant - or sniper! (8)
12 A bothersome annoying person (8)
14 Has an effect upon (7)
16 A soft thin paper used as a kerchief (6)
18 The verbal act of requesting (6)
19 A woman's close-fitting foundation garment (5)
22 An opening that permits escape or release (4)

Colossal Book of Crosswords

ACROSS

7 A fancy dock for small yachts and cabin cruisers (6)
8 The act of paying for the use of something (6)
9 Bake in a kiln - rife! (4)
10 The quality of being holy - scanty it! (8)
11 Move by degrees in one direction only - chatter! (7)
13 Discoloured with mildew spots, like an old book (5)
15 Tangle or complicate - laver! (5)
17 A sweet served as the last course of a meal (7)
20 Used in or intended for inhaling (8)
21 The imperial dynasty of China from 960 to 1279 (4)
22 The quality of threatening evil (6)
23 Assets belonging to a group (6)

DOWN

1 A clear liquid secreted into the mouth (6)
2 Freshwater fish (4)
3 A female spirit who wails (7)
4 A general direction (5)
5 Unpleasantly and excessively suave - uncut sou! (8)
6 Disclosing information about another, with tittle? (6)
12 Ornamental climbing plant (8)
14 A person who belongs to the political left (7)
16 Toughen by a process of gradually heating and cooling (6)
18 A member of the Texas state highway patrol (6)
19 Glazed yeast-raised doughnut-shaped roll (5)
21 A celestial body of hot gases (4)

Colossal Book of Crosswords

ACROSS

7 The main meal of the day (6)
8 Attached something by means of hammer and metal fixings (6)
9 (classical mythology) a being of great strength (4)
10 In an emotionally fierce manner (8)
11 Takes up residence and becomes established (7)
13 A sailing ship - macks! (5)
15 Passing from physical life (5)
16 Let go - see earl! (7)
18 Stops along railway for loading and unloading (8)
19 Finishes, terminates (4)
21 Drawn slowly or heavily (6)
22 Being new in a time not long past (6)

DOWN

1 The periodic rise and fall of the sea level (4)
2 By bad luck (13)
3 Be in motion due to some air or water current (7)
4 Alphabetical listing of topics in a book (5)
5 The size of something as given by the distance around it (13)
6 Substitutes a person or thing (8)
12 A native or inhabitant of Egypt (8)
14 Place a value on; judge the worth of something (7)
17 Pens for sheep (5)
20 Refuse to recognise or acknowledge (4)

Colossal Book of Crosswords

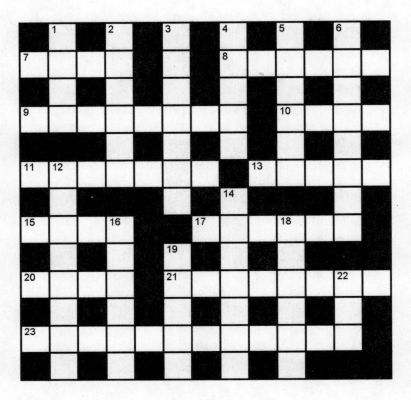

ACROSS

7 Art movement from the 30s (4)
8 Refuse to acknowledge (6)
9 At some indefinite or unstated time (8)
10 A small part that can be considered separately (4)
11 External covering of birds (7)
13 Preliminary races to decide who goes into the final (5)
15 The present location; this place (4)
17 The place after the first, short time (6)
20 A long-handled tool with a row of teeth (4)
21 Most fortunate (8)
23 An amount of money given to a cause (12)

DOWN

1 Indicating the absence of any or all units (4)
2 Worthy of being depended on - no Seth! (6)
3 The largest planet and the 5th from the sun (7)
4 Anointed to stop squeaks? (5)
5 Motor that converts thermal energy to mechanical work (6)
6 Taken into police custody - serrated! (8)
12 Lifting device - lever oat! (8)
14 Thick spicy sauce made from tomatoes (7)
16 Things that happen at a given place and time (6)
18 The place where something begins (6)
19 A basic knitting stitch (5)
22 Estrangement from god (3)

Colossal Book of Crosswords

ACROSS

7 The inner or enclosed surface of something (6)
8 Literature in metrical form (6)
9 An outer garment that has sleeves (4)
10 An inclination to do something - deny cent! (8)
11 Made senseless or dizzy - dunnest! (7)
13 Not fully grown (5)
15 Hold dear (5)
16 Plutonic igneous rock (7)
18 Generic name for certain synthetic materials (8)
19 Let something be known (4)
21 Spiritual being attendant upon God (6)
22 As much as necessary - no huge! (6)

DOWN

1 (archaic) to (4)
2 Set apart from other such things (13)
3 Animal skin made smooth and flexible by tanning (7)
4 Backbone (5)
5 Judgment reached after consideration (13)
6 Jewelry worn around the wrist for decoration (8)
12 Lagging or lingering behind (8)
14 Fell or came down violently (7)
17 The location of something surrounded by other things (5)
20 A written record of the transmissions by a radio station (4)

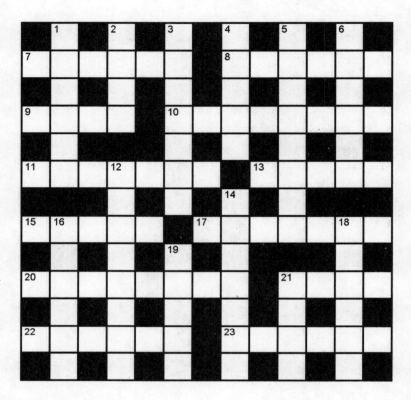

ACROSS

7 Official residence of an exalted person (6)
8 Laughed unrestrainedly and heartily (6)
9 Rub (4)
10 Beliefs that can guide behavior - so either! (8)
11 Looked up to - amid red! (7)
13 Contests of speed (5)
15 Evidence that helps to solve a problem (5)
17 Turn in the opposite direction (7)
20 Animal food for browsing or grazing - purest as! (8)
21 Rub with glasspaper (4)
22 A metal pot for stewing or boiling (6)
23 Athlete, drawer slide rail (6)

DOWN

1 Be subject to change,diverse (6)
2 Suffer from; be ill with (4)
3 Moved into the centre (7)
4 Intense sorrow caused by loss (5)
5 Characteristic way of bearing one's body (8)
6 Very strong or vigorous - see rev! (6)
12 Who you are - tin deity! (8)
14 Time available for ease and relaxation (7)
16 Sheets of any written or printed material (6)
18 The daily event of the sun sinking below the horizon (6)
19 Arrange thoughts, ideas, temporal events, etc. (5)
21 Deliver by singing (4)

Colossal Book of Crosswords

ACROSS

7 Disappear - an shiv! (6)
8 Animate being, creature (6)
9 The arithmetic operation of summing (4)
10 Position 11 in a countable series of things (8)
11 Deceived somebody - kid cert! (7)
13 Adult females (5)
15 Knocks out (5)
17 Utility to warm a building - an eight! (7)
20 Dispute - anger tum! (8)
21 Slender, thin, lose weight? (4)
22 Free from pomp or affectation (6)
23 Utter words loudly and forcefully (6)

DOWN

1 The greatest in vertical size - all ret! (6)
2 Passes away (4)
3 Robbers (7)
4 Competitions for runners (5)
5 A strong sea boat designed to rescue people from a sinking ship (8)
6 Domesticated bovine animals (6)
12 Made unclear or incomprehensible (8)
14 Written messages addressed to a person (7)
16 Great fear (6)
18 Sounds (6)
19 Makes hotter - haste! (5)
21 The fleshy part of the human body that you sit on (4)

Colossal Book of Crosswords

ACROSS

7 Sweater (6)
8 Military land forces (6)
9 Make senseless or dizzy by or as if by a blow (4)
10 High-speed military or naval aircraft (8)
11 Half woman and half fish; lives in the sea (7)
13 Lepidopterous insects - sh tom! (5)
15 A sturdy hand shovel (5)
17 Narrow-leaved green herbage (7)
20 Large outdoor fires (8)
21 Neat (4)
22 Persons who comes from a foreign country (6)
23 A feeling of pleasure and enjoyment (6)

DOWN

1 Faint and difficult to analyse - bluest! (6)
2 Afford access to (4)
3 Deal illegally - car tiff! (7)
4 Sudden very loud noises (5)
5 Any strong feelings (8)
6 Look for, maybe in a party? (6)
12 Changed in form or character (8)
14 Very recently - fly hers! (7)
16 Citizenry - lee pop! (6)
18 Finish - ginned! (6)
19 Arm joint (5)
21 Make a photograph with a camera - teak! (4)

ACROSS

7 Clear liquid secreted into the mouth (6)
8 Ornamental shrub (6)
9 Bird watcher's disguise? (4)
10 Climbing garden plant (8)
11 Short-tailed rodent with large cheek pouches (7)
13 A person who poses for a photographer (5)
15 H2O (5)
17 Fine particles of wood made by sawing (7)
20 Removing waste water through pipes - gardenia! (8)
21 Moving quickly and lightly, nimble (4)
22 To do with dogs or teeth (6)
23 Assets belonging to an individual person or group (6)

DOWN

1 Affectedly genteel, hoity-toity (2-2-2)
2 The amount a salary is increased (4)
3 Annual or perennial herb (7)
4 Having no protecting or concealing cover (5)
5 Inexpensive food (hamburgers or chicken or milkshakes) prepared and served quickly (4,4)
6 Remove or make invisible (6)
12 Stated explicitly or in detail, particular (8)
14 The countries of eastern Asia, not near! (3,4)
16 In a foreign country (6)
18 A light four-wheeled horse-drawn carriage (6)
19 Rubber product - exalt! (5)
21 Make very hot, brown meat in hot pan (4)

Colossal Book of Crosswords

ACROSS

1 Point formed by two intersecting arcs - cups! (4)
3 Toward a lower or inferior state - whin doll! (8)
9 Be a part or attribute of - painter! (7)
10 A synthetic fabric (5)
11 Generally incompetent and ineffectual (5)
12 Examiner - setter! (6)
14 Hear with intention - enlist! (6)
16 A tenant who holds a lease (6)
19 Soft blue-grey mineral; lead sulfide - anlage! (6)
21 A positively charged electrode (5)
24 Currently broadcasting (2,3)
25 Live side by side (2-5)
26 Completely - eternity! (8)
27 Have a tendency or disposition to (4)

DOWN

1 A top (as for a bottle) (3)
2 A brief indulgence of your impulses (5)
4 Rich in decorative detail (6)
5 Fifth of the seven canonical hours; about 3 p.m. (5)
6 Sickness (7)
7 Solo, like the ranger! (4)
8 Snake or child's toy! (6)
11 A small island (4)
13 Affected with madness or insanity (8)
15 Condiment that comes from the ocean (3-4)
17 Hard white substance covering a tooth (6)
18 A wealthy and privileged person, overweight feline! (3,3)
20 Mistake (5)
22 Speak one's opinion without fear or hesitation (5)
23 Move toward, travel toward something (4)

Colossal Book of Crosswords

ACROSS

7 Bird that uses others to hatch young (6)
8 Violent weather conditions (6)
9 A blemish made by dirt (4)
10 A fact about some part (as opposed to general) (8)
11 Most wealthy (7)
13 Not elaborate or elaborated; simple (5)
15 Come to pass, happen (5)
17 Emitting smoke in great volume - go Minsk! (7)
20 People who visit (8)
21 Rotate, possibly political? (4)
23 Very bad in degree or extent (6)
24 Necessary for relief or supply (6)

DOWN

1 A mechanical device that blows up tyres (4)
2 Describe roughly or briefly (6)
3 Have ownership of (7)
4 Inquired about - a desk? (5)
5 Relating to human society and its members (6)
6 A strong drive for success (8)
12 At an angle - nice lind! (8)
14 Witty, fun - in magus! (7)
16 Brought together (6)
18 Touched with the lips - is desk! (6)
19 Someone who fights (5)
22 A distinct part, thing - mite! (4)

Colossal Book of Crosswords

ACROSS

7 Cows (6)
8 Reduced speed (6)
9 Strike one's hands together (4)
10 The distinct personality of an individual (8)
11 Broken partially but keeping its integrity (7)
13 Where horses compete for speed - acres! (5)
15 Fighter or dog (5)
17 A prominent aspect of something (7)
20 Centurions, samurais, crusaders (8)
21 A socially awkward or tactless act (4)
22 Achieved harmony of opinion (6)
23 Directed one's gaze towards (6)

DOWN

1 Loftiest in style - rat ell! (6)
2 Halt! (4)
3 Based upon, taken from (7)
4 Posed a question to (5)
5 A binding agreement (8)
6 A small sofa (6)
12 Fruit with a single hard stone - cheer sir! (8)
14 Reflexive form of "her" - re shelf! (7)
16 Any of a range of colours between red and yellow (6)
18 Kept in check - denier! (6)
19 Small lakes (5)
21 A small slit for inserting a coin (4)

ACROSS

7 Electric wall sockets - indicates with finger (6)
8 The wife of your uncle (6)
9 Gratis, for nothing, out of jail! (4)
10 Replied to question - new dares! (8)
11 Estimates based on little or no information (7)
13 Further or added - throe! (5)
15 Normal (5)
16 Supported from above - nigh nag! (7)
18 The action of touching with the hands (8)
19 Undergoing an experiment (4)
21 A male member of a royal family (6)
22 Assigns a grade or rank to - crosse! (6)

DOWN

1 IV (4)
2 An inclination to support - sing redundant! (13)
3 Broke free, got out, leaked (7)
4 Reason that something happened (5)
5 An inquiry into unfamiliar or questionable activities (13)
6 XIX (8)
12 On or of upper floors of a building (8)
14 Greatest in size of those under consideration (7)
17 Depleted of strength or energy (5)
20 Perceived by sight (4)

Colossal Book of Crosswords

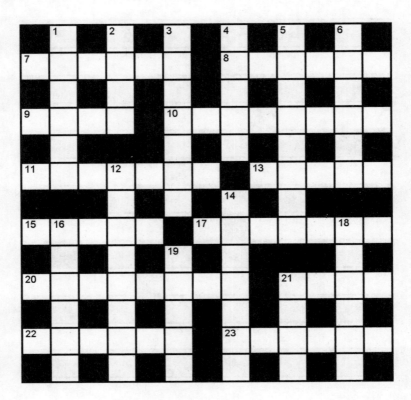

ACROSS

7 Restore by replacing a part (6)
8 On a ship, train, plane or other vehicle (6)
9 Cook and make edible by putting in a hot oven (4)
10 An example regarded as typical of its class (8)
11 Sitting, as on a branch (7)
13 Youthful attendants at official functions (5)
15 Very recently, as in wed? (5)
17 Having much flesh (especially fat) (7)
20 The lowermost portion of a structure (8)
21 Exposes one's body to the sun (4)
22 A story about mythical or supernatural beings (6)
23 General conscious awareness - nesses - come to them! (6)

DOWN

1 Act in an apt manner - have be! (6)
2 Put money aside regularly (4)
3 Entered party uninvited - her cads! (7)
4 Animal enclosures (5)
5 Exercising influence or control (8)
6 Fall below 0 degrees centigrade (6)
12 Institutions of further or higher education (8)
14 Most rapid (7)
16 An implement used to erase something, rubber (6)
18 When the sun begins to fall below the horizon (6)
19 Small drops of sweat - based! (5)
21 Went under (4)

Colossal Book of Crosswords

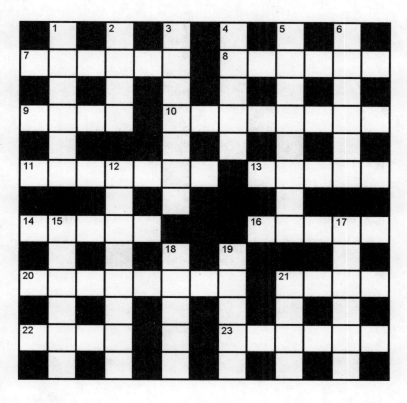

ACROSS

7 A thin plate or layer, animal in reverse! (6)
8 Soft light-coloured wood - end nil! (6)
9 A US coin worth one tenth of a dollar (4)
10 Fabric from which bed sheets are made (8)
11 Screaming female ghost (7)
13 A framework for holding wood - shore! (5)
14 Keen (5)
16 The act of lending money at an exorbitant rate (5)
20 Someone new to a field or activity (8)
21 Mentally healthy; free from mental disorder (4)
22 Animal hunted for food or sport (4)
23 American religious sect and type of furniture (6)

DOWN

1 Docking facility - airman! (6)
2 The physical magnitude of something (4)
3 Herb, served in sauce with fish (7)
4 Of time long past (5)
5 Unpleasantly and excessively suave, smarmy (8)
6 Name of Margaret Thatcher's husband (6)
12 Climbing garden plant, Lathyrus odoratus (8)
15 Temper, nan lea! (6)
17 Melt (fat, lard, etc.) to filter out impurities (6)
18 Tangle or complicate - laver! (5)
19 A leavening agent, used to raise dough (5)
21 A pole of wood or metal used to support rigging (4)

Colossal Book of Crosswords

ACROSS

7 Render capable or able for some task (6)
8 Road consisting of a pair of parallel rails (6)
9 Certain (4)
10 Tries - matt pets! (8)
11 A mixture of lime or gypsum with sand and water (7)
13 Newspaper writers and photographers (5)
15 Away from another or others (5)
17 The decision of a court on issues of fact or law (7)
20 Having the power to bring into being (8)
21 A polite name for any woman (4)
22 Joined or combined (6)
23 A beverage (6)

DOWN

1 Occurring or payable every year (6)
2 Having a strong healthy body (4)
3 Made less tense or rigid (7)
4 Express an idea, etc. in words (5)
5 Shaped or worked, forged - armed hem! (8)
6 Sports equipment that is worn on the feet (6)
12 Persons working in the service of another (8)
14 The absence of sound (7)
16 A father or mother (6)
18 Let the head fall forward through drowsiness (6)
19 Breezy, blowy (5)
21 Take out of the ground, of root crops (4)

Colossal Book of Crosswords

ACROSS

1 Having worth or merit or value (6)
4 Endure, bear (6)
9 The justification for some act or belief (7)
10 Pastry cups with fillings of fruit or custard (5)
11 Clean with hard rubbing (5)
12 Make impure (7)
13 Cake flavoured with ginger, also man! (11)
18 Cleanest - twist he! (7)
20 Of or relating to or caused by tides (5)
22 Sound of any kind (5)
23 Set free, let go (7)
24 Lengthwise cracks in wood (6)
25 Models of excellence or perfection (6)

DOWN

1 Broad in scope or content (6)
2 Make reference to (5)
3 A bag used for carrying money, especially by women (7)
5 Up to a time that (5)
6 Directions for making something (7)
7 Hurried - rude sh! (6)
8 The degree of hotness or coldness of a body (11)
14 The first letter of a word (7)
15 Thrown into a state of agitated confusion - let drat! (7)
16 Moves in a curve - gin SSW! (6)
17 Kips, naps, slumbers (6)
19 Something that happens - nee TV! (5)
21 Work intended for performance by actors (5)

Colossal Book of Crosswords

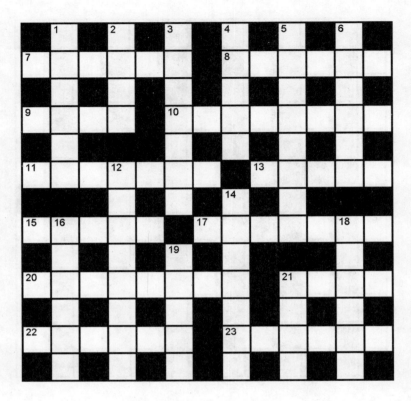

ACROSS

7 A ceremonial procession - pad ear! (6)
8 Hinged or detachable flat sections of table (6)
9 Part played by actor (4)
10 Parts of something, could be chemical (8)
11 Hoodwinked (7)
13 Sweet juicy gritty-textured fruit, Pyrus communis (5)
15 Kind of music (5)
17 Most quickly (7)
20 Damaged by blows or hard usage (8)
21 Plumbing fixture (4)
22 A position on a scale of intensity (6)
23 General conscious awareness (6)

DOWN

1 Bestow a privilege upon (6)
2 Characteristic of a man (4)
3 Umpire, the chief official (7)
4 Evidence that helps to solve a problem (5)
5 The lowest part of a house - below ground level (8)
6 A sweet liquid secretion (6)
12 A human being - rue carte! (8)
14 Toughest, most difficult (7)
16 Sprang, bounded, jumped (6)
18 The daily event of the sun sinking below the horizon (6)
19 Pushed for something (5)
21 A very small sum (4)

Colossal Book of Crosswords

ACROSS

7 Sufficient (6)
8 Without speed (6)
9 Bypass, rubbish container (4)
10 Above your head; in the sky - heave rod! (8)
11 Accept without verification or proof (7)
13 Animal food for browsing or grazing (5)
15 Month for fools? (5)
17 Propels boat, splashes in sea with feet? (7)
20 Physical energy or intensity (8)
21 A characteristic state or mode of living (4)
22 A unit of instruction (6)
23 Comes to pass - crocus! (6)

DOWN

1 Limbless scaly elongate reptiles, in grass? (6)
2 A low-cut shoe without fastenings (4)
3 Selects (7)
4 Inquired about (5)
5 Nervous or agitated - berth ode! (8)
6 Rests on the surface of water - of SALT! (6)
12 Everything that exists anywhere (8)
14 The latest and most admired style in clothes (7)
16 Summarised or abridged, plant? (6)
18 Earnest and conscientious activity (6)
19 Getting older - an gig! (5)
21 Be without (4)

Colossal Book of Crosswords

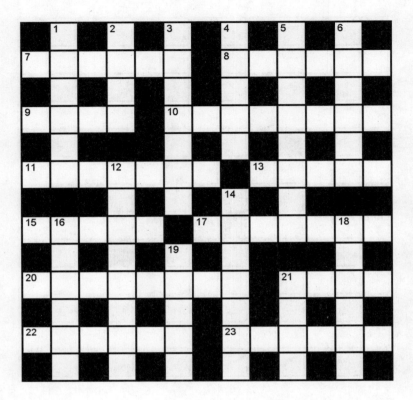

ACROSS

7 Elongated crescent-shaped yellow fruit (6)
8 Any substance that causes injury or illness or death of a living organism (6)
9 Prepare with dry heat in an oven (4)
10 An institution of higher education (8)
11 Low-lying wet lands with grassy vegetation (7)
13 The precise location of something - Pinot! (5)
15 Cover with a material such as stone (5)
17 A film about life in the western US, cowboy (7)
20 Activity leading to skilled behavior (8)
21 Hosiery - cloth covering for the foot (4)
22 Keeping out of sight, for protection and safety (6)
23 Thing an archer aims at - get rat! (6)

DOWN

1 A nation in northern North America (6)
2 A person's partner in marriage (4)
3 Emerge from the eggs; of birds, fish, or reptiles (7)
4 Put into service - go for job (5)
5 A boat designed to rescue people (8)
6 Contemporary - mend or! (6)
12 Not general, about some particular thing (8)
14 Altitudes - eighths! (7)
16 Fearful, scared (6)
18 More wealthy (6)
19 Monarchs (5)
21 Group into sizes, colours, etc (4)

Colossal Book of Crosswords

ACROSS

7 The gradual beginning or coming forth (6)
8 Every 60 minutes (6)
9 A blood vessel (4)
10 A response that reveals a person's feelings (8)
11 Books of maps (7)
13 Thick, centre, middle - St dim! (5)
15 Fast, rapid, bird! (5)
17 The sound of a bell (7)
20 Reckless or malicious behavior - if chimes! (8)
21 Tastelessly showy - ludo! (4)
22 A story about mythical or supernatural beings (6)
23 Beat (6)

DOWN

1 Pressing, needed now! (6)
2 Sweep majestically, also royal bird! (4)
3 Make shorter (7)
4 Corn (5)
5 The stealing of cattle (8)
6 Permits - owl las! (6)
12 Speaking or behaving in an artificial way (8)
14 Disagrees - rid effs! (7)
16 A person whose occupation is to serve at table (6)
18 Zero (6)
19 Pay close attention to; give heed to (4)
21 Narrative songs with a

Colossal Book of Crosswords

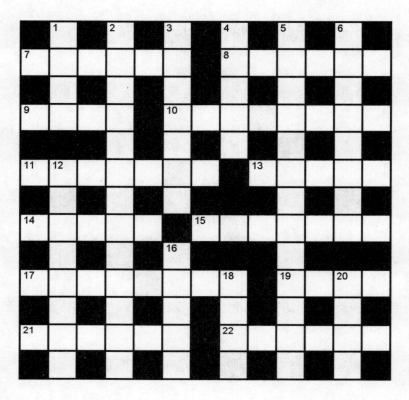

ACROSS

7 The quality of being funny (6)
8 Small air-breathing arthropod (6)
9 Singles - nose! (4)
10 Suitable to or characteristic of drama (8)
11 Fell down, as if collapsing (7)
13 Not younger, having greater age (5)
14 The name of a work of art or literary composition (5)
15 The amount per unit size (7)
17 Turn the oar, while rowing (8)
19 Pertaining to adult male persons! (4)
21 The expression on a person's face - set cap! (6)
22 Ached, for something (6)

DOWN

1 Destroy completely; damage irreparably (4)
2 Future prospects or potential (13)
3 Wooden supports on stringed instruments (7)
4 The contestant you hope to defeat (5)
5 A public or private structure (13)
6 A mishap (8)
12 The whole collection of existing things (8)
16 Relaxes for a while (5)
18 Your consciousness of your own identity (4)
20 Be obliged, required, or forced to (4)

Colossal Book of Crosswords

ACROSS

7 Occupation for which you are trained (6)

8 A thief who steals from someone (6)

9 We Have, in short! (4)

10 The act of guiding or showing the way (8)

11 Brass instrument (7)

13 Steer clear of (5)

15 Unsharp, possibly instrument (5)

16 Situated in a particular spot or position (7)

18 Self-contained parts of a larger composition (8)

19 Keen on, as in "---- rock music" (4)

21 At a distance, like a TV control? (6)

22 Open shoe (6)

DOWN

1 An account describing incidents or events (4)

2 The act of examining the properties of something (13)

3 Sweep across or over (7)

4 The Hellenic branch of the Indo-European family (5)

5 Shortenings, Shortened forms of words (13)

6 During the intervening time (8)

12 Lessened the intensity of; calmed (8)

14 Have ownership (7)

17 Brought into something against your will! (5)

20 The other one from this (4)

Colossal Book of Crosswords

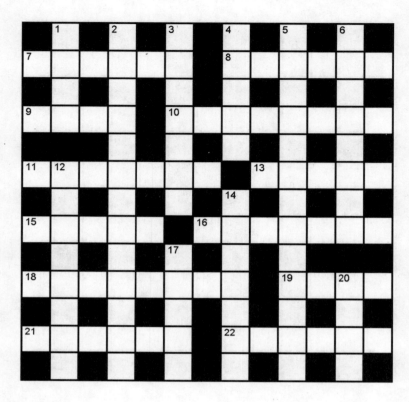

ACROSS

7 Characterised by variety (6)
8 United by being of the same opinion (6)
9 Disabled in the feet or legs (4)
10 Made ready or fit or suitable beforehand (8)
11 Saves, lives - secures! (7)
13 Gives temporarily; let have for a limited time (5)
15 Bed linen (5)
17 A struggle between rivals (7)
20 Social units living together - I fails me! (8)
21 A mark left by the healing of injured tissue (4)
22 Insect having biting mouthparts (6)
23 Did military service (6)

DOWN

1 A large and stately mansion (6)
2 Exhaust though overuse - out! (4)
3 Acquired as your own by free choice (7)
4 Blocks of solid substance (such as soap or wax) (5)
5 Something used to beautify (8)
6 Fight against or resist strongly (6)
12 A retail shop where medicines are sold (8)
14 Have as an attribute, knowledge, or skill (7)
16 Marked by emotional heat; vehement (6)
18 Weighing machines (6)
19 Someone who works underwater (5)
21 Ride the waves of the sea with a board (4)

Colossal Book of Crosswords

ACROSS

1 Overly diluted; thin and insipid - arty we! (6)
4 Like down or as soft as down, flossy (6)
9 Not constipated - err Gaul! (7)
10 The significance of a story or event (5)
11 Solid-hoofed herbivorous quadruped (5)
12 November 5th feature (7)
13 Bringing back to mind, recalling (11)
18 Able or likely to do harm (7)
20 Part of staircase (5)
22 An instance of some kind (5)
23 Pounded, beat - the dump! (7)
24 Most recent (6)
25 A characteristic to be considered (6)

DOWN

1 Meriting respect or esteem (6)
2 Panthera tigris (5)
3 Alleviate or remove (7)
5 Yellow oval fruit with juicy acidic flesh (5)
6 Concerning the affairs of other nations (7)
7 Shouted (6)
8 A measure of how likely it is that some event will occur (11)
14 Devout, sincere - nearest! (7)
15 Saves from something - cur sees! (7)
16 A place of worship that has its own altar (6)
17 Approval (6)
19 Examines by touch (5)
21 Fruit or type of computer (5)

Colossal Book of Crosswords

ACROSS

7 Soak up (6)
8 Everything you own (6)
9 Stop at railway platform? (4)
10 Serve as an excuse for - an pixels! (8)
11 Contain as a part (7)
13 Use language, talk (5)
15 Rapid simultaneous discharge of firearms (5)
17 Putting goods onto a train or lorry - do algin! (7)
20 Make less or smaller (8)
21 Come together (4)
22 At rest - please! (6)
23 Tidily (6)

DOWN

1 Get hold of something (6)
2 Where the leg begins - also a measure (4)
3 Watch attentively (7)
4 The rate of some repeating event, beat, pace (5)
5 Secure with a strap; of sprained joints, having no cash! (8)
6 A fixed number of lines of verse (6)
12 Witnessed at first hand (8)
14 A person - see moon! (7)
16 Causing or fraught with or showing anxiety (6)
18 A slender pointer for indicating a reading (6)
19 Temporary lodgings in the country for travellers (5)
21 Denote or connote, tight fisted! (4)

Colossal Book of Crosswords

ACROSS

7 Intense and profound fear, genre of film (6)
8 Plays boisterously - strops! (6)
9 Pteridophyte, frondy plant (4)
10 Wheel in car or committee (8)
11 Reproduced by printing (7)
13 Normal, same drink in the pub? (5)
15 Any dialect of the language of ancient Rome (5)
16 Black plastic music discs before CDS! (7)
18 Most unclean (8)
19 Serving item for food or hand out dirt! (4)
21 A 60th part of a minute (6)
22 Support for artists - van sac! (6)

DOWN

1 Finished and completed (4)
2 The way that words are said - puritanic noon! (13)
3 Humiliated or depressed completely (7)
4 Inquired about (5)
5 Exchanging messages (13)
6 Any distinctive flag (8)
12 Became fully aware or cognisant of (8)
14 Any of various plants of the genus Lactuca (7)
17 Poised for action - deary! (5)
20 Distance across aircraft wings or bridge (4)

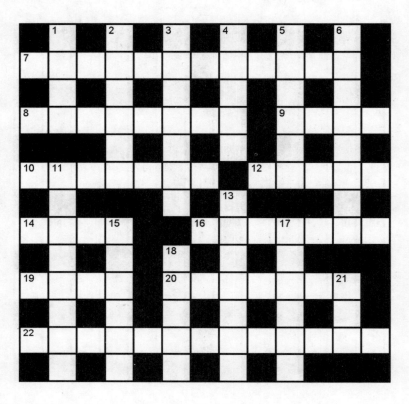

ACROSS

7 Maker, producer - fracture an um! (12)

8 Perceiving by inhaling through the nose (8)

9 A space reserved for sitting (4)

10 In the middle (7)

12 A pipe through which liquid is carried away (5)

14 A hemispherical roof (4)

16 Produces - a erects! (7)

19 A person who invites guests (4)

20 Being ten more than ninety (7)

22 Standing above others in character (13)

DOWN

1 Having an exaggerated sense of self-importance (4)

2 A set of clothing (with accessories) - it tofu! (6)

3 Wealth in the form of money or property (7)

4 Plan, organise, and carry out an event (5)

5 India Rubber (6)

6 Artistic - reactive! (8)

11 Financially rewarding - Neo comic! (8)

13 Function word - poor nun! (7)

15 Type of large car or land (6)

17 The act of apprehending (6)

18 Be distinguished or eminent, as if polished! (5)

21 A deer, a female deer (sing along!) (3)

Colossal Book of Crosswords

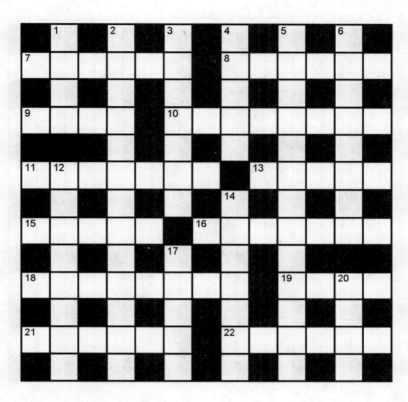

ACROSS

7 Having less money or being lower in quality (6)
8 What the pigs said! do Nike! (6)
9 A distinctive style or manner, carrying blood! (4)
10 Bony structure of animals (8)
11 Round yellow to orange fruit (7)
13 An analytic or interpretive literary composition (5)
15 An illusory feat, tricks - think Paul Daniels! (5)
16 Taking it easy - red axle! (7)
18 Area (8)
19 Could be floppy, magnetic? (4)
21 Get rid of, maybe a stain (6)
22 Saucy French dance (6)

DOWN

1 Watering pipe for garden (4)
2 Ron up inaction -The manner of uttering a word (13)
3 Lawns are made up of these (7)
4 Small velvety-furred burrowing mammal (5)
5 Capacity for rational thought - sing redundant! (13)
6 Drink made with lemons! (8)
12 Successfully completed or brought to an end (8)
14 Salad ingredient (7)
17 What trains run on (5)
20 Bottom or where you put it! (4)

Colossal Book of Crosswords

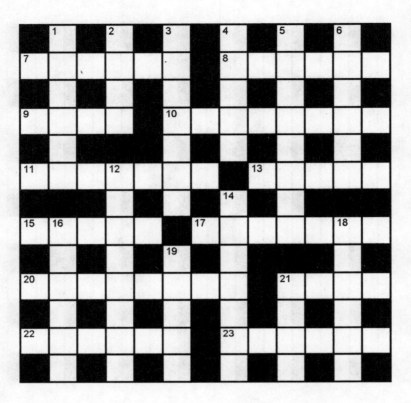

ACROSS

7 Characterised by variety, assorted (6)
8 Having a heading or caption, going in the direction of (6)
9 Cook by putting in a hot oven (4)
10 Came before - deep cred! (8)
11 Accomplishes, achieves - a cheers! (7)
13 Groups of cattle or sheep (5)
15 Directed or put a question; sought an answer to (5)
17 Most tolerant or lenient (7)
20 Upper-case letters (8)
21 Oceans (4)
22 Device for boiling water or a drum! (6)
23 Expresses an idea, etc. in words (6)

DOWN

1 Harm done to something - mad age! (6)
2 A light informal meal (4)
3 Changed in order to improve, altered (7)
4 A cry or shout of approval, hip! hip! (5)
5 Walk consisting of a paved area for pedestrians (8)
6 Have faith or confidence in, rely on (6)
12 Scientists who specialises in chemistry (8)
14 Made up of - Scots in! (7)
16 Spectacles that are darkened, keeps out of sun (6)
18 One suit on a deck of cards (6)
19 Kept back, rescued (5)
21 Make tight; secure against leakage (4)

Colossal Book of Crosswords

ACROSS

7 Concerned with religion or religious purposes (6)
8 Having a heading or caption, could be pig? (6)
9 No other place but this one (4)
10 Exact sameness - tin deity! (8)
11 Clad (7)
13 Declare or acknowledge to be true (5)
15 Lie obliquely (5)
17 Subject matter, substance - see mags! (7)
20 Force, take, or pull apart (8)
21 The collection of rules imposed by authority (4)
23 Very strong or vigorous - see rev! (6)
24 Having vision, not blind (6)

DOWN

1 The finishing line for a foot race (4)
2 Issue commands to others - err sod! (6)
3 Looked up to (7)
4 Good heart - Urge on or encourage esp. by shouts (5)
5 Sampled by mouth - stated! (6)
6 A gradual sinking to a lower level (8)
12 Made easier to bear (8)
14 Let go, set free, like a handbrake? (7)
16 Closer (6)
18 Metal used in jewellry (6)
19 Money paid to government from earnings (5)
22 Part of bird, most have two! (4)

Colossal Book of Crosswords

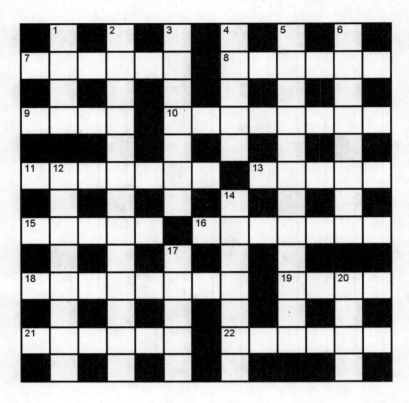

ACROSS

7 Exercise authority over; as of nations (6)
8 The feet of ungulate mammals (6)
9 A course of related exercises and ostures (4)
10 Doing well, growing - hiring TV! (8)
11 Break, vacation (7)
13 A single serving of a beverage (5)
15 A kind of pain; something sudden and painful (5)
16 The reason why - sea cube! (7)
18 People who fight for a cause (8)
19 Thing, an individual instance (4)
21 Lower, like a voice - peered! (6)
22 Possessors (6)

DOWN

1 On one's own, singly (4)
2 States of connectedness between people (13)
3 Occurring at the beginning, of a name? (7)
4 A visual display of information (5)
5 Speech used for informal exchange of views (12)
6 The idea that is intended - am ensign! (8)
12 Got, procured, found (8)
14 Stress (7)
17 Rips, liquid from eyes (5)
20 Make money through work (4)

Colossal Book of Crosswords

ACROSS

7 Bedding that keeps a person warm in bed (6)
8 Not vegetable or mineral! (6)
9 Cab (4)
10 Newspaper writings (8)
11 Prior to a specified or implied time (7)
13 Having nothing inside (5)
15 A cutting weapon with a long blade (5)
16 The act of touching physically (7)
18 Water falling in drops from vapour condensed in the atmosphere (8)
19 Close, not far (4)
21 Model of excellence or perfection of a kind (6)
22 Required, wanted to complete something (6)

DOWN

1 Comfy seat for more than one person (4)
2 The largest inland sea (13)
3 Land masses surrounded by water (7)
4 Where we all live, soil (5)
5 Situations, sometimes beyond control? (13)
6 Regal, cites jam! (8)
12 Low lying areas, not highlands! (8)
14 Getting cooler, lowering temperature (7)
17 The narrowing of the body between the ribs and hips (5)
20 Long time - sage! (4)

Colossal Book of Crosswords

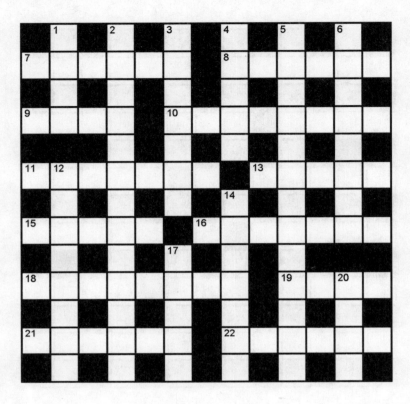

ACROSS

7 A device that attracts iron (6)
8 Shut, no longer open (6)
9 Wear out - confused rite! (4)
10 Easily damaged (8)
11 The first performance (as of a theatrical production), first night (7)
13 Beneath, like Milk Wood? (5)
15 Compass point (5)
16 Having the least wealth (7)
18 Not having all the facts, lacking knowledge (8)
19 A succession of notes forming a distinctive sequence (4)
21 10 years (6)
22 Prepared for eating by applying heat (6)

DOWN

1 Cab (4)
2 From or between other countries (13)
3 Leaner, especially in college (7)
4 Climb a mountain (5)
5 The strength of a solution - not concertina! (13)
6 Unable to settle (8)
12 Turned over with a plough (8)
14 Sort of lenses (7)
17 Dislikes intensely; feels antipathy or aversion towards (5)
20 A condition requiring relief (4)

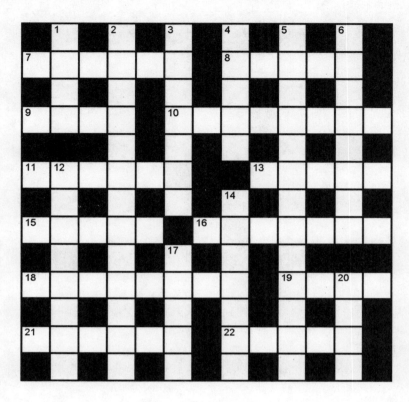

ACROSS

7 A way of acting or behaving (6)
8 A unit of weight = one sixteenth of a pound (5)
9 A door-like movable barrier in a fence (4)
10 Hard bony structure of humans (8)
11 A male member of a royal family (6)
13 Begin, jump with surprise (5)
15 Pleasing to the sense of taste (5)
16 Spectacles worn to protect the eyes (7)
18 Strong and active physically or mentally (8)
19 Try something out, exam, cricket match (4)
21 Make a logical or causal connection (6)
22 Item of cutlery (5)

DOWN

1 Molten rock from a volcano (4)
2 Belonging to at least two or more nations (13)
3 Clothed, like crab? (7)
4 Have a great affection or liking for (5)
5 An inquiry into questionable activities (13)
6 Available source of wealth (8)
12 Became fully aware or cognisant of (8)
14 Be composed of (7)
17 A structure taller than its diameter (5)
20 A musical composition with words (4)

ACROSS

7 Be subject to change (6)
8 Seas (6)
9 Atomic number 30 - metallic element (4)
10 Gave out, like a job - a designs! (8)
11 Digestive organ (7)
13 In a higher place (5)
15 Money awarded to winner in libel trial for legal fees (5)
16 Problems, difficulties, bother (7)
18 Extending or moving from a higher to a lower place (8)
19 Where you live? (4)
21 In accord, went along with, signed up to (6)
22 Sufficient (6)

DOWN

1 Hire car with driver (4)
2 Situation, could be suspicious? (13)
3 Move forward, payment made to author for novel (7)
4 Cooked bread (5)
5 Place where you and others live (13)
6 Short break, in a performance (8)
12 Detailed, leaving no stone unturned (8)
14 Baby beds (7)
17 Useful gadget, ready to hand (5)
20 Fools or drinking vessels for tea! (4)

Colossal Book of Crosswords

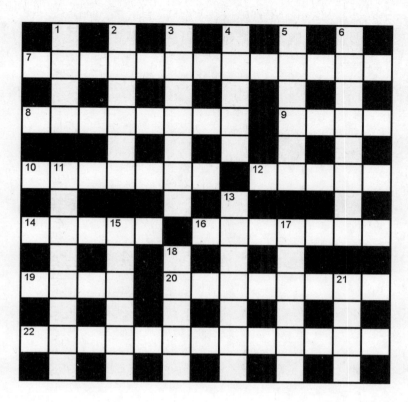

ACROSS

7 Conducting a test or investigation, trying out (13)
8 Takes the place or moves in place of (8)
9 Cut down to the desired size or shape (4)
10 House number, street, town, postcode (7)
12 Garden stores (5)
14 Stay clear from; keep away from (5)
16 Cheerio! (4-3)
19 Halt (4)
20 A long narrow sled (8)
22 Complete attention; intense mental effort (13)

DOWN

1 Metal rod supporting wheels (4)
2 Room under house, sometimes for wine (6)
3 To consider or examine in speech or writing (7)
4 A general conscious awareness, hopefully common (5)
5 Spasm of pain in the side from running (6)
6 Lacking in sympathy and kindness (8)
11 Dedication, feelings of ardent love (8)
13 Thieves (7)
15 The striking of one body against another (6)
17 One of the elements that collectively form a system of numbers (6)
18 Abounding in rocks or stones, sort of ground? (5)
21 The smallest component of an element (4)

Colossal Book of Crosswords

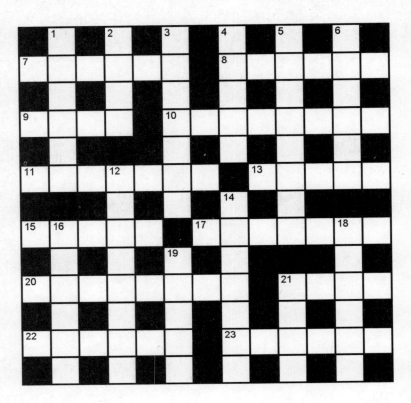

ACROSS

7 Be in charge of, possibly a football club? (6)
8 Astonished (6)
9 Number - baker's dozen less 4 (4)
10 Small fruits with a single stone (8)
11 Gave information or notice to (7)
13 A contest of speed (5)
15 Cycles (5)
17 Let go, set free (7)
20 Pointers, confused, from food! (8)
21 Caused to go somewhere - like a letter (4)
22 Comfy seat for more than one (6)
23 Let for money; of housing (6)

DOWN

1 Made something more diverse (6)
2 Bottom of something (4)
3 Fruits, with cream? (7)
4 An identifying or descriptive marker (5)
5 Characteristic way of bearing one's body (8)
6 Very strong or vigorous, harsh (6)
12 Who you are (8)
14 Pudding (7)
16 Jewish republic in southwestern Asia (6)
18 Time in the evening at which the sun begins to fall (6)
19 Plunges head first into water (5)
21 Male human offspring (4)

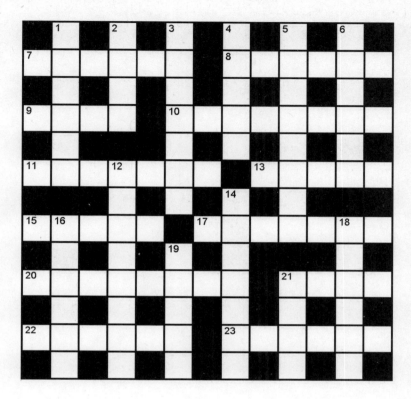

ACROSS

7 Sturdy grass used to make cane furniture (6)
8 Pair, two people (6)
9 Depend on (4)
10 Social or professional status or reputation (8)
11 A form of capital punishment (7)
13 Before all others, the leader (5)
15 A loose outer garment, goes with dagger? (5)
17 Suitcases (7)
20 A state of misfortune or affliction (8)
21 Paper or similar covering of a gift (4)
22 A conical shaped device for pouring liquid (6)
23 Sugary treats (6)

DOWN

1 Photographic recording device (6)
2 Do as instructed (4)
3 Homes, cover for equipment (7)
4 Sea (5)
5 Hugging lovingly (8)
6 Any of various organs - nag LSD! (6)
12 Keeping watch over (8)
14 What something is used for (7)
16 An association of sports teams, like the football ..... (6)
18 Any creature of exceptional size (6)
19 Home for crab, snail or oyster (5)
21 Cry (4)

Colossal Book of Crosswords

ACROSS

7 A short musical passage (6)
8 Having a crew (6)
9 An open flat-bottomed boat (4)
10 The distinct personality of an individual (8)
11 100 of these equals 1 Deutsche Mark (7)
13 Smell (5)
15 A minor nature goddess (5)
16 A series of acts at a night club (7)
18 Badly made or finished, tacky (8)
19 Lazy (4)
21 Persons who own (are legal possessors of) a business (6)
22 Distance, duration, time period (6)

DOWN

1 Thyself ;(archaic) (4)
2 Condiments on table, in pots (4,3,6)
3 An excess of liabilities over assets (7)
4 Cause to move forward with force (5)
5 UN (6,7)
6 Glass tube closed at one end, for babies? (4-4)
12 Spoiled and covered with larvae of flies (3-5)
14 Shoes - a sole fastened by straps to the foot (7)
17 Run after with the intent to catch (5)
20 After the expected or usual time; delayed (4)

ACROSS

7 Genre of film - scary! (6)
8 Determining the sum of two or more numbers (6)
9 Wood fixing device (4)
10 Without any noise or sound (8)
11 Concerned, disquieted (7)
13 Number one (5)
15 Travels through water using arms and legs (5)
17 Wax colouring sticks (7)
20 Hour that war ended (8)
21 Title (4)
22 Heavenly body (6)
23 One who reads! (6)

DOWN

1 Salad ingredient (6)
2 Using speech rather than writing (4)
3 Narrow-leaved green herbage: grown as lawns (7)
4 Bird of prey, old comic! (5)
5 Establish the identity of someone (8)
6 The brothers of your father or mother (6)
12 Taking away (8)
14 Bowmen and women, radio programme? (7)
16 With violent and uncontrollable passion (6)
18 Health care workers (6)
19 Blemishes in wood (5)
21 The provision of money temporarily (usually at interest) (4)

Colossal Book of Crosswords

ACROSS

7 Making something, sort of industry (13)
8 Prickling, a kind of pain - singing + T (8)
9 Cleaning bar (4)
10 Got on the train, nailed up (7)
12 Chips are french ones! (5)
14 Exhausts, wears out, fatigues (5)
16 Tooth doctor (7)
19 Exploding buried device (4)
20 Apertures (8)
22 Invisible (6)
23 Sort of horse, made of wood! Historical (6)

DOWN

1 Stop, train stop (4)
2 Jogger, long carpet (6)
3 Part of government, cupboard (7)
4 Place where actors ply their trade, coach? (5)
5 Rubber device for removing pencil or pen (6)
6 Someone who enters by force in order to conquer (8)
11 Personal beliefs or judgments (8)
13 Under (7)
15 Number in football team (6)
17 Suit maker (6)
18 Get on, horse (5)
21 Happy little Gladice (4)

Colossal Book of Crosswords

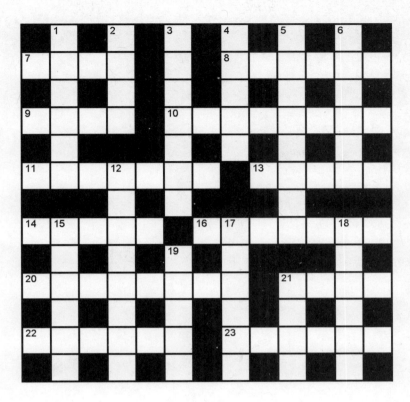

ACROSS

7 Collection of facts from which conclusions may be drawn (4)
8 Great fear (6)
9 Part of face (4)
10 Brought together, harvested? (8)
11 A monarchy in northwestern Europe (7)
13 The highest in an ordering or series (5)
14 Collective word for sheep (5)
16 Computer application (7)
20 The time immediately following sunset (8)
21 The protective covering on top of a building (4)
22 Punishment intended as a warning to others (6)
23 Protect by insurance (6)

DOWN

1 On the contrary, instead - her art! (6)
2 The first light of day (4)
3 Complete electrical path, lap of racing arena (7)
4 Things (5)
5 Falling behind, hanging down as a plant (8)
6 Tall buildings (6)
12 Difficult to handle; requiring great tact (8)
15 A professional person authorised to practice law (6)
17 Hold on to, keep back (6)
18 Alongside, on a ship (6)
19 A substance that exerts some force or effect - at gen! (5)
21 State of calm, not active (4)

Colossal Book of Crosswords

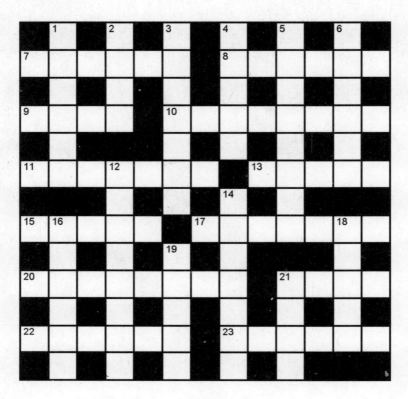

ACROSS

7 A collection of things wrapped together (6)
8 Pictures (6)
9 What something is used for (4)
10 Something that treats the symptoms of disease (8)
11 Catching up with, Deriving benefit from (7)
13 Lacking seriousness; given to frivolity, like a kipper? (5)
15 Making use of (5)
17 Pulled slowly or heavily (7)
20 Most distant (8)
21 Certain (4)
22 Not so long ago (6)
23 Exhales abruptly, when one has a chest cold (6)

DOWN

1 Former communist country in East Europe (6)
2 Determines the sum of (4)
3 Section or one part of a whole (7)
4 Discovers something (5)
5 Walking steadily and rhythmically and in step with others (8)
6 Relied on for support, at an angle? (6)
12 The decade from 1890 to 1899 (8)
14 People who express reasoned judgments (7)
16 Looked at unblinkingly (6)
18 Soil, this planet (5)
19 Trials conducted for diagnostic purposes (5)
21 Liquid food (4)

Colossal Book of Crosswords

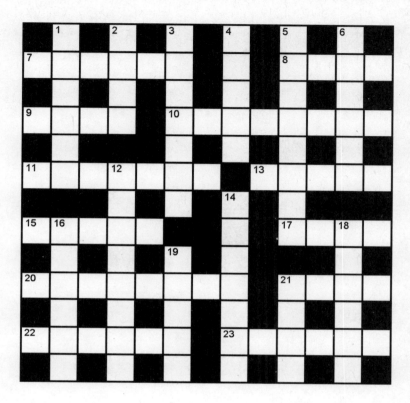

ACROSS

7 Characterised by variety (6)
8 Historic periods (4)
9 An occurrence of something (4)
10 Pleasing by delicacy or grace; not imposing (8)
11 Gets to a certain point (7)
13 Greeting (5)
15 Makes cake in oven (5)
17 Any piece of work that is undertaken (4)
20 A wheeled vehicle drawn by horses (8)
21 Delivered by singing (4)
22 Intensely or extremely bad (6)
23 A person who sings (6)

DOWN

1 Barbaric, brutal (6)
2 TV programme going out as it happens (4)
3 Changed or altered to suit a purpose (7)
4 Wounds resulting from biting (5)
5 Most distant (8)
6 Show, unveil (6)
12 Fruits with a single hard stone (8)
14 Let go, set free (7)
16 Astonished (6)
18 Feels something, general conscious awareness (6)
19 Computer man - Bill (5)
21 Slide beneath the waves (4)

ACROSS

7 Royal seat (6)
8 Jail (6)
9 Child's transport (4)
10 Does a routine on stage, acts (8)
11 Blocks of 10 years (7)
13 Travels in a sail powered boat (5)
15 The skilled practice of a practical occupation (5)
17 A proceeding (usually by a court of law) (7)
20 Naughty behaviour (8)
21 Torture instrument or herb store (4)
22 Precious stones (6)
23 Noon (6)

DOWN

1 Pay by credit card or attack! (6)
2 Inhabitant of garden soil (4)
3 Humanity, folks, population (6)
4 A drama set to music (5)
5 Extinct former inhabitant of earth (8)
6 Not out of the ordinary (6)
12 Have an emotional or cognitive impact upon (8)
14 Scent (7)
16 Pulled back (a horse) (6)
18 The food and drink of the gods; (6)
19 In the middle of (5)
21 Naughty or crude (4)

277

Colossal Book of Crosswords

ACROSS

7 Musical instruments, they could be grand (6)
8 Money from business, after expenses! (6)
9 Sound bounced back from surface (4)
10 Height, above sea level (8)
11 Given or presented with (7)
13 One of 7 across! (5)
15 Put on scales to calculate weight (5)
16 Ask for, maybe a record on the radio (7)
18 Sea creatures, half fish half women (8)
19 Metal (4)
21 At an angle, relied on for support (6)
22 A series of hills or mountains (6)

DOWN

1 Metal (4)
2 Giving hope or support to someone (13)
3 Got away, broke free (7)
4 Pimples or beauty? (5)
5 Monies given towards a campaign (13)
6 Conclusions (8)
12 At whatever place (8)
14 Relaxation time (7)
17 Breezy (5)
20 Unlocked, free access (4)

ACROSS

1 The largest ocean in the world (7)
5 Monies owed (5)
8 Held within something (9)
10 Single, 1 (3)
11 Employees or wooden stick (5)
13 The furthest or highest degree of something (7)
14 Markedly new or introducing radical change (13)
16 Directions for making something (7)
18 8 (5)
20 Travel across snow on thin plastic runners (3)
21 Copy of something, form of flattery? (9)
23 Frock, clothe (5)
24 Sewing or knitting equipment (7)

DOWN

1 Guitar pluckers or starts a fight? (5)
2 Tin container (3)
3 Scared (7)
4 Intense mental effort (13)
6 Bent wood that returns when thrown (9)
7 The painted structures on a stage (7)
9 Part of morse code (3)
12 Make publicity for; try to sell (a product) (9)
14 Declined, not given permission (7)
15 Work (machinery), repair by surgery (7)
17 Counting quantity, with tens and hundreds (5)
19 Looks after (5)
22 Sick (3)

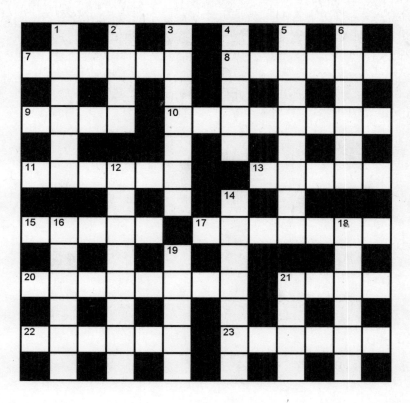

ACROSS

7 The occupation for which you are trained (6)
8 Bring together (6)
9 Other than what is under consideration or implied (4)
10 Types of plant, going up a mountain (8)
11 Predatory arachnid (6)
13 Web-footed long-necked migratory aquatic bird (5)
15 Sea (5)
17 Precipitation (7)
20 The person you have to beat (8)
21 Reach a state, relation, or condition (4)
22 Comport oneself properly (6)
23 Make a total by combining numbers (6)

DOWN

1 Pace of horse in race (6)
2 Nowhere else, in this place (4)
3 General consumer item, type of shop (7)
4 Once more, repeated (5)
5 Difficult to move, like a mule? (8)
6 Game played at Wimbledon (6)
12 A cut across a fabric that is not at right angles to a side (8)
14 Not complete (7)
16 Secondary representations of an original (6)
18 Giving names to something (6)
19 Number of brides for brothers? (5)
21 (computer science) the symbolic arrangement of data (4)

ACROSS

7 A visible suspension in the air of particles (6)

8 Units of weight equal to one sixteenth of a pound (6)

9 Fishing devices (4)

10 Bony structure (8)

11 Women's sleeveless undergarments, bears! (7)

13 Up to a time that (5)

15 Keep or lay aside for future use (5)

16 Operation that segregates items into groups (7)

18 Train arrival and departure places (8)

19 Promise, sworn (4)

21 Take away (6)

22 Vibrated back and forth, disturbed (6)

DOWN

1 Remove or make a photograph (4)

2 Thoughtfulness (13)

3 Sweeping or painting devices (7)

4 Musical sounds or jottings (5)

5 Company located in a number of countries (13)

6 Feelings of ardent love, dedication (8)

12 Has the right to something (8)

14 Is made up of (7)

17 Book, unusual (5)

20 Objective case of they (4)

Colossal Book of Crosswords

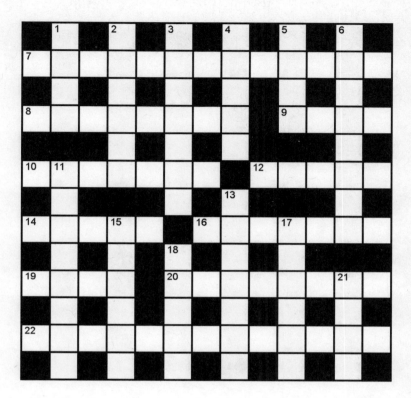

ACROSS

7 Making, building, constructing (13)
8 Strikingly beautiful or attractive (8)
9 A blow from a flat object (4)
10 Taken with you, transported on a stretcher (7)
12 Wept, shouted out (5)
14 Looks directly at - visages (5)
16 Dental surgeon, orthodontist (7)
19 Animal, pessimistic stock market outlook (4)
20 Gladdest, most pleased (8)
22 The act of making up your mind (13)

DOWN

1 An actor's portrayal of someone in a play (4)
2 Type of bean or athlete (6)
3 Government body or storage unit (7)
4 Actor's domain, coach? (5)
5 Plant with sword-shaped leaves (4)
6 Armies who enter by force in order to conquer (8)
11 Woken up (8)
13 Assisting, lending a hand (7)
15 Acquired or deserved by one's efforts (6)
17 30 (6)
18 Hit someone, heavy dull sound (5)
21 Fired a gun (4)

Colossal Book of Crosswords

ACROSS

1 Numbered or proceeding by tens; based on ten (7)
5 Looked directly at (5)
8 The size of the distance around something (13)
9 Second person pronoun; the person addressed (3)
10 Youngsters between 13 and 19 (9)
12 Small air-breathing arthropod (6)
13 Tapped affectionately on the head (6)
15 Letter from bank detailing transactions (9)
16 To a complete degree or to the full extent (3)
18 Books of facts and knowledge (13)
20 Covered in dust, also Springfield! (5)
21 Stretches out over a distance (7)

DOWN

1 Go bad or rotten (5)
2 Situation, sometimes financial (13)
3 Facial hair (9)
4 Raised up, possibly spirits (6)
5 A long way away (3)
6 Intense thought (13)
7 Fully clothed (7)
11 Flat (9)
12 In place of (7)
14 Far away TV control (6)
17 Does not win (5)
19 Weep (3)

ACROSS

7 The way that you do something (6)
8 A place of risk or peril (6)
9 Cost to travel, price of ticket (4)
10 Man's name, short version of Stephen (5)
11 Connected to a computer to make copies (7)
13 Tale (5)
15 Rubbish (5)
16 Wanted, amorously (7)
18 Extinct terrestrial reptile of the Mesozoic era (8)
19 Tiny leafy-stemmed flowerless plants (4)
21 A person who belongs to the sex that can have babies (6)
22 Open shoe (6)

DOWN

1 Molten rock (4)
2 From or between other countries (13)
3 Breaks violently or noisily, car accidents (7)
4 Snake - mathematically inclined? (5)
5 Fun, something done or visited for pleasure (13)
6 Available source of wealth or material (8)
12 Became aware of, it dawned upon me? (8)
14 Closest (7)
17 A hen that lays eggs, single thickness (5)
20 Sudden cold spell (4)

Colossal Book of Crosswords

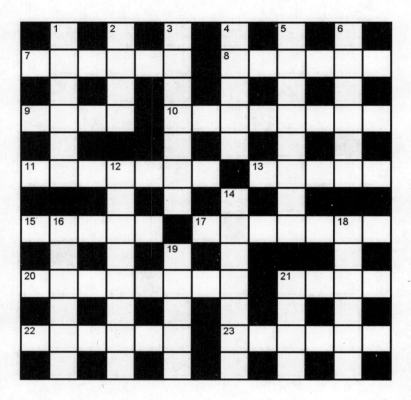

ACROSS

7 Female parent (6)
8 Possessing (6)
9 Characteristic of false pride (4)
10 Ruled over (8)
11 Destructive windstorm (7)
13 Minimal in magnitude (5)
15 The opening through which food is taken in (5)
17 A relatively flat highland (7)
20 Domestic fowl bred for flesh or eggs (8)
21 Baby beds with high sides (4)
22 Any liquids suitable for drinking (6)
23 Come up with an idea before anyone else (6)

DOWN

1 Fruit eaten as vegetable in salad (6)
2 The protruding part of the lower jaw (4)
3 An event resulting in great loss and misfortune (7)
4 Unravel a mystery, crack a crime (5)
5 Most angry (8)
6 If not (6)
12 Perceiving (8)
14 Stretchable (7)
16 Persons who are not us (6)
18 Playing a part on stage (6)
19 Conscious awareness, could be common (5)
21 Dwelling for early humans (4)

Colossal Book of Crosswords

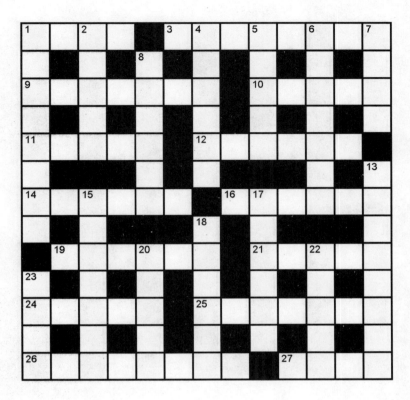

ACROSS

1 Sort of music from the 60s and 70s (4)
3 Month (8)
9 Lowered, in price (7)
10 Cat (5)
11 Load carried by ship (5)
12 Additions to contracts - derris! (6)
14 Has a good chance of being the case (6)
16 Crescent-shaped yellow fruit (6)
19 Any person, no one in particular (6)
21 Style of jazz played by big bands in the '30s (5)
24 Any long raised strip (5)
25 A small cosmetics case with a mirror (7)
26 Drink (8)
27 Back end, rise up (4)

DOWN

1 In a stringent manner - cry stilt! (8)
2 Beneath (5)
4 Put up with, tolerate (6)
5 Fast, dangerous water (5)
6 Country (7)
7 Toy on string (2-2)
8 Place of learning for children (6)
13 Female child (8)
15 A country with a king as head of state (7)
17 Take to be true without proof (6)
18 Cordoned off by a structure, sold stolen goods (6)
20 Sea (5)
22 A visual representation of an object (5)
23 To do with the mouth (4)

Colossal Book of Crosswords

ACROSS

7 Review, announcement, perceive (6)
8 Jewish republic (6)
9 Goes into place perfectly (4)
10 A verbal commitment which should be kept (7)
11 Witty, fun (7)
13 The extent of something from side to side (5)
15 Imprecise but fairly close to correct, approx (5)
17 Nag, black and white striped animal (6)
20 Outside (8)
21 Explosive device (4)
22 What you mean to do (6)
23 Allow, parking badge for example (6)

DOWN

1 A silvery soft waxy metallic element (6)
2 Children or young goats (4)
3 Retaining, like a goal! (7)
4 Of lesser importance or stature or rank (5)
5 Laudatory, expressing thanks for something (8)
6 A building material (6)
12 Grip and press firmly (7)
14 Where racehorses train, and at what speed? (7)
16 Fighting in a ring (6)
18 Stay (6)
19 Fastening tied in rope or string (4)

Colossal Book of Crosswords

ACROSS

7 Move up and down repeatedly, like a rubber ball (6)
8 An administrative unit of government (6)
9 Any activity that is performed alone (4)
10 The day after today (8)
11 Quickly, rapidly (7)
13 Go along with, be in accord (5)
15 An item inserted in a written record (5)
16 Direct a question at someone, where you live (7)
18 Photographic film before printing, no! (8)
19 The rear part of an aircraft (4)
21 An informal form of address for a man (6)
22 Made a sound like a dog (6)

DOWN

1 Game played on horseback or in water (4)
2 Experiencing physical discomfort (13)
3 Capable of reproducing (7)
4 Place where crops are grown for food (5)
5 Ice boxes, cooling devices (13)
6 Two-wheeled vehicles operated by foot (8)
12 Walked aimlessly (8)
14 A word that modifies something other than a noun (6)
17 Looks at carefully; studies mentally, vistas (5)
20 Wild goat of mountain areas of Eurasia (4)

Colossal Book of Crosswords

ACROSS

7 Artillery gun that is usually on wheels (6)
8 Money available for a client to borrow (6)
9 A delicate decorative woven fabric (4)
10 Made bigger, like a photograph (8)
11 Bath cleaners from the sea bed! (7)
13 Once more (5)
15 Compass point (5)
17 Positions on a scale, like centigrade (7)
20 Lacking basic knowledge (8)
21 Ripped (4)
23 Turned into (6)
24 Clothes protectors for cooks or woodworkers (6)

DOWN

1 Volcanic rock (4)
2 Not seen or perceived (6)
3 Exhaled spasmodically, as when hay fever strikes! (7)
4 Part of fish skin, musical progression (5)
5 Not a good thing to show a bull! (3,3)
6 In like or similar manner (8)
12 To break and turn over earth with a plough (8)
14 Out of gear, not on one side or another (7)
16 Middle of an insect (6)
18 Take back, like a library book? (6)
19 Challenges (5)
22 One step on a ladder (4)

ACROSS

7 A ceremonial procession with marching (6)
8 Affected with wonder - am daze! (6)
9 A hemispherical roof (4)
10 Place where plays are performed (7)
11 Game played with willow on leather! (7)
13 Answer (5)
15 Sacked, pulled trigger on gun (5)
17 Competition, argue for something (7)
20 Upper case letters (8)
21 Kitchen fixture (4)
22 A long wooden bench with a back (6)
23 Crooner (6)

DOWN

1 A visible suspension in the air (6)
2 Flower holder (4)
3 Paint pot or water boiler (6)
4 Monies paid for labour (5)
5 Most distant (8)
6 Show, make clear and visible (6)
12 Apothecary (7)
14 Is made up of (7)
16 Girl's name (6)
18 Going down of the sun (6)
19 Less intense colour due to exposure to light (5)
21 Mentally OK (4)

Colossal Book of Crosswords

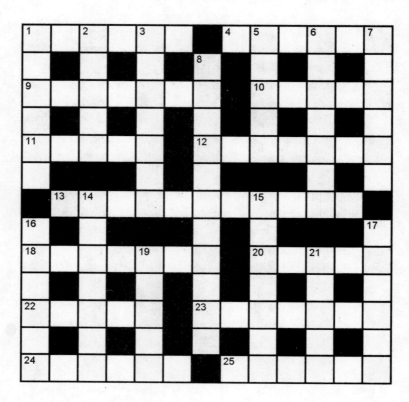

ACROSS

1 Small creature (6)
4 Strikes with disgust or revulsion (6)
9 Hair cleaner (7)
10 Do not eat food, go away (5)
11 Clean vigorously (5)
12 Ran at a moderately swift pace, like a horse (7)
13 Straight away with no delays (11)
18 Flat area of land (7)
20 Make reference to (5)
22 Full of sound, mostly unwanted? (5)
23 Made it possible for something to happen (7)
24 Fingers or computer numbers (6)
25 View - set cap! (6)

DOWN

1 Be insistent and refuse to budge (6)
2 Ringo the beatle (5)
3 Able to do something without help (7)
5 Greeting, Hi! (5)
6 Bordering on a coast (7)
7 Reliable, firm, stable - as a rock? (6)
8 Gave to, was a factor (11)
14 The message that is intended or expressed (7)
15 Warnings with implied violence (7)
16 Unsealed, started in business (6)
17 Have trust in; trust in the truth or veracity of (6)
19 Pyramid building country (5)
21 Untrue (5)

Colossal Book of Crosswords

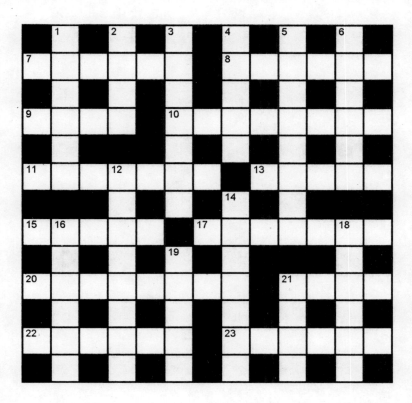

ACROSS

7 Pigment (6)
8 Beast, creature (6)
9 Animals kept for pleasure (4)
10 Roaring decade in USA1 (8)
11 Get away (7)
13 Thick (5)
15 More than one goose! (5)
17 Highest temperature (7)
20 Crawling, on hands and knees perhaps (8)
21 Garden tool store (4)
22 Come into sight or view (6)
23 Frightened (6)

DOWN

1 Controlling influences (6)
2 Places where animals are kept on display (4)
3 Work produced using pen and ink? (7)
4 Removed, perhaps photo? (5)
5 Filthiest (8)
6 Short newspapers (6)
12 Replied (8)
14 Having greatest length (7)
16 Continent (6)
18 Appeared to be (6)
19 Yearbook (5)
21 Bottom, place to sit (4)

Colossal Book of Crosswords

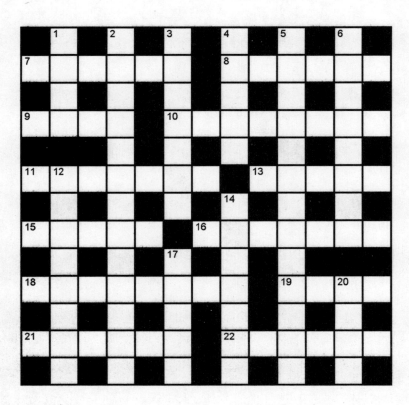

ACROSS

7 Country (6)
8 People who possess something (6)
9 Unattractive, duckling perhaps? (4)
10 Transporting, perhaps a baby? (8)
11 Told off, berated (7)
13 Mess up lines in play (5)
15 Kipped, napped, dozed (5)
16 Aerodrome (7)
18 Formal event like an opening perhaps (8)
19 From which we get venison (4)
21 Middle sized (6)
22 Jumped (6)

DOWN

1 Pull along the ground (4)
2 Book of facts (13)
3 Fruits served with cream (7)
4 Entrance covers and 60s band! (5)
5 More than one of 2 down! (13)
6 Move from one team to another (8)
12 Institutions of higher education (8)
14 Two wheeled transport (7)
17 Types of gear or animal infestation! (5)
20 Equal, divisible by two (4)

Colossal Book of Crosswords

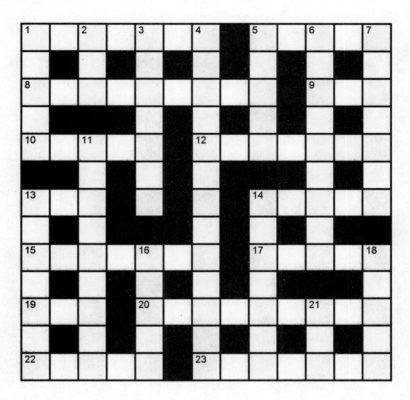

ACROSS

1 Type of aircraft (7)
5 Produced on a loom (5)
8 Fitted in place (9)
9 Gamble (3)
10 Horizontal surface for holding objects (5)
12 Destructive wind (7)
13 European Economic Community in short (3)
14 Goes out (5)
15 Homes of royals (7)
17 Sisters of your father (5)
19 Fishing equipment (3)
20 Terminate or take out, get rid of (9)
22 Take clothes off for money (5)
23 Jumper, hot person? (7)

DOWN

1 Winged insects (5)
2 Type of fuel (3)
3 Deal in drugs, cars (7)
4 Human attachments, dealings (13)
5 Broad in scope or content (5)
6 A shaky motion (9)
7 Whimsical ideas (7)
11 Moving stair (9)
13 Gets bigger (7)
14 Look at with great care (7)
16 Inexpensive (5)
18 Pointed weapon (5)
21 Play a role, part of a play (3)

Colossal Book of Crosswords

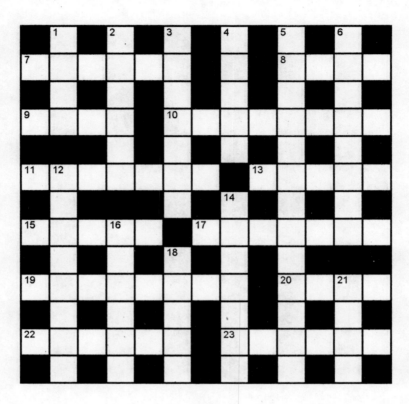

ACROSS

7 A way of acting or behaving (6)
8 Christmastime (4)
9 Great anger (4)
10 Minimal staffing (8)
11 Produced on a press (7)
13 Bad weather (5)
15 Known information (5)
17 Eye protectors (7)
19 Strong and active physically or mentally (8)
20 The act of flipping a coin (4)
22 Act in a controlled manner (6)
23 Cutlery for soup (6)

DOWN

1 Computer information (4)
2 Relating to the Andes (6)
3 Frocks (7)
4 Submitted to pressure (5)
5 Criminal inquiry (13)
6 Available materials to get the job done (8)
12 Be fully aware or cognizant of (8)
14 Own (7)
16 Name of man or tank engine (6)
18 Casts ballot, ballots cast (5)
21 Went under the sea (4)

Colossal Book of Crosswords

ACROSS

6 Prevent from inheriting (6)
7 Flamboyant, showy (6)
8 An expression of some desire (4)
9 Respectful or considerate act (8)
10 Gangster linked to organised crime (7)
12 Style of abstractionism popular in the 1960s; (2,3)
14 Be worthy of or have a certain rating (5)
15 Bedding rolled up for carrying (3-4)
17 Thread used by surgeons to bind a vessel (8)
18 A short nail (4)
20 Building material (6)
21 Give new life or energy to (6)

DOWN

1 High fidelity sound system (2-2)
2 Ahead in development; complex or intricate (13)
3 A disrespectful laugh (7)
4 Happening or done after a surgical operation (4-9)
5 A singer of folk songs (8)
7 A conduit to carry off smoke (4)
11 Biased (3-5)
13 Deprive through death (7)
16 A matching set of furniture (5)
19 A small restaurant, coffee bar (4)

Colossal Book of Crosswords

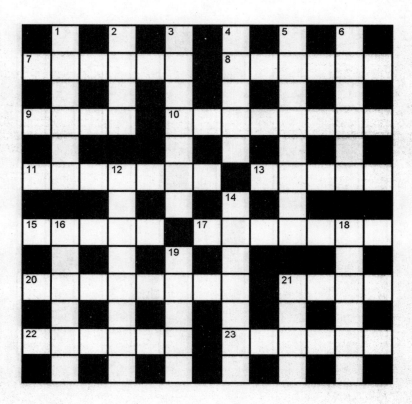

ACROSS

7 Type of monumental stone (6)
8 Group of people assembled to sing together (6)
9 Evidence that helps to solve a problem (4)
10 Joins together (8)
11 Relied upon, had faith in (7)
13 Sweets, covers in mud? (5)
15 Takes up challenge (5)
17 People who frequently find fault (7)
20 On top, in charge (8)
21 Delivered by singing (4)
22 A native or inhabitant of India (6)
23 said clearly (6)

DOWN

1 Suit maker (6)
2 Capable (4)
3 Attains or gets to (7)
4 Perfume (5)
5 Weather prediction (8)
6 Father's sister (6)
12 Detail, not general (8)
14 From Britain (7)
16 Approximately, about this amount (6)
18 Transfer to another (6)
19 Sort of owl (5)
21 Seen in the night sky (4)

Colossal Book of Crosswords

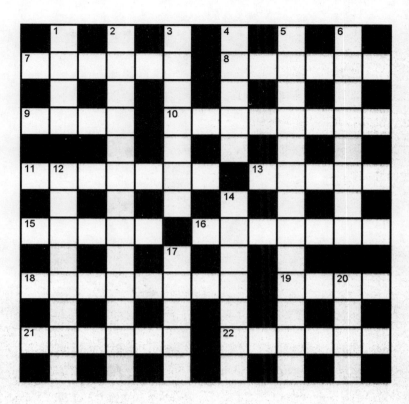

ACROSS

7 Select (6)
8 Give work to (6)
9 Groups of things (4)
10 Ancient wine jars (8)
11 Person at college (7)
13 Remove wallpaper (5)
15 A committee having supervisory powers (5)
16 At an angle, on a lamp post? (7)
18 Has within it (8)
19 Incoming sea water on coast (4)
21 Pretend not to see (6)
22 Dozen (6)

DOWN

1 Item of footwear (4)
2 Thoughtfulness (13)
3 What is left (7)
4 Looks furtively (5)
5 Chances, sometimes they knock (13)
6 Music is written using this (8)
12 Painstakingly careful and accurate (8)
14 Thickness (7)
17 Supplied at no cost (5)
20 Plunge into water (4)

Colossal Book of Crosswords

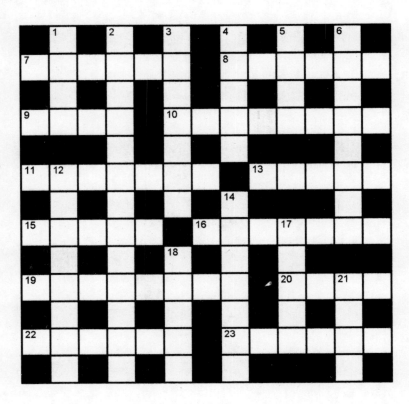

ACROSS

7 Artist's workshop (6)
8 Soldiers (6)
9 Joint in leg (4)
10 In unison, as a group (8)
11 Beats, regular recurrences (7)
13 Correct (5)
15 Make laugh (5)
16 Ask for something (7)
19 Propelling oneself through the water (8)
20 Lazy (4)
22 Beverages (6)
23 Looked after like a garden? (6)

DOWN

1 Knock out (4)
2 Public promotion of some product or service (13)
3 These go up when you drink a toast (7)
4 Type of coach (5)
5 Door fastener (4)
6 Formal communications at wedding (8)
12 School work done at home (8)
14 What you don't like if you have vertigo (7)
17 Organisation of employees (5)
18 Before all the others (5)
21 Untruths (4)

Colossal Book of Crosswords

ACROSS

7 Fastened down, trapped (6)
8 Square cloth used for wiping the nose (6)
9 A reply that repeats what has just been said (4)
10 Heartbeat (5)
11 Deprived of food (7)
13 Girl's name (5)
16 The last (24th) letter of the Greek alphabet (5)
17 Female siblings (7)
19 Shook with fear or cold (8)
20 Golf tournament (4)
22 Gets on horseback (6)
23 Steps from one floor to another (6)

DOWN

1 Portable computer storage (4)
2 Giving hope or support (13)
3 Altered in some way (7)
4 Teachers' writing stuff? (5)
5 Girl's name (4)
6 Film controller (8)
12 The day after today (8)
14 Not based on fact; dubious (8)
15 Craziest (7)
18 The soft tissue of the body (5)
21 Make, as a wage (4)

Colossal Book of Crosswords

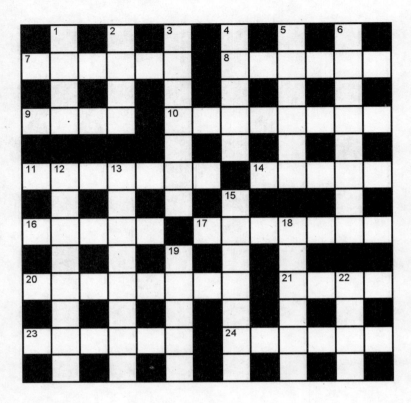

ACROSS

7 Detective (6)
8 Sexual relationships (6)
9 Unfasten (4)
10 Look like (8)
11 Less expensive (7)
14 List of entries at back of book (5)
16 Learn a craft (5)
17 An event that accomplishes its intended purpose (7)
20 A state of extreme ruin (8)
21 A period of time spent in military service (4)
23 Closed so tightly as to be watertight (6)
24 Sufficient (6)

DOWN

1 Scale drawing of a structure (4)
2 New monetary unit in Europe (4)
3 Object that impedes free movement (7)
4 Severe (5)
5 Archer (6)
6 Wheeled vehicles for shopping (8)
12 Female heroes (8)
13 Characterised by friendship and good will (8)
15 Very reluctant to give out information (7)
18 Fine thread for sewing (6)
19 Learn by reading books (5)
22 A strong restless desire (4)

Colossal Book of Crosswords

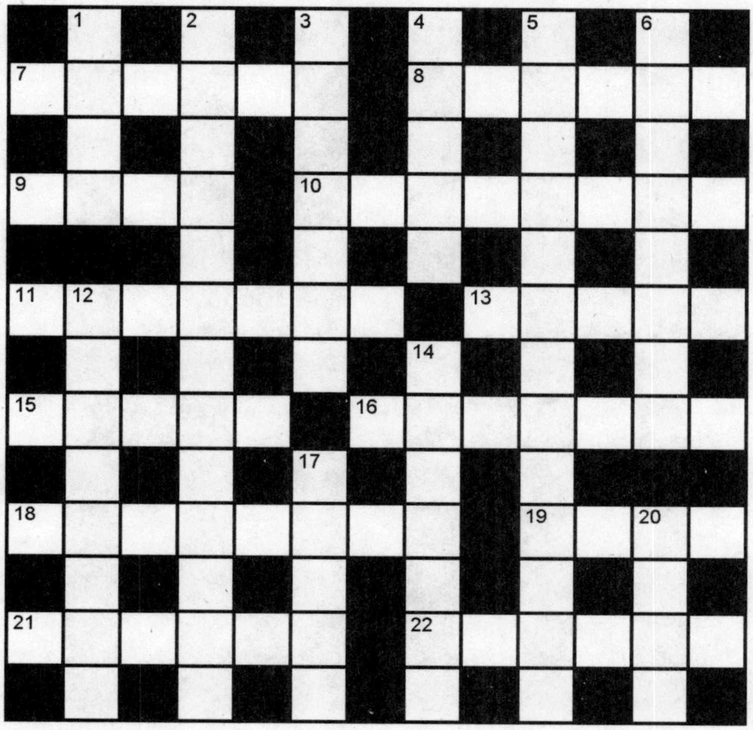

ACROSS

7 An alloy of copper and tin (6)
8 Wound around like a snake (6)
9 Nil (4)
10 Formal spoken communications (8)
11 Outdoing or overcoming (7)
13 Heat ore for metals (5)
15 Fastening things (5)
16 Relies on (7)
18 Police workplaces (8)
19 Compass direction (4)
21 Went in wind powered boat (6)
22 Not long ago (6)

DOWN

1 Gratis (4)
2 Sadly (13)
3 Motives (7)
4 Played part on stage (5)
5 Distance round wheel (13)
6 Showed, unveiled (8)
12 From Egypt (8)
14 Determine length (7)
17 Trousers of ribbed cloth (5)
20 Male children (4)

Colossal Book of Crosswords

ACROSS

1 Going out with (6)
4 Written announcement (6)
9 From Africa (7)
10 Precise amount (5)
11 Hurriedness (5)
12 Become aware of (7)
13 Acquainting (11)
18 Do impression of (7)
20 Knock over (5)
22 Pottery and country (5)
23 Larval frog or toad (7)
24 Knocks first ball over net (6)
25 Follows prey (6)

DOWN

1 End of life (5)
2 Fruit pies (5)
3 Atomic (7)
5 Sung play (5)
6 From Italy (7)
7 One or the other (6)
8 Components for cookery (11)
14 Louder (7)
15 Expresses possibility (5)
16 Discotheques (6)
17 Strain (6)
19 Cognisant (5)
21 Ruin, go bad (5)

ACROSS

7 Kindness (6)
8 Pressed (6)
9 Groups (4)
10 Manoeuvring with a wheel (8)
11 Touched (7)
14 Urn contents (5)
16 Animals, tolerates (5)
17 Flags for trooping (7)
19 Balm, emollient (8)
21 Good looker, pottery item (4)
23 Inclination to approve (6)
24 Support material for oil paint (6)

DOWN

1 Remove (4)
2 Person in charge (4)
3 Ladies' garments (7)
4 Units of length equal to 1760 yards (5)
5 Writing to each other (13)
6 Sleigh puller at Christmas (8)
12 Single pip playing card (3)
13 Length of time (8)
15 Type of lens (7)
18 Jewel from oyster (5)
20 Terrible Russian? (4)
22 Leave in water (4)

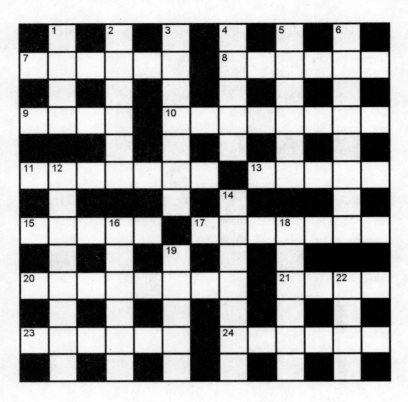

ACROSS

7 Earlier, in a short time (6)
8 Torn (6)
9 Selling at reduced cost (4)
10 Expected, believed (8)
11 Impressed, published (7)
13 Look at with fixed eyes (5)
15 Components (5)
17 Violent wind (7)
20 Strong and active (8)
21 Job (4)
23 Turned into (6)
24 Beholding (6)

DOWN

1 Couch (4)
2 Hidden (6)
3 Came down violently (7)
4 Ensnares (5)
5 New growth of a plant (6)
6 Directed for treatment (8)
12 Came to understand (8)
14 Own (7)
16 Big Tom! (6)
18 Spice (6)
19 Pugilist (5)
22 Went under (4)

Colossal Book of Crosswords

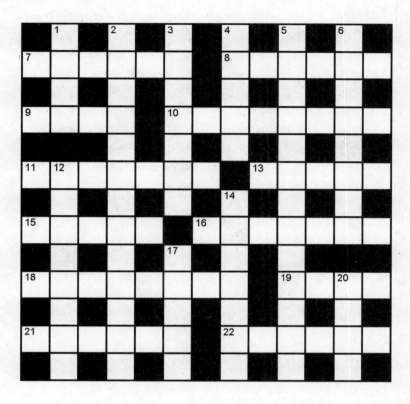

ACROSS

7 Different (6)
8 Cause to move (6)
9 Capital city in Ukraine (4)
10 Get back, recover (8)
11 Hold down, persecute (7)
13 Sort of bopper? (5)
15 Christmas song (5)
16 Self centred (7)
18 Monocle (8)
19 Effigy that is worshipped (4)
21 Chest of drawers (6)
22 Mural (6)

DOWN

1 Against (prefix) (4)
2 Smooth talker! (6-7)
3 Push down button (7)
4 Cattiness, malevolence (5)
5 Member of a police force (6,7)
6 Retainers (8)
12 Duckbilled creature (8)
14 Compose verses; put into verse (7)
17 Item of fact derived from measurement (5)
20 One time only (4)

ACROSS

7 Fine meal made from cereal grain (6)
8 Advanced level (1-5)
9 Give up, surrender (4)
10 Lathyrus odoratus, plant (8)
11 Tearless (3-4)
13 Offensively malodorous (5)
15 Chewed nut (5)
16 Fine particles of wood (7)
18 Grandiloquence (8)
20 Neither good nor bad (2-2)
22 Edict (6)
23 Move unsteadily, with a rocking motion (6)

DOWN

1 Curse (4)
2 Used to locate explosive mines (4-9)
3 Master key (7)
4 Supply food ready to eat, for parties (5)
5 Cleaning wand with feathers! (7-6)
6 Study of DNA and modification (8)
12 Fish eggs (3)
14 The dead body of an animal (7)
17 Official who made public announcements in town (5)
19 Part of shoe (4)
21 Rise rapidly (4)

Colossal Book of Crosswords

ACROSS

7 Paper that turns red in acid (6)
8 Moral philosophy (6)
9 Coffin stand (4)
10 Beneath (5)
11 Ugly site (7)
13 Sham to distract (5)
15 Herb (5)
16 Highest mast (7)
19 Horse eye patches (8)
20 Turn to liquid by heating (4)
22 Fresh, not yet utilised (6)
23 Exaggerate, do to excess (6)

DOWN

1 High Fidelity (2-2)
2 A genre of French painting (13)
3 Part of river near sea (7)
4 Requirements (5)
5 What the Light Brigade did (6)
6 Places to skate (3-5)
12 Racehorse in second year (8)
14 Writer of War and Peace (7)
17 Actor who communicates entirely by gesture (6)
18 Abounding with or resembling weeds (5)
21 A polite name for any woman (4)

ACROSS

6 Boatyard (6)
7 Rework old material (6)
9 Reduced instruction set computer, by the letter! (4)
10 The appropriate word, French (3,5)
11 Musician (7)
13 Beautify (5)
15 A sudden short attack (5)
16 Monsieur Chevalier (7)
18 Tropical fern (4-4)
19 For fear that (4)
21 Coniferous tree (6)
22 A seat for the rider of a horse (6)

DOWN

1 Wise Men (4)
2 Assorted, sundry (13)
3 Mask to protect against gas`attack (3-4)
4 A mutual promise to marry (5)
5 Scapula (8-5)
8 Exposing human folly to ridicule (7)
12 Outings of self-aggran disement (3,5)
14 Heartfelt (7)
17 Rise in the temperature of the body (5)
20 Unaccompanied (4)

309

Colossal Book of Crosswords

ACROSS

7 Type of hat (6)
8 Early ancestors? (6)
9 Garden party (4)
10 Ceremonial or emblematic staffs (8)
11 A flask for carrying water (7)
13 Spooky (5)
15 Watercourse (5)
16 Toughest (7)
19 Draw out (8)
21 Type of window (4)
23 Deprive, strip away (6)
24 Man's name, confused fasten! (6)

DOWN

1 Pallid (4)
2 Leather with a hard glossy surface (6,7)
3 Screaming ghost (7)
4 A small thin crisp cake or cookie (5)
5 P.G.Wodehouse's Wooster (6)
6 Curatives (8)
12 Cassius Clay became Muhammad ... (3)
14 Illusion, imagination (7)
17 Cartoon great Walt (6)
18 Containing or composed of fat (5)
20 Water falling in drops from sky (4)
22 Box lightly (4)

Colossal Book of Crosswords

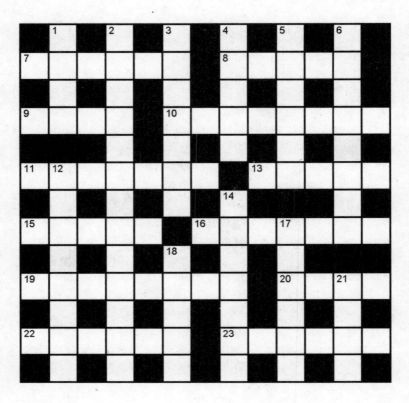

ACROSS

7 Chosen job path (6)
8 Girl's name (5)
9 Microbe, bacteria (4)
10 Utter words with spitting rage! (8)
11 Into parts or pieces (7)
13 Israeli statesman, start! (5)
15 Smooth surface on a cut gemstone (5)
16 Sailor (7)
19 Soviet policy of free discussion (8)
20 A bunch of feathers or hair (4)
22 Agitation (6)
23 Shoe for summer (6)

DOWN

1 Bogus (4)
2 Epidemic roseola (6,7)
3 Staff carried by bishops (7)
4 Wire, flex, transmission line (5)
5 A large hemispherical brass or copper drum (6)
6 Broadcast via television (8)
12 An aeroplane that can land on water (8)
14 Sacrament signifying rebirth in Christ (7)
17 Aim, design, purpose (6)
18 Value (5)
21 Wear away at the edge (4)

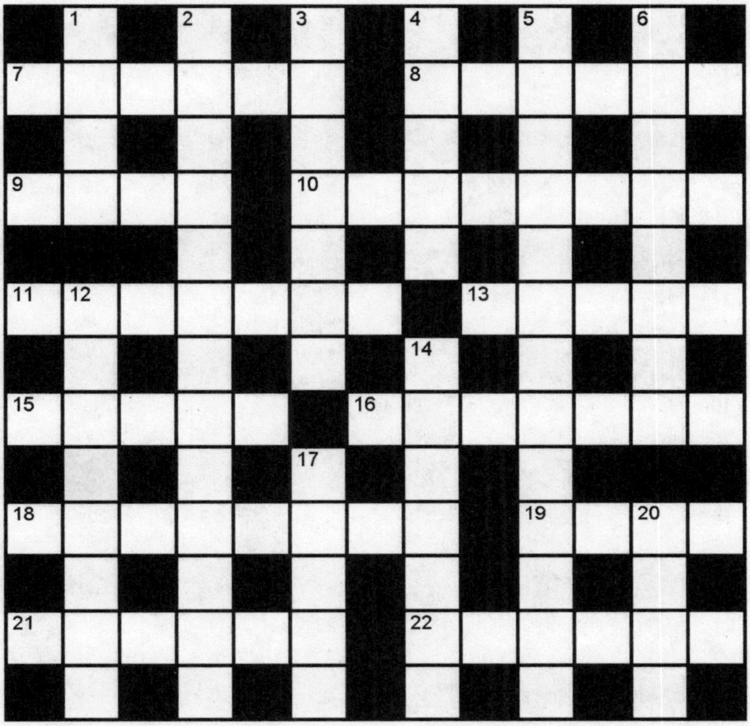

311

ACROSS

7 Main meal (6)
8 Conclusion, Finishing (6)
9 Give up (4)
10 Lessened (8)
11 Grounds for doing something (7)
13 Loft (5)
15 Atomiser (5)
16 A communication (7)
18 Military personnel (8)
19 Mothers in short (4)
21 Inclined (6)
22 Haphazard (6)

DOWN

1 Be fond of (4)
2 Agreement (13)
3 Developing (7)
4 Started (5)
5 Ad (13)
6 Expulsion of air from the nose (8)
12 Blows up (8)
14 Free time (7)
17 Unwanted plants (5)
20 Temper (4)

Colossal Book of Crosswords

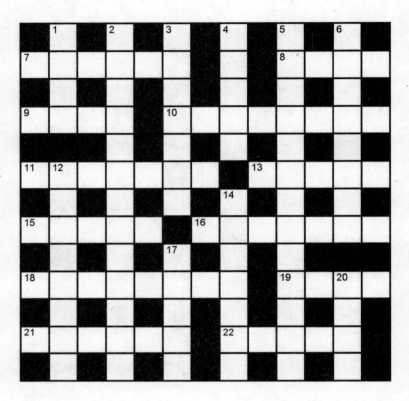

ACROSS

 7 An Asian temple (6)
 8 First ever garden (4)
 9 Man's name, shortened (4)
10 Climbing garden plant (8)
11 Drain cock on ship (7)
13 Beelzebub (5)
15 Mindless (5)
16 Powder from cutting wood (7)
18 American game (8)
19 Type of window or ribbon (4)
21 Conflict, struggle (6)
22 Fragrance (5)

DOWN

 1 Coffee shop (4)
 2 The two adulterous persons (2-11)
 3 Annual or perennial herb (7)
 4 Canny, shrewd (5)
 5 Cleaner - feathers on a stick (7-6)
 6 Study of human heredity and DNA (8)
12 A heavy reddish mineral - can bairn! (8)
14 Deserving or inciting pity (7)
17 Provide or supply food for event (5)
20 Building place (4)

Colossal Book of Crosswords

ACROSS

7 Summerhouse (6)
8 Egg dish, with cheese or ham perhaps (6)
9 Bring aircraft to earth (4)
10 Smash a liquid against a surface (8)
11 Minimal clothing worn by stripper (1-6)
13 Spiral (5)
16 Duck for down (5)
17 Fill to satisfaction (7)
19 Scare monger (8)
20 Pinnacles (4)
22 Mother or father (6)
23 The cloak as a symbol of authority (6)

DOWN

1 Volcanic rock (4)
2 Kind and generous (6-7)
3 A sudden unexpected piece of good fortune (7)
4 Expresses possibility (5)
5 100th part of dollar (4)
6 Italian monk who founded an order (8)
12 Boatload, amount of cargo held (8)
14 Expelling from property (8)
15 A period of time during which there is armed conflict (7)
18 Number, retirement age for some (5)
21 The soft inner part of a tooth (4)

Colossal Book of Crosswords

ACROSS

7 Hard work and political party (6)
8 Briefly closed an eye (6)
9 Descended from Jacob (4)
10 Mistakenly believed (8)
11 Burdened with, like a horse? (7)
14 Chips (5)
16 Tired (5)
17 For the most time (7)
20 Territory, having a nurse? (8)
21 Face cover (4)
23 Forest gods (6)
24 Heavy closely woven fabric (6)

DOWN

1 Strongbox (4)
2 Gear wheels (4)
3 Swept (7)
4 Brushed (5)
5 Inside (6)
6 Match officials (8)
12 North and South America, also cup (8)
13 This Parker was an american writer (7)
15 Get in touch with (7)
18 American space mission/craft (6)
19 In the middle of (5)
22 Remain (4)

Colossal Book of Crosswords

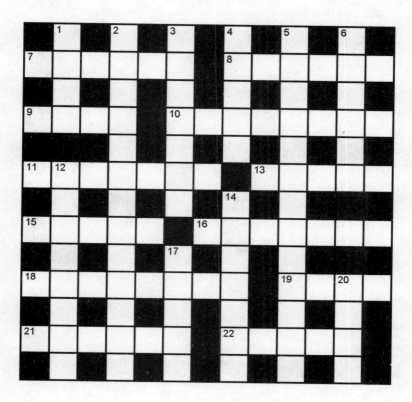

ACROSS

7 Malevolence (6)
8 A practitioner of voodoo (6)
9 Small american coin (4)
10 A bag for food that a customer did not eat (5,3)
11 Naval rank (7)
13 Freshwater carnivorous mammal (5)
15 Great pain (5)
16 Heartfelt (7)
18 (pathology) like a reed or tube (8)
19 Keen on something (4)
21 Ill-tempered or annoyed (6)
22 Should, had better (5)

DOWN

1 Hack (4)
2 Musical notation - the number of beats (4-9)
3 The head of a tribe or clan (7)
4 Part of leg (5)
5 One-piece tight-fitting undergarments for women (4,9)
6 Mental infirmity as a consequence of old age (6)
12 An aerial engagement (3-5)
14 (H2SO4) a highly corrosive acid (7)
17 A resin used in adhesives and paints, (5)
20 Bye-bye (2-2)

Colossal Book of Crosswords

ACROSS

7 Spittle (6)
8 Sharp, sharp angle (5)
9 Administer, punishment? (4)
10 Ceremonial staff (7)
11 Diameter of a tube or gun barrel (7)
14 Lukewarm (5)
16 Beverage (5)
17 Rare black and white mammals (6)
20 Put off, draw attention away from (8)
21 Window operating system (4)
23 Edict (6)
24 So thin as to transmit light (5)

DOWN

1 The top of the head (4)
2 A digestive juice (4)
3 Scottish girls? (7)
4 Hesitate (5)
5 Aquatic reptiles with shell and flippers (6)
6 Cures (8)
12 A commercial airplane (8)
13 A device for lighting or igniting fuel (7)
15 Christen (7)
18 Cleaning cloth (6)
19 Gentleman's gentleman (5)
22 Agile (4)

Colossal Book of Crosswords

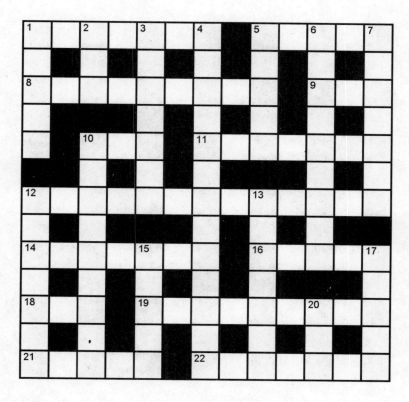

ACROSS

1 Exaggerate one's acting (7)
5 Summarise briefly (5)
8 Obtained illegally (3-6)
9 A major division of geological time (3)
10 Rest on a chair (3)
11 Large cat has a tawny coat with black spots (7)
12 Compulsive (13)
14 Car part, part of the the cooling system? (3-4)
16 A structure attached to the exterior of a building (5)
18 The sound made by a pigeon (3)
19 A cargo ship designed to carry crude oil (3-6)
21 A long narrow excavation in the earth (5)
22 A short-handled receptacle into which dust can be swept (4-3)

DOWN

1 Popeye's girlfriend (5)
2 Long thin fish (3)
3 Disciple (7)
4 Gossiped (6-7)
5 A musical form (5)
6 A gallant or courtly gentleman (9)
7 Enthusiastic approval (7)
10 Addicted to a drug (6,3)
12 Humourless; unnecessarily solemn (2-5)
13 Children with no parents (7)
15 A unit of geological time (5)
17 Grey or white wading bird (5)
20 Sleep (3)

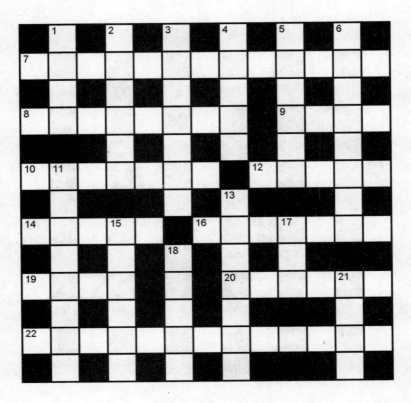

ACROSS

7 A second or new birth (13)

8 Set close together, like eyes? (5,3)

9 Usually large hard-shelled seeds (4)

10 A disgraceful event (7)

12 Of an angle; less than 90 degrees (5)

14 A line spoken by an actor to the audience (5)

16 Medical instruments (7)

19 Heroic (4)

20 Provide or furnish with (6)

22 Type of ferry (4-2-4-3)

DOWN

1 American inventor of the telephone (4)

2 Corresponding exactly (6)

3 Men who row a boat (7)

4 Bring together (5)

5 Cultural (6)

6 The sound of a step of someone walking (8)

11 A covered cistern for waste water (8)

13 A twisting force (7)

15 Easily handled or managed (6)

17 Headwear (3)

18 Backbone (5)

21 Bequeathed (4)

Colossal Book of Crosswords

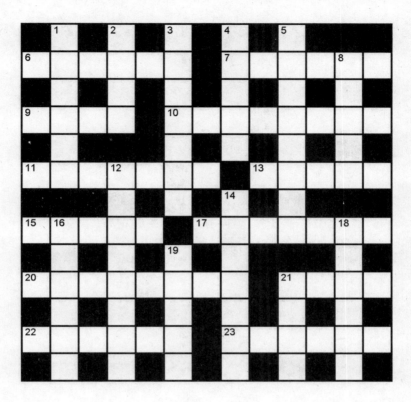

ACROSS

- **6** Aircraft take off strip (6)
- **7** Different (6)
- **9** Not difficult (4)
- **10** Resort, refuge (8)
- **11** To say or state again (7)
- **13** Number 1 (5)
- **15** Underground burial chamber (5)
- **17** State of the Vatican City (4,3)
- **20** A feeling of intense dislike (8)
- **21** Disappear gradually (4)
- **22** A fragrant ointment containing a resin (6)
- **23** Ensnare (6)

DOWN

- **1** Being up to particular standard or level (2,4)
- **2** Amiss (4)
- **3** Add water or moisture (7)
- **4** Full of juice (5)
- **5** Inflammatory disease of the lungs (8)
- **8** Legal fees (5)
- **12** Express the same message in different words (8)
- **14** Aimed at, indicated (7)
- **16** Make visible or known (6)
- **18** Make attractive or lovable (6)
- **19** Gadget - I smog! (5)
- **21** Garden party (4)

ACROSS

7 Table linen - ask dam! (6)
8 Voucher, possibly football based? (6)
9 Biblical wise men (4)
10 Flesh of any of a number of wild game birds (4-4)
11 Forget, before relearning something? (7)
13 Say clearly (5)
15 Moving quickly and lightly (5)
17 Quicksilver (7)
20 Ride on water towed by boat (5-3)
21 In this place (4)
23 Dog house (6)
24 Penny-pinching (6)

DOWN

1 Short paratrooper (4)
2 A small overnight bag for short trips (6)
3 Directed toward heaven or the sky (7)
4 Berate (5)
5 Any cohesive unit such as a military company (6)
6 Predicament, to do with heated liquid! (3,5)
12 A place to avoid (2-2,4)
14 Cause to turn away from a previous or expected course (7)
16 Stay in bed in the morning (3-2)
18 Come or be in close contact with (6)
19 Any sacred song used to praise the Deity (5)
22 Type of collar, sounds like a dog? (4)

Colossal Book of Crosswords

ACROSS

1 Unknown or unspecified quantity or number (4)
3 Chinese dish created in USA (4,4)
8 Lottery, lucky dip (7)
9 Decorate the surface of by inserting wood (5)
10 A reckless impetuous irresponsible pirate (12)
12 Disqualify (6)
14 Organisation (6)
17 An island in the south Pacific (6)
19 Norse deity (5)
22 A moderate yellow-orange to orange colour (5)
23 Flower petal or Toyota car? (7)
24 Being of striking appropriateness and pertinence (8)
25 Catch sight of, spot (4)

DOWN

1 Farmland left fallow (3-5)
2 Informal term for a mother (5)
4 An interruption, missing piece - is Utah! (6)
5 Pierce with a sharp pin (5)
6 Least attractive (7)
7 Man with an ark (4)
11 Envoy (8)
13 Damage or destroy as if by violence (5-2)
15 Regional and archaic, afraid (6)
16 Large wild animal; lion, tiger (3,3)
18 Thoughts (5)
20 Lounges about (5)
21 A tiny or scarcely detectable amount (4)

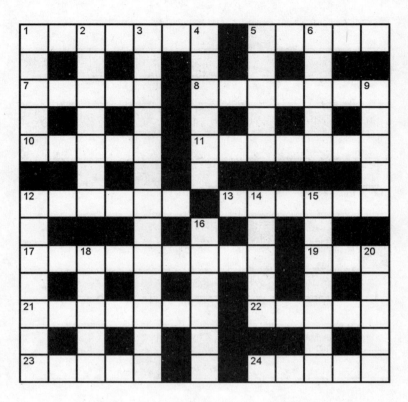

ACROSS

1 Reflexive form of "him" (7)
5 Doglike nocturnal mammal that laughs? (5)
7 An energetic style (5)
8 Of great force or power, also ship (7)
10 Seek someone's favour (5)
11 Warlike - kind of strict law (7)
12 A small earthquake (6)
13 Pretend not to see (6)
17 A passage or expression that is quoted (9)
19 Sacred chest or boat (3)
21 Early childhood (7)
22 Speak one's opinion without fear (5)
23 Deal out, allow to have (5)
24 Cavity in skull, painful when swollen (5)

DOWN

1 Chaos, for the wreaking of.... (5)
2 Large and often sumptuous tent (7)
3 Magnet driven by wire and electricity (13)
4 Youngest daughter of the prophet Mohammed (6)
5 A person who hates (5)
6 Boredom (5)
9 Girl's name (5)
12 Mexican liquor (7)
14 Pungent bulb used in cooking (5)
15 Enthusiastic recognition, often standing (7)
16 A native or inhabitant of Libya (6)
18 Organs, variety meat (5)
20 Leg joints (5)

Colossal Book of Crosswords

ACROSS

7 Not presently active (6)
8 Plant disease resulting in withering (6)
9 The main organ of photosynthesis (4)
10 Longshoreman (4,4)
11 Intransigent, Not capable of being swayed (7)
13 Make dim or indistinct (5)
15 Edible fruit (5)
16 Give in to (7)
18 Bucket for spit (8)
19 A covering to disguise or conceal the face (4)
21 Immerse into a liquid quickly (6)
22 Dangerous coastal rock (4)

DOWN

1 Concern (4)
2 Arrogant (4-9)
3 Scholar (7)
4 By surprise (5)
5 Early photo device without lens - alphameric one! (7,6)
6 Ghostlike (8)
12 A deed made and executed by only one party (4,4)
14 Type of physics and leap! (7)
17 Make a written note of (5)
20 Prophet (4)

Colossal Book of Crosswords

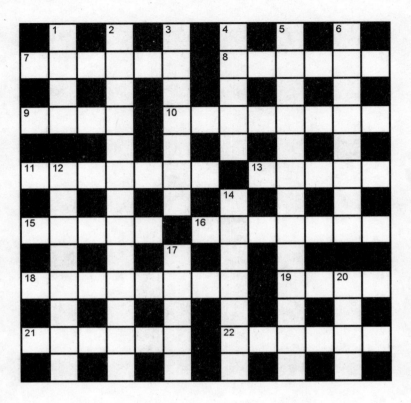

ACROSS

7 Stalks eaten raw or cooked (6)
8 Pantry (6)
9 Rotate rapidly, sometimes politically? (4)
10 Aspiration or dream (8)
11 Something that is lost as a penalty (7)
13 Eight people considered as a unit (5)
15 Wading bird that delivers cartoon children? (5)
16 A formal association (7)
18 Unstable by being overloaded at the top (3-5)
19 Average (4)
21 Aromatic bulbous stem base (6)
22 Store in a silo, as of fodder (6)

DOWN

1 Retain (4)
2 Early cycle with two different sized wheels (5-8)
3 Active, not static (7)
4 Someone who swears you were with them when a crime was committed (5)
5 An advocate of protectionism (13)
6 Most distant, furthest (8)
12 Out of fashion -domed out! (8)
14 Chemical compound - ply Rome! (7)
17 A nautical unit of depth (5)
20 A small stream in box of trill for birds! (4)

Colossal Book of Crosswords

ACROSS

7 A short jacket; worn mostly by women (6)
8 On a vehicle (6)
9 Not mad in any way (4)
10 An ornamental but poisonous flowering shrub - no dealer! (8)
11 Hole where a key is inserted, surgery too (7)
13 Very happily, while being broadcast? (2,3)
15 Coat with a layer of silver or gold (5)
16 To begin with (7)
18 Clapping (8)
19 A Hindu prince or king in India (4)
21 Outdoor meal (6)
22 Possibility, hypothesis (6)

DOWN

1 Deep and often prolonged unconsciousness (4)
2 Long lens for camera (9,4)
3 Eyeglass (7)
4 Narrow towards a point (5)
5 Westminster home of Prime Minister (7,6)
6 Of or involving or contained in the arteries (8)
12 Egg-shaped, ovate - clip tile! (8)
14 Glass tube used for measuring liquid (7)
17 A narrow gorge with a stream running through it (5)
20 12 people in court to weigh evidence (4)

Colossal Book of Crosswords

ACROSS

7 Filled with water (6)
8 Nocturnal wildcat of Central and South America (6)
9 Type of music (4)
10 A comment (usually added to a text) (8)
11 Space by the side of a bed (7)
13 Using the voice; not silently (5)
15 Range (5)
17 Covetous (7)
19 Done on purpose (5)
20 Motor that converts thermal energy to mechanical work (6)
22 Point in time when entries are not accepted (6)
23 Known for (6)

DOWN

1 Ancient heroic tale (4)
2 Car maker, one of a pair (4)
3 Poisonous salt of hydrocyanic acid (7)
4 Itinerary (5)
5 Roman Priestesses dedicated to Vesta (6,7)
6 The capital and largest city of Hawaii; (8)
9 Injection (3)
12 The highest female voice (7)
14 Forget what you have been taught (7)
16 A field on which the buildings of a university are situated (6)
18 Unbending (5)
21 Nothing - colloquially (4)

Colossal Book of Crosswords

ACROSS

6 Poor handwriting (6)
8 O (6)
9 Snug (4)
10 Butt, the thing you aim at (6)
11 Completely enveloping (7)
14 Even surface (5)
16 Change (5)
17 Nocturnal flightless bird of New Zealand (7)
19 Coarse-grained, gritty (8)
21 Input words using a keyboard (4)
23 A two-wheeled horse-drawn covered carriage (6)
24 Stroppy, pushy and aggressive (6)

DOWN

1 A very young child (4)
2 Any of various forms of aluminium oxide (7)
3 Bonkers, with spots on! (5)
4 Power from water passing through a dam (13)
5 Burial ground (8)
7 The sound made by a pigeon (3)
12 Be cruel to (8)
13 Frozen H2O (3)
15 Keep under control ruthlessly (7)
18 A feather or cluster of feathers (5)
20 The loch where the monster lives! (4)
22 A feeling of sympathy and sorrow (4)

ACROSS

7 To agree or express agreement (6)
8 A thick and heavy shoe or accent (6)
9 Make synchronous, in short (4)
10 Having no intelligible meaning (8)
11 Stout-bodied insects with large membranous wings (7)
13 Broker (5)
15 A sudden forceful flow (5)
16 Celebrate (7)
18 Income undeserved or gained without work (8)
19 Number (4)
21 Boilerman, stoker (6)
22 Poor and possibly mischievous city child (6)

DOWN

1 Catch sight of, antique word (4)
2 Credit card processing banks - ants bench-mark! (8,5)
3 Student from Eton (7)
4 Very dark wood (5)
5 The government department in charge of foreign relations (7,6)
6 Less than the speed of sound (8)
12 Exemption from punishment or loss (8)
14 Requisite - flu Eden! (7)
17 Disarm (5)
20 A blood vessel that carries blood (4)

Colossal Book of Crosswords

ACROSS

7 Appetiser (6)
8 Batting time in cricket (6)
9 Wingless blood-sucking parasitic insect (4)
10 The words of an opera or musical play (8)
11 Dwelling (7)
13 Of time long past, as in .... days! (5)
15 Bourbon, sugar and mint over crushed ice (5)
16 Makeup used to darken the eye lashes (7)
18 Device that produces an intense monochromatic beam of coherent light (5)
19 Make a sound like a clock or a timer (4)
21 Mountainous republic of south-central Europe (6)
22 Placed crosswise (6)

DOWN

1 Injure badly by beating (4)
2 Savoury dressings for salad (5-8)
3 An act of narration (7)
4 The state of being disregarded or forgotten (5)
5 Consisting of dialogue - our contritely! (13)
6 Knitted clothing (8)
12 A clear seasoned broth, stock cube (8)
14 Saw used with one hand for cutting metal (4-3)
17 Evergreen treelike Mediterranean shrub, used to make pipes (5)
20 A thin triangular flap of a heart valve, edge (4)

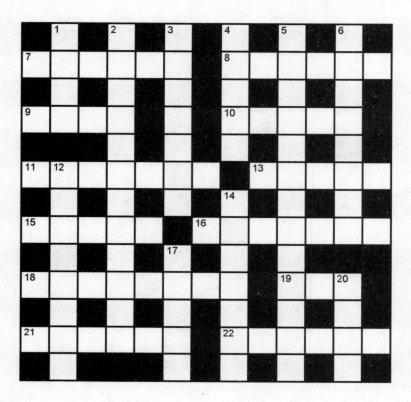

ACROSS

7 Place in a grave or tomb (6)
8 Breathe out (6)
9 Could be hard or floppy - computer item! (4)
10 French right (5)
11 Burdensome responsibility (7)
13 An unusually small individual (5)
15 Large tree branch (5)
16 Army unit smaller than a division (7)
18 B vitamin that prevents beriberi - hit Maine! (8)
19 Strange, sort of number (3)
21 Excessively conventional, lumpy food! (6)
22 A young eagle (6)

DOWN

1 Against, as in freeze? (4)
2 A piano suitable for performances (7,5)
3 Greek god of wine (7)
4 Intoxicating (5)
5 A disease of the respiratory mucous membrane (8-5)
6 Badly timed (3-5)
12 Any new participant in some activity (8)
14 Free from tears (3-4)
17 A woman who tells fortunes (5)
20 They play with the antelope on the range? (4)

Colossal Book of Crosswords

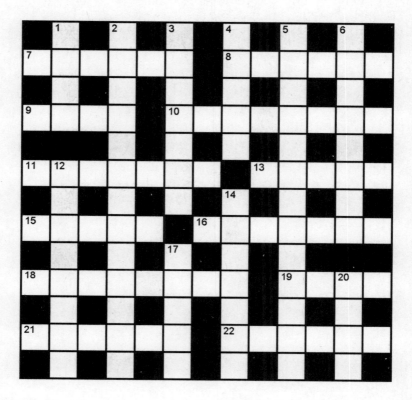

ACROSS

7 The way in which you do something (6)
8 Dignified and sombre in manner (6)
9 Register in a public office or a court of law (4)
10 Unsettled in mind or opinion, dubious (8)
11 Produced under conditions of intense heat (7)
13 Compare (5)
15 Informal terms for a mother (5)
16 Mischievous (7)
18 Chinese-red (8)
19 Curved shape that spans an opening (4)
21 Skin design made by pricking and staining (6)
22 Nocturnal wildcat (6)

DOWN

1 Gully or streambed in North Africa (4)
2 Vague, of uncertain or ambiguous nature (13)
3 A heavy brittle metallic element, atomic number 77 (7)
4 One of a series published periodically (5)
5 Absorbent paper used to dry ink (8-5)
6 Improperly forward or bold (8)
12 Formality in bearing and appearance (8)
14 Taproom (3-4)
17 The superior of an abbey of monks (5)
20 A farm building for housing poultry (4)

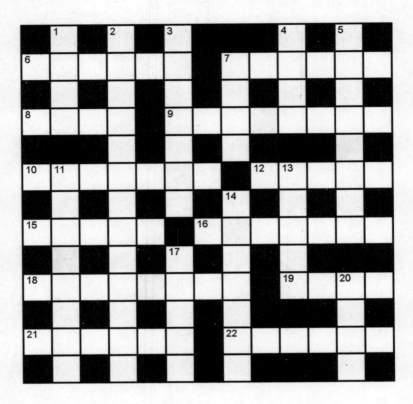

ACROSS

6 Moral philosophy (6)
7 African tree (6)
8 Long skirt popular in the 70s (4)
9 Murder (8)
10 A photograph taken at close range (5-2)
12 Slap with hand to chastise (5)
15 Make more attractive by adding ornament (5)
16 Free time (7)
18 Separate house (8)
19 Title (4)
21 Rain collection system (6)
22 Unravel, untwist, unroll (6)

DOWN

1 An inactive volcano in Sicily (4)
2 Government workers (5,8)
3 A relatively narrow strip of land (7)
4 Ancient metal armband (4)
5 A medieval cleric, one of Canterbury Tales (8)
7 Explosive device (4)
11 Serving spoon full - auld fell! (8)
13 A ski run densely packed with snow (5)
14 Necessary for relief or supply (7)
17 Fish seen in jaws (5)
20 Wreck or destroy (4)

Colossal Book of Crosswords

ACROSS

7 Be expected to (6)
8 Make more subtle or refined (6)
9 43rd President of the United States (4)
10 A broadcast of news (8)
11 Open in French (7)
13 One who gives, possibly organs (5)
15 The basic unit of money in Poland (5)
16 A team representing a college or university (7)
18 Cause fear in, scare (8)
19 Make editorial changes (in a text) (4)
21 Become of; happen to (6)
22 Free (6)

DOWN

1 The imperial dynasty of China from 1122 to 221 BC (4)
2 Behaves like a tyrant (13)
3 A collection of lymphatic tissue in the throat (7)
4 Free-for-all (5)
5 Metal to make valuable coins or jewelry (8,5)
6 Branch (8)
12 Filled with high spirits; filled with optimism (8)
14 The quality of having a superior or more favourable position (7)
17 Fit and supple (5)
20 Part of eye and woman's name (4)

ACROSS

- **7** Stick to something (6)
- **8** Artist's workplace (6)
- **9** Meat from cow (4)
- **10** Conspicuously and offensively loud (8)
- **11** The act of paying money (7)
- **13** Imitate for satirical effect (5)
- **15** Sing softly (5)
- **16** A small rounded boat (7)
- **19** The time between one event and another (7)
- **20** The lowest brass wind instrument (4)
- **22** Streamer, flag (6)
- **23** Fool (6)

DOWN

- **1** Not in action or at work (4)
- **2** Arrogant, big headed (4-9)
- **3** A country person (7)
- **4** An exorbitant or unlawful rate of interest (5)
- **5** Coagulated milk; used to made cheese (4)
- **6** Two-yearly (8)
- **12** A commercial airplane that carries passengers (8)
- **14** Compel (7)
- **17** Marked by practical hardheaded intelligence (6)
- **18** Large long-necked wading bird (5)
- **21** Quality of being active or spirited or vigorous (4)

Colossal Book of Crosswords

ACROSS

7 Something considered choice to eat (6)
8 A quantity (6)
9 A strong restless desire (4)
10 A rectangular column (8)
11 Metal support for logs in a fireplace (7)
13 A brief stanza concluding certain forms of poetry (5)
15 Arm joint (5)
16 A dense growth of bushes (7)
18 A small piece of anything (7)
19 A sign of something about to happen (4)
21 Any physical damage to the body (6)
22 Gear wheels (4)

DOWN

1 Reasonable (4)
2 Without due formalities (13)
3 Sensation or change in bodily function that is experienced by a patient (7)
4 A large gathering of people (5)
5 Taking what is offered or nothing at all (7,6)
6 Letter container (8)
12 Based on or having the nature of an illusion (8)
14 Tending toward white (7)
17 An implement with a shaft and barbed point (5)
20 The boundary of a surface (4)

Colossal Book of Crosswords

ACROSS

6 Breathe spasmodically, and make a sound (6)
7 A thin slice of potato fried in deep fat (6)
9 Deprive (infants) of mother's milk (4)
10 Persons that are not ourselves, throes! (6)
11 Maker, builder (7)
13 A diplomat having less authority than an ambassador (5)
15 Pity (5)
16 Water travel for pleasure (7)
18 Wages (8)
19 A dice is this shape (4)
21 A characteristic to be considered (6)
22 Feeling a need to see others suffer (6)

DOWN

1 Refer to (4)
2 A person who spreads malicious gossip (13)
3 The reason for a court's judgment (7)
4 A theatrical performer (5)
5 Equipment used in fishing (7-6)
8 Swipe, make off with others' belongings (7)
12 Try out before going on stage (8)
14 Devour (7)
17 Combine, get together for strength (5)
20 One dollar US (4)

Colossal Book of Crosswords

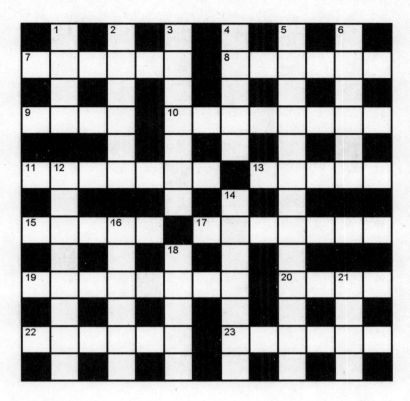

ACROSS

7 A document that can be rolled up, move down computer screen (6)
8 An inclination to want things (6)
9 500 sheets (4)
10 Not liable to error, unfailing (8)
11 100 pfennigs equal 1 Deutsche Mark (7)
13 Open space at the top of a house (5)
15 Therefore (5)
17 Atomic number 33 - poison! (7)
19 Loud and confused and empty talk (8)
20 A musical work that has been created (4)
22 Existing in abundance (6)
23 Transfer power to someone (6)

DOWN

1 Disease of the skin (4)
2 An inhabitant of Normandy (6)
3 Acclaim (7)
4 Mammary gland of bovids (e.g. cows) (5)
5 The spirit of a group, morale (6,2,5)
6 A sultanate in northwestern Borneo (6)
12 A first-year undergraduate (8)
14 Come before (7)
16 Fabric woven from fibres (6)
18 Sorrow caused by loss of a loved one (5)
21 Having the requisite qualities for the job (2,2)

ACROSS

7 Race on skis around obstacles (6)
8 Deliver a hard blow to (6)
9 Star (4)
10 Pattern to ensure consistent results (8)
11 Flemish painter of landscapes (1525-1569) (7)
13 A daily written record, yearbook (5)
15 Reaction between an acid and an alcohol (5)
16 Performer who throws and catches balls (7)
18 Terminate gradually (5,3)
19 Long green edible pods, ladies fingers (4)
21 Tumult (6)
22 Expensive (6)

DOWN

1 The lowest female singing voice (4)
2 Pension claimed by retired persons (3-3,7)
3 Innumerable but many (7)
4 A token that postal fees have been paid (5)
5 Domicile, home (8-5)
6 Escaped without punishment (4-4)
12 Fruits of the rose bush (8)
14 The quality of being just or fair (7)
17 Concern, fret (5)
20 Reign (4)

Colossal Book of Crosswords

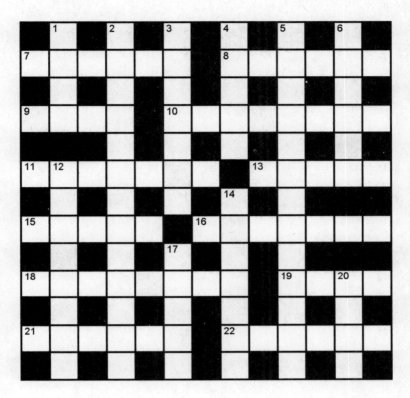

ACROSS

7 The basic unit of money in Spain, pre Euro (6)
8 Performed by a choir (6)
9 12 inches (4)
10 Exhaust (4-4)
11 Practicing great self-denial, cast ice! (7)
13 Take control of (5)
15 Put up with something (5)
16 Parts of a horse (7)
18 Throbs (8)
19 (informal) dubious (4)
21 Reproductive cell - me geta! (6)
22 National song (6)

DOWN

1 Someone who fights for a cause (4)
2 Cleaning device made from bird parts! (7-6)
3 The naval officer in command of a ship (7)
4 Certificate (5)
5 Thursday after Trinity Sunday (6,7)
6 A picnic basket usually with a cover (6)
12 Less than human or not worthy of a human being (8)
14 A male relative (7)
17 Spread by scattering (5)
20 Be agitated or irritated (4)

Colossal Book of Crosswords

ACROSS

7 A drink believed to cure all ills (6)
8 Attachable by a clip (4-2)
9 Japanese beverage from fermented rice (4)
10 Paraded, military style! (7)
11 A vehicle carrying many passengers (7)
13 Young owl (5)
15 Path around a planet taken by a spaceship (5)
16 A person who belongs to the political left (7)
18 Pursue or chase relentlessly, like a dog? (8)
19 Indistinct, fuzzy (4)
21 Disgust so strong it makes you feel sick (6)
22 Pass by, as of time (6)

DOWN

1 Napoleon's first place of exile (4)
2 Showing off (13)
3 Filled to capacity, like a hat? (7)
4 Fruit of the oak tree (5)
5 Overnight security guard (5-8)
6 Young children learning to walk (8)
12 Herb (8)
14 A word for horses used by children (3-4)
17 A roll of tobacco for smoking (5)
20 Vigorous and enthusiastic enjoyment (4)

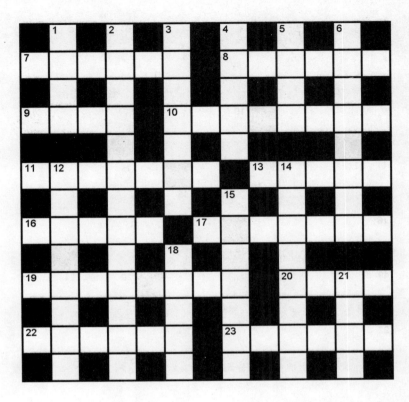

ACROSS

7 Any spherically shaped artifact (6)
8 Sweet dark purple plum (6)
9 Hinge joint in the human leg (4)
10 Practicing complete abstinence from alcohol (8)
11 When one celestial body obscures another (7)
13 Visible disembodied soul of a dead person (5)
16 Tied up (5)
17 Most attractive, lightest (7)
19 Ice cream or water ice on a wooden stick (3-5)
20 A deposit of valuable ore (4)
22 A hat tied under the chin (6)
23 Plants with sword-shaped leaves (6)

DOWN

1 Worked natural fibers into a thread (4)
2 Window covering with thin strips (8,5)
3 Tidiest (7)
4 From whence milk comes (5)
5 Little ammunition (4)
6 Thick dark syrup (8)
12 Breed of thick-coated medium-sized dogs (8)
14 Of or relating to heraldry (8)
15 Look after children while parents go out (4-3)
18 Dish on which food is served (5)
21 Regime of eating (4)

ACROSS

7 Summerhouse (6)
8 Pungent rhizome used in cookery (6)
9 Fold (4)
10 Leather from the hide of a deer (8)
11 Attribute - is caber! (7)
13 Type of beer (5)
16 Type of bread (5)
17 The time of life when sex glands become functional (7)
19 A person who alarms others needlessly (8)
20 Muscular diaphragm in the eye (4)
22 An addition that extends a main building (6)
23 Coloured stick of composition wax (6)

DOWN

1 Beseech (4)
2 Easily moved by another's distress (6-7)
3 The basic unit of money in Nicaragua (7)
4 Heron (5)
5 Encumbrance (4)
6 Living in a particular place (8)
12 Gregarious birds (8)
14 A native or inhabitant of the United States (8)
15 The administration of law (7)
18 A stingy hoarder of money (5)
21 A material effigy that is worshipped as a god (4)

Colossal Book of Crosswords

ACROSS

7 Doctor who turned into Mr Hyde (6)
8 Unusual mental ability (6)
9 Musical notation (4)
10 Bon voyage, what to do with a naughty footballer? (4-3)
11 Forsake, leave behind (7)
13 Put your signature on something (4)
15 Bring together (5)
16 Any opponent of technological progress (7)
18 Coiled chambered fossil shell (8)
19 Went on horseback (4)
21 Martial art (6)
22 In waiting, Not presently active (6)

DOWN

1 Any small compartment (4)
2 Impaired in function (13)
3 Produce or yield flowers (7)
4 A substance that exerts some force or effect (5)
5 Lacking regard for the rights or feelings of others (13)
6 A tea party, punch up in bread factory? (3,5)
12 Fertilizer made of ground bones (4-4)
14 The outermost region of the sun's atmosphere (7)
17 Bestowed, handed over (5)
20 Declare untrue; contradict (4)

Colossal Book of Crosswords

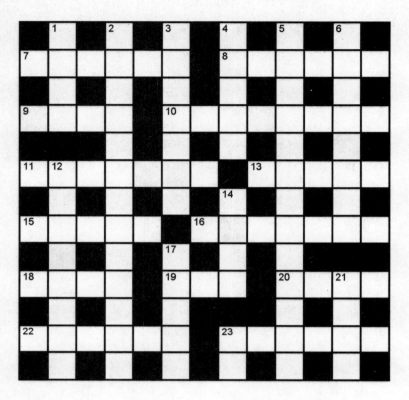

ACROSS

7 Two-piece bathing suit (6)
8 Subject to legal action (6)
9 A notable achievement (4)
10 A band around the collar of a garment (8)
11 The system of production and distribution and consumption (7)
13 Not the same one or ones already mentioned (5)
15 Animal, force (5)
16 Deteriorate in health (7)
18 Town in Scotland (4)
19 Number (3)
20 Make a mess of (4)
22 Stimulate sexually (4-2)
23 Long strip for decoration or advertising (6)

DOWN

1 Measure of distance (4)
2 Someone already renting a property you buy (7,6)
3 Assign in incorrect name to, mains me! (7)
4 Colour - or lack of? (5)
5 Underground tunnels occupied by rabbits (6-7)
6 Horse vision adjusters (8)
12 Anterior portion of the brain (8)
14 Short memorandum! (4)
17 Bad smell (5)
21 Wild goat (4)
23 Degree (2)

Colossal Book of Crosswords

ACROSS

7 The passage to the stomach and lungs (6)
8 Large tent (3,3)
9 Dextrous, skilled (4)
10 Can be used - bleep oar! (8)
11 Seasoned campaigner? (7)
13 Thin and metallic in sound; lacking resonance (5)
15 Currently in progress (5)
17 The official residence of a dean (7)
20 Resembling, derived from, containing glass (8)
21 Average (2-2)
22 Multiply by three (6)
23 From the start (6)

DOWN

1 Solid food prepared from the pressed curd of milk (6)
2 Agile ruminant (4)
3 A low stool to rest the feet (7)
4 A monastery ruled by an abbot (5)
5 Agricultural, farming (8)
6 A woman's foundation garment (4-2)
12 Self-aggrandisement (3,5)
14 Sitting, period of time (7)
16 A monastery of friars (6)
18 Slice of bacon (6)
19 A framework that supports climbing plants (5)
21 Where a web page will be found? (4)

Colossal Book of Crosswords

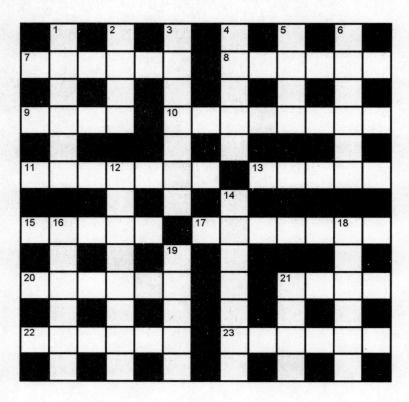

ACROSS

7 The basic unit of electric current (6)
8 Number in football team (6)
9 Waterless (4)
10 Number XIV (8)
11 Metal casing in which a train of gears is sealed (7)
13 A quantity of paper; 24 or 25 sheets (5)
15 Charm, enchantment (5)
17 Baby dogs (7)
20 Connecting the notes; in music (6)
21 Unknown or unspecified amount (4)
22 Cavalryman armed with a lance (6)
23 A waterproof overshoe, mainly US (6)

DOWN

1 Come out from somewhere (6)
2 Have or hold in one's hands (4)
3 Edible fish, shellfish, etc (3-4)
4 A connected series or group (5)
5 Money owed (4)
6 Thin covering, often of wood (6)
12 Trust, dependency (8)
14 Backache (7)
16 Pay for something before receiving it (6)
18 Entangle or catch in, or as if in, a mesh (6)
19 Goods vehicle (5)
21 Threads from worms! (4)

Colossal Book of Crosswords

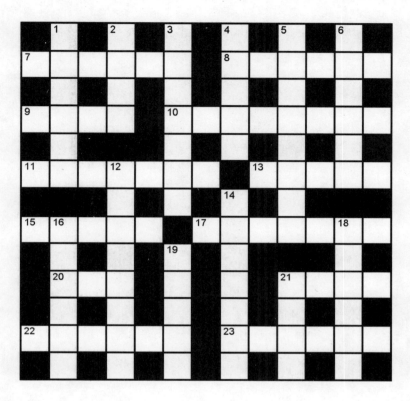

ACROSS

7 Everything you own (6)
8 Be quiet! (4,2)
9 Make a raucous noise (4)
10 The unwritten literature of a culture (8)
11 Smoked herring (7)
13 Descend swiftly, as if on prey (5)
15 Fold in a garment (5)
17 Mottled buff and white owl (4,3)
20 Animal doctor (3)
21 A clear liquid secreted into the mouth (4)
22 Unroll, as a banner (6)
23 Difficult to please, fussy (6)

DOWN

1 Attack someone physically or emotionally (6)
2 A large piece of fabric on a boat (4)
3 Brochure (7)
4 Any sacred song used to praise the Deity (5)
5 A brief report (8)
6 The size of a book whose pages are made by folding a sheet of paper twice to form four leaves (6)
12 Herbaceous plant (8)
14 Search thoroughly, making a mess! (7)
16 Being alive (6)
18 Capriciousness (6)
19 A support for books (5)
21 Hard graft (4)

Colossal Book of Crosswords

ACROSS

7 Provide a detailed plan or design (3,3)
8 Fervent believer (6)
9 Select, digging implement (4)
10 Kiss - locate us! (8)
11 An alloy of mercury with another metal (7)
13 Excessively fat (5)
15 A small portable timepiece (5)
17 A brilliant solo passage (7)
20 High status importance (8)
21 A regular payment by a tenant (4)
22 Prepare musical instrument (4,2)
23 Oxygenate, blow air through (6)

DOWN

1 A soft silvery metallic element of the alkali earth group, used in meal! (6)
2 Employment (4)
3 Thick cushion used as a seat, also empire! (7)
4 A native of inhabitant of the Czech Republic (5)
5 Likely to fail or be inaccurate (8)
6 Unborn child (6)
12 Someone to who a license is granted (8)
14 An entrance that can be closed by a gate (7)
16 Metal protection used in knightly combat (6)
18 Celestial point (6)
19 Awkward, Not elegant (5)
21 Not widely distributed, undercooked? (4)

Colossal Book of Crosswords

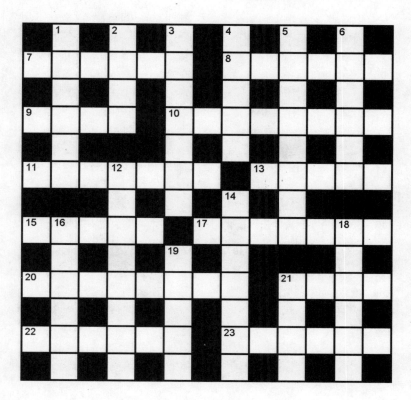

ACROSS

7 Deceive (6)
8 Surprisingly and unceremoniously brusque (6)
9 A notable achievement (4)
10 Herbaceous plant - a staunch! (8)
11 Astral (7)
13 Headgear for girls and frenchmen? (5)
15 Sharp (5)
17 Fake, alter (7)
20 Lucky clover? (4-4)
21 Small rodents (4)
22 An officer of the church (6)
23 Stereotyped behavior (6)

DOWN

1 Determine the existence of (6)
2 Placed the foot (4)
3 Night wear (7)
4 A unit of weight for precious stones (5)
5 Pig's feet (8)
6 Type of tree (6)
12 The literary intelligentsia (8)
14 The waging of armed conflict (7)
16 A plant of the genus Trifolium (6)
18 Care for the face (6)
19 Any distracting manouver (5)
21 An inferior dog (4)

Colossal Book of Crosswords

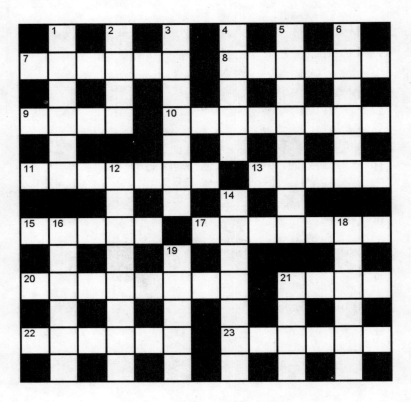

ACROSS

7 A source of danger (6)
8 Inexpensive lodging for youngsters (6)
9 Wild plum (4)
10 Acceptance as satisfactory (8)
11 Deviation from the normal (7)
13 Further or added (5)
15 An unforeseen development in a plot (5)
17 The membrane in the ear (7)
20 Tending to cure or restore to health (8)
21 An aggressive remark (4)
22 Colourless watery fluid of blood and lymph (6)
23 Furniture with drawers (6)

DOWN

1 Large long-jawed oceanic sport fish (6)
2 Very heavy wind - Beaufort 7 to 10 (4)
3 In a perfect world? (7)
4 A small cut of meat including part of a rib (5)
5 Mixed (8)
6 Allow air to get into (6)
12 A female massager (8)
14 Brush kangaroo (7)
16 Hebdomadally (6)
18 Cheerful (6)
19 The largest of the satellites of Saturn (5)
21 An abrupt spasmodic movement, idiot! (4)

ACROSS

7 Highly seasoned fatty sausage (6)
8 Perception by means of the eyes (6)
9 An examination conducted by word of mouth (4)
10 Tip (8)
11 They speak louder than words (7)
13 Barter (5)
15 Later on (5)
17 The children of your aunt or uncle (7)
20 Lightweight handheld collapsible canopy (8)
21 The rate of moving (4)
22 All of the inhabitants of the earth (6)
23 A breakfast food prepared from grain (6)

DOWN

1 Cloth, material (6)
2 Tumble American winter! (4)
3 Devouring greedily - ping gig! (7)
4 Written piece of schoolwork (5)
5 Needs, has to have (8)
6 Brought together (6)
12 Frozen dessert (3-5)
14 Leaves of plant dried for smoking (7)
16 Well known (6)
18 Ambrosia (6)
19 A strong current of air or explosion (5)
21 Segment, component (4)

Colossal Book of Crosswords

ACROSS

7 Place to see films (6)
8 Persons not us (6)
9 Cream off (4)
10 Precise or exact (8)
11 Began (7)
13 1st (5)
15 A visual representation (5)
17 Characterised by great swelling waves or surges (7)
20 Green transparent gemstones (8)
21 Anticipated outcomes (4)
22 Pick out (6)
23 Eating (6)

DOWN

1 A summons issued to an offender (6)
2 Concrete or wooden support in house (4)
3 Car homes (7)
4 Covered entrance (5)
5 Pleasing or delighting (8)
6 Puts pen to paper (6)
12 Considered or deemed to be (8)
14 A grant paid by a government (7)
16 One who belongs to a group (6)
18 The act of putting a person into a non-elective position (6)
19 Fabric (5)
21 The sister of your father (4)

Colossal Book of Crosswords

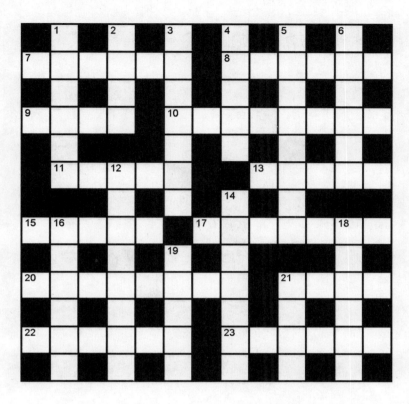

ACROSS

7 Atomic number 27 (6)
8 7th planet from the sun (6)
9 Thing (4)
10 Crop grown for its enlarged roots (4,4)
11 A garment worn on the upper half of the body (5)
13 Lose blood from one's body (5)
15 Express an idea, etc. in words (5)
17 Someone engaged in warfare (7)
20 Retired but retaining title (8)
21 Be unsuccessful, in an exam maybe? (4)
22 Give pleasure to; be pleasing to (6)
23 Writer of books (6)

DOWN

1 As yet unborn child (6)
2 Damage (4)
3 To say or state again (7)
4 A person who gives private instruction (5)
5 Relating to vessels that circulate fluids (8)
6 A sudden outburst (as of protest) (6)
12 Occurring within (8)
14 A law officer (7)
16 Violent agitation, ruction (6)
18 Reverent petition to a deity, prayer (6)
19 Inhaled anaesthetic (5)
21 Destiny (4)

Colossal Book of Crosswords

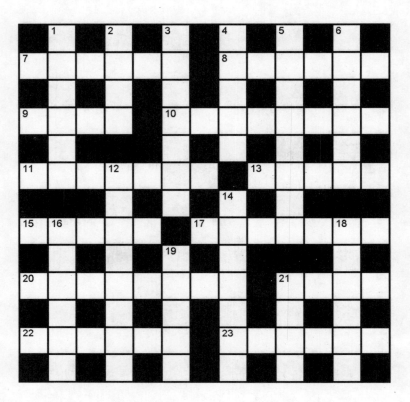

ACROSS

7 Showing a brooding ill humour (6)
8 A child who has lost both parents (6)
9 The top edge of a vessel (4)
10 The time of day immediately following sunset (8)
11 Spray can (7)
13 Play boisterously (5)
15 A convent ruled by an abbess (5)
17 Beyond what is natural (7)
20 Having no toll levied for its use (4-4)
21 Posterior part of a human (4)
22 Go away, leave (6)
23 A musical composition of 3 or 4 movements of contrasting forms (6)

DOWN

1 Party in the evening (6)
2 A mass of small bubbles (4)
3 Decorate (7)
4 A magazine devoted to strip cartoons (5)
5 Dried hulled pea; used in soup (5,3)
6 Assemble or get together (6)
12 Jump across or leap over (8)
14 A substance that produces a fragrant odour when burned (7)
16 A fan run by an electric motor (6)
18 Conformity with some aesthetic standard (6)
19 A fact that has been verified (5)
21 A financial institution (4)

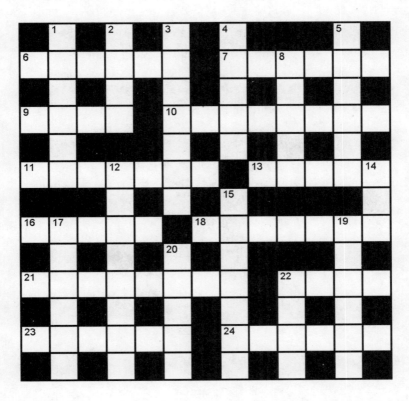

ACROSS

6 Shape with 4 equal length sides (6)
7 Rise and move, as in waves (6)
9 Festival (4)
10 Make vital, get going, inject life into (8)
11 A light shade of blue (3-4)
13 A firm open-weave fabric (5)
16 Powder of ground roasted cacao beans (5)
18 Damage or destroy as if by violence (5-2)
21 Strikingly beautiful or attractive (8)
22 A transparent deep red gemstone (4)
23 Reproductive cell - ate Meg! (6)
24 Not at all out of the ordinary (6)

DOWN

1 Mouse noise (6)
2 Valley, possibly of tears? (4)
3 Great warmth and intensity (7)
4 Die away (5)
5 A dwarfed ornamental tree (6)
8 Of a pale purple colour (5)
12 Pre guide girls? (8)
14 Chart (3)
15 Form a mental image (7)
17 Money paid out (6)
19 Optimistic, feeling good (6)
20 Snake (5)
22 Unusual underdone meat (4)

ACROSS

7 A fine coating of oxide, weathering (6)

8 Melt lard in order to separate out impurities (6)

9 Cycle (4)

10 Ghostlike (8)

11 Spirit (7)

13 Cash (5)

15 Overhang of a roof (5)

17 An artist of consummate skill (7)

20 Pour water on (8)

21 Chinese dynasty (4)

22 Belonging to one by birth (6)

23 Looked at with fixed eyes (6)

DOWN

1 Spittle (6)

2 A digestive juice (4)

3 Colourful swirled pattern popular in the 70s (7)

4 Clean with one's bill, of birds (5)

5 Ingratiating in manner or speech (8)

6 Capture again, as of an escaped prisoner (6)

12 A fact about some part (as opposed to general) (8)

14 Countries of eastern Asia (3,4)

16 In a foreign land, out and about (6)

18 Forest fire fighter (6)

19 Single thickness (5)

21 Fake or pretend (4)

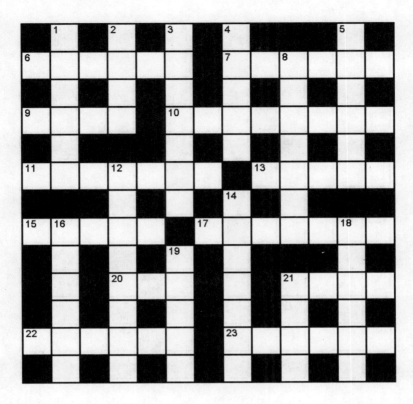

ACROSS

6 Freudian term for sexual urge or desire (6)
7 A large military unit (6)
9 Disease of the skin (4)
10 Corn pancake from Mexico (8)
11 Currently happening, continuing (7)
13 Warhorse (5)
15 Eight people considered as a unit (5)
17 African flightless bird (7)
20 The centre of a city or wheel (3)
21 Present (4)
22 Behavior - no digs! (6)
23 Small depression under the shoulder joint (6)

DOWN

1 Mineral (6)
2 Sit and travel on the back of animal (4)
3 Indicate by signs (7)
4 Far beyond the norm (5)
5 Sheep dog breed (6)
8 Sparkle brightly (7)
12 Projection (8)
14 Not having or involving sex (7)
16 Attachable by a clip - no clip! (4-2)
18 Box in which a corpse is buried or cremated (6)
19 Ill-treatment (5)
21 Precious or semiprecious stones (4)

Colossal Book of Crosswords

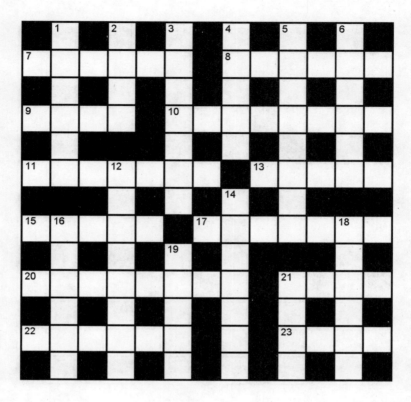

ACROSS

7 Small wolf native to North America (6)
8 Inconsistent in quality, pimply (6)
9 A measured portion of medicine (4)
10 Army unit smaller than a division (8)
11 Place or set apart (7)
13 Alloy of iron with small amounts of carbon (5)
15 Poised for action (5)
17 Any dramatic scene (7)
20 Central stone at top of arch, also cops? (8)
21 Past times (4)
22 Emperor of Japan, Gilbert & Sullivan play (6)
23 Shed tears (4)

DOWN

1 Happy (6)
2 Greater than (4)
3 Give to, in marriage (7)
4 Employment, custom (5)
5 Not containing metal (3-5)
6 Position on an issue (6)
12 Guiding star (8)
14 Threatening or foreshadowing evil (7)
16 A medicine that induces nausea (6)
18 Exceedingly sudden and unexpected (6)
19 Hot chocolate (5)
21 Swerves - usually on a boat (4)

ACROSS

7 Child with no parents (6)
8 Harsh (6)
9 Sound made by a dog (4)
10 Remove the strings from an instrument (8)
11 Pale grey; ash-coloured (4)
13 Someone who works metal (5)
15 Approximately (especially of a date) (5)
17 Art movement, 1920s and 30s, using geometrics (3,4)
20 One type of christian (8)
21 Animal enclosure (4)
23 Wine (6)
24 A wise and trusted guide and advisor (6)

DOWN

1 Animation, comes from confused biro! (4)
2 Dubious looking character (6)
3 Income from capital investment (7)
4 A bottomless gulf or pit (5)
5 Enough members to have a meeting (6)
6 Possessing an extraordinary ability to attract (8)
12 Appropriate for a condition or occasion (8)
14 The basic unit of money in Greece (7)
16 Come or be in close contact with, stick together (6)
18 Socially or conventionally correct (6)
19 Dish on which food is served (5)
22 A feeling of considerable warmth or pride (4)

Colossal Book of Crosswords

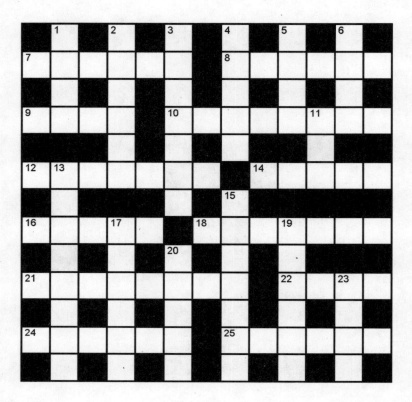

ACROSS

7 Portable computer (6)
8 Absent without permission (6)
9 Champion (4)
10 Pleasantly optimistic (8)
12 Firefighter if male (7)
14 Slanderous defamation (5)
16 Decoration made by fitting pieces of wood into prepared slots (5)
18 Dessert of stewed or baked fruit (7)
21 Relating to cells - all cruel! (8)
22 A small bottle (4)
24 Give advice to (6)
25 A truncated cloth cone mounted on a mast (6)

DOWN

1 Something that rises rapidly and dies away (4)
2 Serving no useful purpose - I toe so! (6)
3 Exceptional, extra (7)
4 An inhalation anaesthetic (5)
5 Rough projection left on a workpiece (4)
6 French for tyre (4)
11 A fixed charge for a privilege (3)
13 An indirect (and usually malicious) implication (8)
15 Deteriorate, rust (7)
17 French - with milk (2,4)
19 Russian physiologist worked with dogs (6)
20 Change (5)
23 A shade of blue tinged with green (4)

Colossal Book of Crosswords

ACROSS

7 Design made of small pieces of coloured stone or glass (6)
8 The middle region of the body of an arthropod (6)
9 Not at all or in no way (4)
10 Scope for freedom (8)
11 Ornamental cloth pad worn on the shoulder (7)
13 Any thick messy substance (5)
15 Tree bearing syrup? (5)
17 Crowned head (7)
20 A feeling of mild anxiety (8)
21 A very young child (4)
23 An occupation for which you are especially well suited (6)
24 Proved to have done a crime (6)

DOWN

1 Game played on horseback (4)
2 French boat (6)
3 Surgical cutting instrument (7)
4 Say clearly (5)
5 A grand and imposing entrance (6)
6 Epidemic over a wide geographical area (8)
12 A member of an ancient Jewish sect (8)
14 Collage (7)
16 Fluid (6)
18 Even though (6)
19 A metric unit of capacity (5)
22 Where you soak your body to clean it! (4)

Colossal Book of Crosswords

ACROSS

7 A ceremonial procession (6)
8 Small plants, often on old stones (6)
9 An impression in a surface (4)
10 H2O from the tap (3-5)
11 Old clothes dryer that squeezed clothes (7)
13 Malicious burning to destroy property (5)
15 Gentleman's gentleman (5)
17 A person who belongs to the political left (7)
20 Monocle (8)
21 Any loose flowing garment (4)
23 With tattle is gossip! (6)
24 Slice of bacon (6)

DOWN

1 Valley (4)
2 Cane used in furniture making (6)
3 The meteorological conditions (7)
4 Run away to get married (5)
5 Oblong cream puff (6)
6 Willing to give and share unstintingly (8)
12 Premixed packs of ingredients (5-3)
14 In a frenzy as if possessed by a demon (7)
16 Number (6)
18 Push forcefully (6)
19 A hen that lays eggs (5)
22 Fermented alcoholic beverage (4)

Colossal Book of Crosswords

ACROSS

7 Elaborate French cake? (6)
8 Colour (6)
9 Wise men (4)
10 Type of parrot (8)
11 Waterproof coat (7)
13 Escargot (5)
15 The contestant you hope to defeat (5)
17 Sausages - that explode?! (7)
20 Direction indicator (8)
21 Long, usually formal, woman's dress (4)
23 Tree and nut (6)
24 In plenty, abounding (6)

DOWN

1 Short paratrooper (4)
2 A natural talent (6)
3 Not very intelligent or interested in culture (7)
4 A drama set to music (5)
5 Smashed, could be record? (6)
6 Another motive (8)
12 Not friendly - iliac nim! (8)
14 Loss, could be natural when people leave a job? (7)
16 Sunshade (6)
18 Titter (6)
19 One of a number of projections on a gear (5)
22 Hospital suite of rooms or beds (4)

Colossal Book of Crosswords

ACROSS

7 True (6)
8 The ability to see (6)
9 Capable (4)
10 Bring into being, start something off (8)
11 Specify individually, list (7)
13 Wood from Lebanon? (5)
15 Break (5)
16 Game like basketball (3,4)
19 Uncontrolled laughter (8)
21 Story (4)
23 Person authorised to conduct religious worship (6)
24 Complain, game bird! (6)

DOWN

1 The fleshy red crest on the head of the domestic fowl (4)
2 Exchange or buy back for money (6)
3 In the beginning, at the start (2,5)
4 Egg-shaped (5)
5 An ancient writ (6)
6 The sound of a step of someone walking (8)
12 A .45-caliber submachine gun (5-3)
14 A motley assortment of things (7)
17 A round fastener sewn to shirts and coats (6)
18 A thin porridge (5)
20 Streetcar (4)
22 A strong sexual desire (4)

Colossal Book of Crosswords

ACROSS

7 Female parent (6)
8 Has a good chance of being the case (6)
9 In the way indicated (4)
10 Being or having an unknown source (8)
11 Come before (7)
13 London art gallery (4)
15 Fruit of the oak tree (5)
17 Extricate from entanglement (7)
20 Avitaminosis caused by lack of thiamine (vitamin B1) (8)
21 Take off - a hat (4)
22 Someone held in bondage, slavery (6)
23 A state of deep-seated ill-will (6)

DOWN

1 Food that fulfills the requirements of Jewish dietary law (6)
2 The other one from that (4)
3 Small explosive bomb thrown by hand (7)
4 South American cud-chewing animal (5)
5 Hard structure provides a frame for the body of an animal (8)
6 Cupboard (6)
12 Knitted jacket (8)
14 A person who does not acknowledge your God (7)
16 Place of child care (6)
18 Prove to be false or incorrect (6)
19 Greeting (5)
21 Gentlewoman (4)

Colossal Book of Crosswords

ACROSS

7 Make a cake (4)
8 Altercation (6)
9 Crazy bird? (4)
10 Used on the high seas (3-5)
11 Pear-shaped tropical fruit (7)
13 Hirsute (5)
15 Fabric (5)
17 Bolshy (7)
20 Blatant or sensational promotion (8)
21 Strike sharply, as in some sports (4)
23 Involuntary expulsion of air from the nose (6)
24 Coiffure (6)

DOWN

1 A circle of light around the sun or moon (4)
2 Feverish (6)
3 Exterior (7)
4 Viscera and trimmings of a butchered animal (5)
5 An Asian temple (6)
6 A drop of rain (8)
12 A treacherous or vicious act (8)
14 Wasting away (7)
16 Lever used to turn the rudder on a boat (6)
18 Orchidaceous plant (6)
19 3 (5)
22 The probability of a specified outcome (4)

Colossal Book of Crosswords

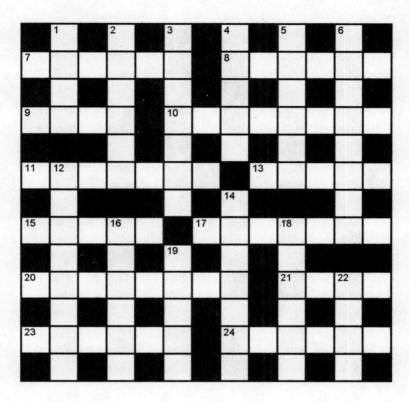

ACROSS

7 Diplomatic representative of the Pope (6)
8 Motivated by concern with the alleviation of suffering (6)
9 Thyself ;(archaic) (4)
10 The final aggregate (3,5)
11 A standard or typical example, image (7)
13 A series of poems or songs on the same theme (5)
15 Skill in an occupation or trade (5)
17 Ridicule with satire (7)
20 A vaguely specified social event (8)
21 (old-fashioned) at or from or to a great distance (4)
23 Up-to-date appliance (3,3)
24 Raise the price of something after agreeing on a lower price (6)

DOWN

1 US President (4)
2 Pronounce not guilty (6)
3 Causing or able to cause nausea (7)
4 The subject matter (5)
5 Represent in bodily form (6)
6 Sunken or depressed engraving or carving on a stone - ligation! (8)
12 Cut of meat from a pig (4-4)
14 The savage and excessive killing of people (7)
16 Groom-to-be (6)
18 A public square with room for pedestrians (6)
19 A stupid foolish person (5)
22 Voluntary contributions to aid the poor (4)

Colossal Book of Crosswords

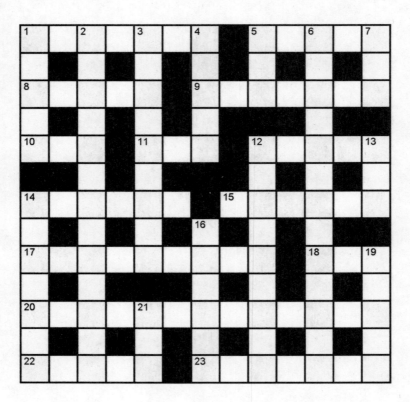

ACROSS

1 Substitute a person or thing for another (7)
5 A stingy hoarder of money (5)
8 Colour similar to that of wood or earth (5)
9 Your basis for belief or disbelief (7)
10 File a suit against (3)
11 Positive response (3)
12 Sarcasm (5)
14 Corpulent (6)
15 The polar region (3-3)
17 A particular course of action (9)
18 A woolen cap of Scottish origin (3)
20 Refrigerator and freezer all in one unit (6-7)
22 A smooth fabric of silk or rayon (5)
23 Lockjaw (7)

DOWN

1 Picture puzzle (5)
2 Person who works the projector in a cinema (13)
3 Irritation (9)
4 The boundaries of a surface (5)
5 Cow noise (3)
6 Old age pensioner, as was (6,7)
7 Short Rosalind (3)
12 The amount by which something increases (9)
13 Dog noise (3)
14 Overpriced deals (3-4)
16 A meal at which guests help themselves (6)
19 Female horses (5)
21 Strong liquor flavoured with juniper berries (3)

Colossal Book of Crosswords

ACROSS

7 The countries of Asia (6)
8 Advertising motto (6)
9 Building block (4)
10 Furthermore - remove or! (8)
11 Stalemate (7)
13 Out of bed (5)
15 Thin layers of rock used for roofing (5)
17 Odd, peculiar (7)
20 A mild rebuke or criticism (8)
21 A city district of central London (2-2)
23 A test of the suitability of a performer (3,3)
24 Being approximately average (6)

DOWN

1 Strong desire to do something (4)
2 Hat (6)
3 List in order (7)
4 A male monarch or emperor (4)
5 Able to absorb fluids (6)
6 Betting (8)
12 Bush to go round? (8)
14 Printing plate made by dipping in acid (7)
16 Sort of flat fish (6)
18 Soak up (6)
19 Overly eager speed, and possibly less speed! (5)
22 Get better (4)

Colossal Book of Crosswords

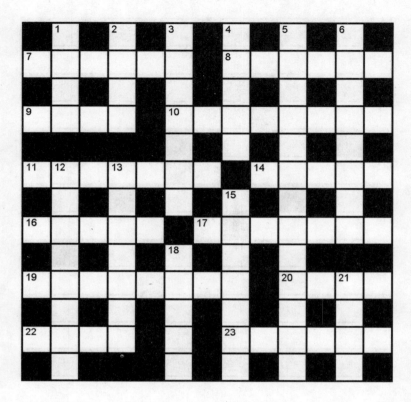

ACROSS

7 A range of mountains, also type of car? (6)
8 A state of extreme poverty (6)
9 Yobbo (4)
10 Shaped like a ring, advertisement (8)
11 Breathing device for diving (7)
14 Give out, like warrants (5)
16 Girl's name (5)
17 After the event (7)
19 Easily irritated, fractious (8)
20 Tools for cutting internal screw threads (4)
22 Composer (4)
23 Deprive of food (6)

DOWN

1 Spanish surrealist painter (4)
2 Unruly child (4)
3 School book carrier (7)
4 Reject with contempt (5)
5 Lacking material form or substance (13)
6 Accumulated wealth, sometimes buried by pirates (8)
12 Not containing or made from metal! (3-5)
13 Touch up, as a photograph (7)
15 Tooth doctor (7)
18 Lady, as in dear sir or .... (5)
21 Cover with stones to make road or path (4)

Colossal Book of Crosswords

ACROSS

7 A man who has sex with and is supported by a woman (6)
8 A game played on an ice rink (6)
9 Happy (4)
10 One million million (8)
11 Metal loops into which rider's feet go (7)
13 Not refined or processed (5)
15 A very small spot (5)
17 Platform projecting from wall of building (7)
20 Mishap (8)
21 A dramatic work (4)
23 Help (6)
24 Small fish (6)

DOWN

1 A small bottle or ampoule (4)
2 Horse food (6)
3 Dais, podium (7)
4 Of them or themselves, belonging to them (5)
5 Relating to or using sight (6)
6 Under a moral obligation to someone (8)
12 Cast repeatedly in the same kind of role (8)
14 A period of time during which there is armed conflict (7)
16 A crucial stage or unstable situation (6)
18 Dealing with (6)
19 The end of life (5)
22 Succulent plants used in shampoo (4)

Colossal Book of Crosswords

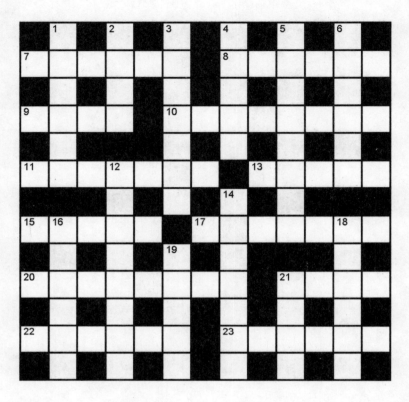

ACROSS

7 An inclination to want things (6)
8 Turns litmus paper blue (6)
9 Civil unrest (4)
10 An international organisation that helps sick and wounded (3,5)
11 Presaging ill-fortune, worrying (7)
13 Shiny and tough and flexible plastic (5)
15 Someone who drives a taxi for a living (5)
17 Maybe, possibly (7)
20 Dumps on someone else, unloads (8)
21 Hard candy in a stick with letters in it? (4)
22 Small (6)
23 Boat steering device (6)

DOWN

1 Boredom (6)
2 Dye with a colour (4)
3 A wrestling hold (4,3)
4 Rice field (5)
5 A minor short-term fight (8)
6 Showy (6)
12 Aristocracy (8)
14 Time for relaxation (7)
16 Abreast of, knowing the latest (French) (2,4)
18 A wooden strip forming part of a fence, non flying! (6)
19 Tower built by Noah's descendants (5)
21 Do again (2-2)

Colossal Book of Crosswords

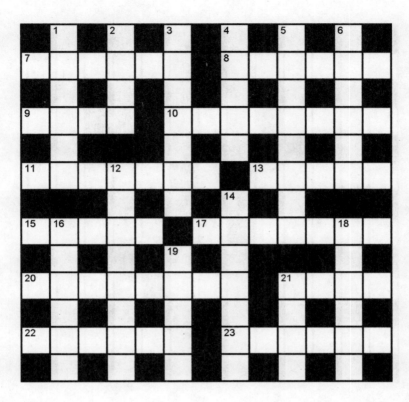

ACROSS

7 A violent denunciation (6)
8 Colour (6)
9 Glorify (4)
10 Not suitable or right or appropriate (8)
11 Rumour (7)
13 Edge tool used in shaving (5)
15 Of which person? (5)
17 A woolen fabric (7)
20 Water ice on a small wooden stick (3-5)
21 The basic unit of money in Turkey (4)
22 Female sibling (6)
23 Sharpness of vision (6)

DOWN

1 Become wider (6)
2 Dance orchestra (4)
3 In the shape of a coil (7)
4 A slender graceful young woman (5)
5 Contestants who lose the contest (4-4)
6 A short jacket; worn mostly by women (6)
12 Unhesitating (8)
14 Emulator (7)
16 Feverish, very busy (6)
18 A mistake in printed matter (6)
19 (used of opinions and actions) far beyond the norm (5)
21 Tastelessly showy or noisy (4)

ACROSS

7 A rude expression intended to offend (6)

8 Informal terms for journalist (6)

9 A speech defect (4)

10 Linear unit, also french for line (5)

11 We (2)

12 Make flat or flatter (7)

14 Precious stone or gem (5)

16 Normal (5)

18 Inexpensive showy collectible (7)

21 Place where you might buy 18? (4-4)

22 Part of ear (4)

23 Fight against (6)

24 Small rounded wartlike protuberance on a plant (6)

DOWN

1 Script or lettering style - in caul! (6)

2 Leap (4)

3 Artificially formal (7)

4 Accepted or habitual practice (5)

5 Without controls (4,4)

6 Greater than 90 degrees (6)

13 Adhesive friction (8)

15 Type of gas for heating (7)

17 Clothes that cover little! (6)

19 Preserve a dead body (6)

20 Small mouselike mammal (5)

22 A woman of refinement (4)

ACROSS

6 Put into words or an expression (6)

7 Something badly botched or muddled (4,2)

8 Travel on the surface of water (4)

9 Repaired area on clothing (5)

11 Make lacework by knotting or looping (7)

13 Very intense, ardent (5)

15 Israeli statesman (1913-1992) (5)

17 Boots with nailed soles (7)

20 Two objects or people that do not go together (8)

21 Polish and make shiny (4)

22 Of or relating to similar to bears (6)

23 Be abundant or plentiful (6)

DOWN

1 One sixth of a polo match (6)

2 Having or displaying affection (4)

3 Crying (7)

4 A state of friendship and cordiality (5)

5 Latex from trees (6)

10 Grey or white wading bird (5)

12 One of a group of three sharing public administration or civil authority especially in ancient Rome (8)

14 Dynamic (2-5)

16 Someone who leaves one country to settle in another (6)

18 A very young child (birth to 1 year) (6)

19 Freshwater carnivorous mammal (5)

21 The part of the face above the eyes (4)

Colossal Book of Crosswords

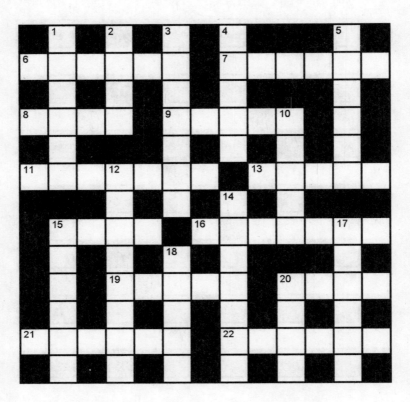

ACROSS

6 Two-channel sound (6)
7 Measured lengthwise (6)
8 The highest adult male singing voice (4)
9 Destiny, (Hinduism and Buddhism) (5)
11 Let go, free from restraint (7)
13 Smelled very bad! (5)
15 Add name to cheque, direction indicator (4)
16 Hansen's disease (7)
19 Instruction to horse? (3,2)
20 Little argument (4)
21 Root vegetable (6)
22 With milk, in France (2,4)

DOWN

1 Purloined (6)
2 Group of three (4)
3 Studious (7)
4 Speak out without thinking (5)
5 Technical terminology (6)
10 Showy daisylike flower (5)
12 Hiring for work (8)
14 The name of the day that is added during a leap year (4-3)
15 A hereditary military dictator of Japan (6)
17 Ending of a word (6)
18 Time or beat (5)
20 Thin clay slab used in bathrooms (4)

Colossal Book of Crosswords

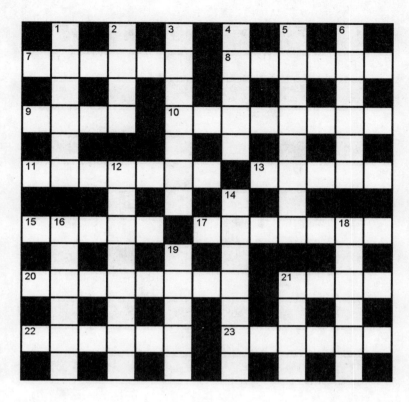

ACROSS

7 Assemble or get together (6)
8 Important football match (3-3)
9 Brought into existence (4)
10 Distance travelled per unit time (8)
11 Hold spellbound (7)
13 Make improvements or corrections (5)
15 Dwell, stay with (5)
17 One who sees and reports a crime (7)
20 Atomic number 62 - I am arums! (8)
21 Twisted toward one side, as plans go? (4)
22 A small low motor vehicle (2-4)
23 Castrate, used with animals (6)

DOWN

1 Colour or leave on island (6)
2 Avoid and stay away from deliberately (4)
3 Of little importance (7)
4 The skin that covers the top of the head (5)
5 Astronaut, male (8)
6 Baby cat (6)
12 Retreat, den, secret place (8)
14 Very hard native crystalline carbon (7)
16 A fire (usually on a hill or tower) (6)
18 A detailed critical inspection of a house (6)
19 A mark used to indicate the word should be repeated (5)
21 Greenish blue (4)

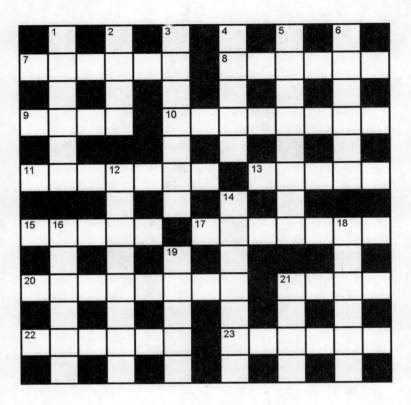

ACROSS

7 Gracefully slender; moving with ease (6)
8 An immense cloud of gas and dust in space (6)
9 Flower (4)
10 Fueled with oil (3-5)
11 Massive Egyptian memorial (7)
13 Derived from ethane by the removal of one hydrogen atom (5)
15 Underground burial chamber (5)
17 Not protected by trademark (7)
20 Huge destructive waves (8)
21 A secret move (to avoid paying debts)! (4)
22 Someone who obtains pleasure from inflicting pain (6)
23 A storage compartment (6)

DOWN

1 To an excessive degree, maybe protective? (6)
2]Money for the poor (4)
3 Type of active exercise (7)
4 The brother of your father (5)
5 Strong green liqueur (8)
6 Tired, ready for bed (6)
12 Part of book and cause of illness in some people (8)
14 Of or relating to tension (7)
16 One who is playfully mischievous (6)
18 More than one of 9? (6)
19 Struck, slapped, knocked down (5)
21 Turn to look at (4)

Colossal Book of Crosswords

ACROSS

7 At or near the north pole (6)
8 Exchange, light operating device (6)
9 Measure of land (4)
10 Offer a lower price than competitors (8)
11 Atom, to poise! (7)
14 Forward in time or order or degree (5)
16 Shaggy-maned humped bovid (5)
17 Final stages of an extended process of negotiation (7)
19 Larger than normal for its kind (8)
21 Snoopy, prying (4)
23 Farther than (6)
24 Hero not getting credit for deeds (6)

DOWN

1 Man's name (4)
2 An infection of the eyelid (4)
3 Rough cider (7)
4 Actor's line spoken to audience (5)
5 Any organism of microscopic size (5-8)
6 Make used (to something) (8)
12 Menial servants (8)
13 As well, in addition, plus, also... (3)
15 An artless innocent young girl (7)
18 Blouse with a sailor collar (5)
20 Public disorder (4)
22 Plumbing fixture (4)

Colossal Book of Crosswords

ACROSS

5 Make a more or less disguised reference to (6)
7 Against the wind (6)
9 Petty quarrel (4)
10 Fizzy drink (8)
11 In an extreme degree (7)
13 Apologetic (5)
15 Printing mark meaning to cancel (4)
17 A clothing fabric in a plaid weave (7)
20 Come near to (8)
21 A Hindu prince or king in India (4)
22 Play boisterously, frolic (6)
23 Make less or smaller than before (6)

DOWN

1 An enclosed conduit for a fluid (4)
2 Cello player (7)
3 Extremely pleasing to the sense of taste! (5)
4 A final performance (4-4)
6 Plant with purple-blue flowers (5)
8 The lowest point of anything (5)
12 Outside (8)
14 Part of horse (7)
16 Formal headgear and Fred Astair film (3-3)
18 Showing humiliation or submissiveness (6)
19 Dry land (5)
21 Naughty or unfinished (crude) (4)

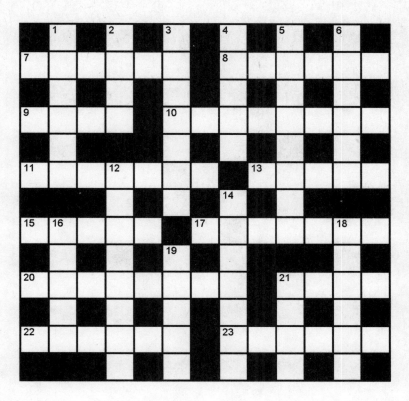

ACROSS

7 Provide a detailed plan or design (3,3)
8 A long pin for holding meat (6)
9 Bladderlike structure that may be abnormal (4)
10 Total forgetfulness (8)
11 Without moral standards or principles (7)
13 Flexible twig of a willow tree (5)
15 Squeeze tightly between the fingers (5)
17 Destroy the peace or tranquility of (7)
20 Whatever person - hover mew! (8)
21 Obviously contrived to charm (4)
22 A sultanate in northwestern Borneo (6)
23 The production of a litter of pigs (6)

DOWN

1 A ravine formed by a river (6)
2 Failed to win (4)
3 Thick cushion used as a seat (7)
4 Any sacred song used to praise the Deity (5)
5 Heavy and compact in form or stature (8)
6 Take away (6)
12 Moving toward one (8)
14 The middle area of the human torso (7)
16 The rarified fluid said to flow in the veins of the Greek gods (6)
18 The food allowance for one day (6)
19 An egg-shaped object (5)
21 A heavy open wagon, often horsedrawn (4)

Colossal Book of Crosswords

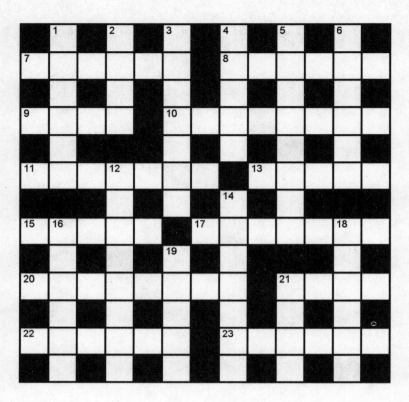

ACROSS

7 Dig over field with tractor (6)
8 Imparted skills or knowledge to (6)
9 Be without (4)
10 Attracting or delighting (8)
11 Poisonous salt of hydrocyanic acid (7)
13 Additional, not this one (5)
15 A person authorised to act for another (5)
17 A boat for communication between ship and shore (7)
20 A sheikhdom of eastern Arabia (3,5)
21 A British imperial capacity measure (4)
22 Disinherit (6)
23 Artificial (6)

DOWN

1 Morally degraded (6)
2 (in cricket) a score of nothing (4)
3 Screens, protects (7)
4 Place to act (5)
5 Bulb filament material (8)
6 Whine and complain (6)
12 Where your neighbour lives? (4-4)
14 Feeling sick (7)
16 Long eared burrowing animal (6)
18 French dance (6)
19 Liquid colour used to decorate walls (5)
21 Short paratrooper (4)

Colossal Book of Crosswords

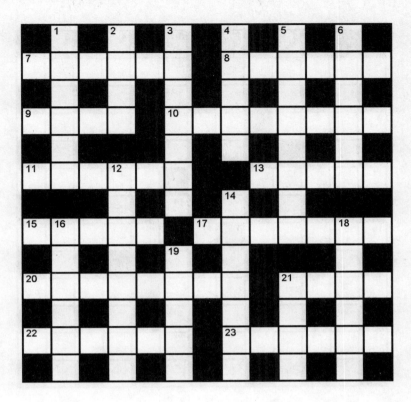

ACROSS

7 Small motor vehicle for fun driving (2-4)
8 Composer (6)
9 Have confidence or faith in (4)
10 (computer science)at the same time as reality, without delay (4-4)
11 The capital of Turkey (6)
13 Foam (5)
15 Not In My Back Yard! Initially (5)
17 Scots instrument (7)
20 Astound, amaze (8)
21 The inner surface of the hand and tree (4)
22 Confederate, associate (6)
23 Look up to, want to be like (6)

DOWN

1 Dignified and sombre in manner (6)
2 Not difficult (4)
3 Lasting for ever (7)
4 Sea (5)
5 Vegetables grown for the underground part (4,4)
6 Fate (6)
12 The food and drink of the gods (8)
14 Tip of missile (7)
16 Inner part of shoe, sometimes removeable (6)
18 Trifling sum (6)
19 Silly, like a kipper (5)
21 Ceremonial elegance (4)

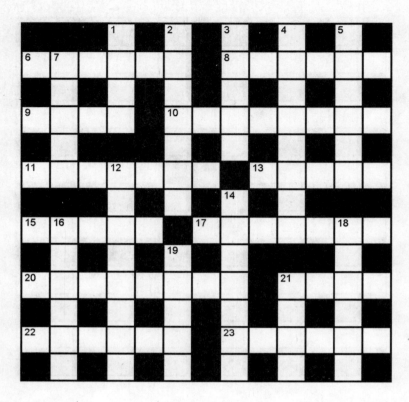

ACROSS

6 An anxiety disorder (6)
8 A rational motive for a belief or action (6)
9 Make well (4)
10 Make urban or city-like (8)
11 Imitate (7)
13 Incompetent (5)
15 Social error, faux pas! (5)
17 Root vegetable (7)
20 In any place (8)
21 A reproduction of a written record (4)
22 Wine (6)
23 Belonging to them (6)

DOWN

1 A slender double-reed instrument (4)
2 A volcanic island republic in Melanesia (7)
3 Podicipitiform seabird (5)
4 Wages, money from employment (8)
5 Malicious report about other people (6)
7 Stem of beans and peas used for thatch (5)
12 The principal work of your career (4-4)
14 Complete outfit (clothing and accessories) for a new baby (7)
16 Chronological records (6)
18 Unclean, tainted (6)
19 A bed on a ship or train (5)
21 Persons serving on a ship (4)

Colossal Book of Crosswords

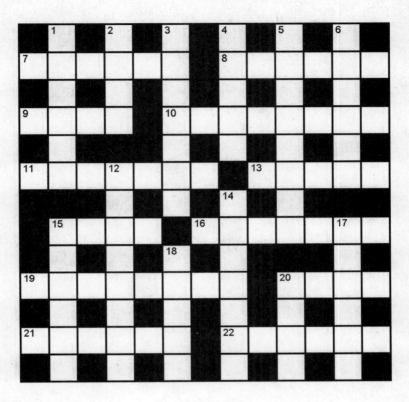

ACROSS

7 Diagnostic test (6)
8 Grounds of a college (6)
9 Burden, load (4)
10 1000000000000 (8)
11 Abounding in or covered with flowers (7)
13 Frequently (5)
15 A mood or display of sullen aloofness (4)
16 Where the jury sit (4-3)
19 (informal) Stupid incompetent people (4-4)
20 Kill off surplus animals to ensure food for rest (4)
21 Plumbing fixture that sprays water over you (6)
22 Remove, take away - (stop from wages) (6)

DOWN

1 Communication that encodes a message (6)
2 A musical work (4)
3 Something that baffles understanding (7)
4 Cheap fabric (5)
5 Literally young fish - insignificant people (5-3)
6 A sudden outburst or fuss over something (6)
12 Game birds suitable for food (4-4)
14 Exterior (7)
15 Wrap in, swaddle (6)
17 According to the clock (6)
18 A daily written record (5)
20 The closing section of a musical composition, finale (4)

Colossal Book of Crosswords

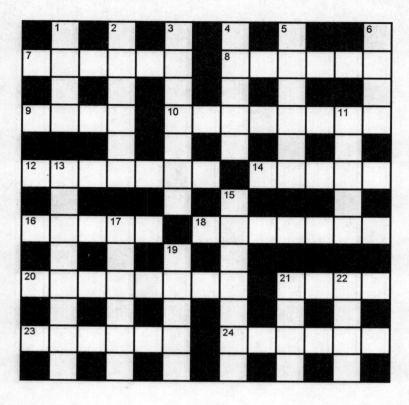

ACROSS

- **7** Bathroom sponge (6)
- **8** Give information or notice to, advise of (6)
- **9** Wise men (4)
- **10** Small, remote and insignificant - no heroes! (3-5)
- **12** Government order imposing a trade barrier (7)
- **14** Begin, commence (5)
- **16** Type of sailing boat (5)
- **18** Someone who is skilled at analysing data (7)
- **20** A five-sided polygon (8)
- **21** Nymph who was spurned by Narcissus (4)
- **23** Wall painting (6)
- **24** Accomplishing something by scheming or trickery (6)

DOWN

- **1** Star, could be super? (4)
- **2** Continent (6)
- **3** From one end or side to the other (7)
- **4** Go in (5)
- **5** The greatest possible degree (6)
- **6** Shelter for cows (4)
- **11** Rides the waves of the sea with a board (5)
- **13** Bush or tree, to go round? (8)
- **15** Nameless - know nun! (7)
- **17** Of an angle; between 90 and 180 degrees (6)
- **19** An Eskimo hut (5)
- **21** An inactive volcano in Sicily (4)
- **22** Orifice (4)

ACROSS

7 Exercises to strengthen the abdomen (6)
8 Supernatural forces and events (6)
9 Unable to speak (4)
10 Untypical, irregular (8)
11 Strongly and firmly constructed - tells we! (4-3)
13 A submersible warship (1-4)
15 Crazy (5)
17 Small dining area in alcove off kitchen (7)
20 Getting onto a horse (8)
21 Microphone, short version (4)
22 A fungus causing decay in timber (3,3)
23 Ghost, strong drink (6)

DOWN

1 Be or play a part of or in, number (6)
2 Naked (4)
3 One who has escaped (7)
4 Small vascular growth on surface of mucous membrane (5)
5 Sketchy handwriting or quick notes (8)
6 Type of Llama (6)
12 A celebrity who is an inspiration to others (8)
14 Largest (7)
16 On a ship, train, plane or other vehicle (6)
18 Fool or hoax (4-2)
19 Young cat, combined stake monies (5)
21 Injure or wound seriously (4)

Colossal Book of Crosswords

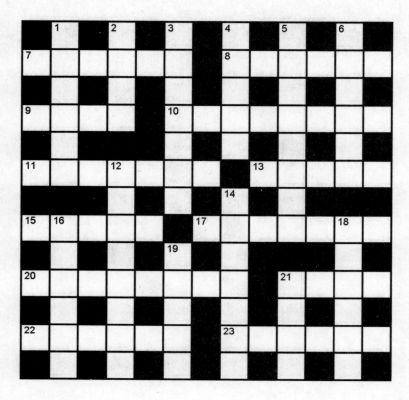

ACROSS

7 The power to entice or attract (6)
8 Followed orders or instructions (6)
9 A seductive woman (4)
10 To do with the sea (8)
11 Lie back and relax (7)
13 French composer of Carmen (5)
15 Amusing (5)
17 Government income from taxation (7)
20 A small spoon (8)
21 Young deer (4)
22 Animal or insect pests (6)
23 Improve or perfect by pruning or polishing (6)

DOWN

1 Late time of life (3-3)
2 Fleshy hindquarters (4)
3 Leftover, oddment (7)
4 Clear up, possibly liquids (3-2)
5 Associated with women and not with men (8)
6 Prove negative; show to be false (6)
12 Marked by dejection from being alone (8)
14 Entering again, return of space craft (2-5)
16 Inconsistent in quality (6)
18 Become less tense (6)
19 Cause injuries or bodily harm to (5)
21 A small high-pitched flute (4)

389

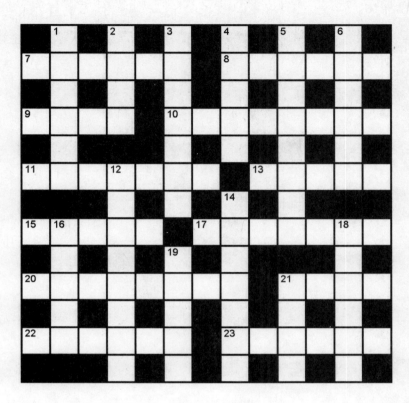

ACROSS

7 Secretive or illicit sexual relationship (6)
8 A Greek island (6)
9 Religious ritual, sometimes last (4)
10 Toilet (8)
11 In contrast to (7)
13 Any of several evergreen plants (5)
15 Turn red with embarrassment (5)
17 Exercising weight, not dumb! (3-4)
20 Extramarital sex (8)
21 Air pollution by a mixture of smoke and fog (4)
22 Brought together (6)
23 Intrusion (6)

DOWN

1 The near or foreseeable future (6)
2 Reduced visibility due to dust, smoke etc. (4)
3 Not devious (7)
4 A room equipped with toilet facilities (5)
5 A very small person or fairy tale person (3,5)
6 Of or relating to or containing iron (6)
12 Protect from heat, cold, noise, etc. (8)
14 Look after children for pay (4-3)
16 Filled with a great quantity (5)
18 Bath sponge (6)
19 Poised for action (5)
21 The founder of a family (4)

Colossal Book of Crosswords

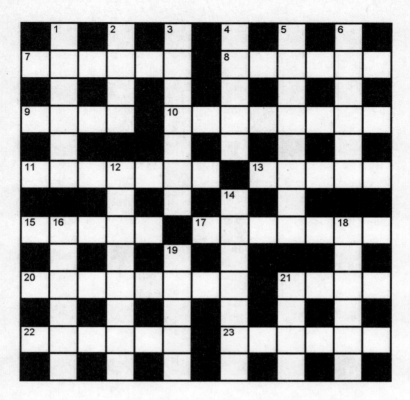

ACROSS

7 Blocks of wood to hold wheels on a hill (6)
8 Communication by word of mouth (6)
9 At no cost or charge (4)
10 Vastness of size or extent (8)
11 Contrary to or forbidden by law (7)
13 Bourbon, sugar and mint over crushed ice (5)
15 Break down - pears! (5)
17 A quantity of no importance (7)
20 Soldiers who fight on foot (8)
21 A port in southern Lebanon (4)
22 A yell to rally a group of soldiers in battle (3-3)
23 Pleasantly (even unrealistically) optimistic (6)

DOWN

1 Performed by a chorus or choir (6)
2 Dull persistent pain (4)
3 Practicing great self-denial - cast ice! (7)
4 Cravat and horse race meeting (5)
5 White wine flavoured with aromatic herbs (8)
6 An edge tool for cutting grass (6)
12 An occurrence of something (8)
14 A drinking mug in the shape of a stout man (4-3)
16 Temper, toughen by heating and cooling (6)
18 Not out of the ordinary (6)
19 Remains where put - ladies undergarment (5)
21 Pipe or underground railway (4)

ACROSS

7 Attempted by employing effort (6)
8 Mushroom - coprinus (3-3)
9 Front part of a vessel, golfer's shout! (4)
10 Above comparison (8)
11 A prominent aspect of something, boast (7)
13 Not moving (5)
15 Appeal or request earnestly (5)
17 Of or characteristic of or resembling a lion (7)
20 Solo dance performed by sailors (8)
21 Lie adjacent to another (4)
22 Mar or spoil the appearance of (6)
24 A powerful circular current (6)

DOWN

1 Pointless - I toe so! (6)
2 Deteriorated through use or stress (4)
3 A late afternoon or evening worship service (7)
4 Muscle connector (5)
5 Bony structure of humans (8)
6 Liege subject (6)
12 Track based transport, part of bridal gown (5)
14 Hold back (7)
16 Slacken off (6)
18 The state that precedes vomiting (6)
19 Men's partners in marriage (5)
21 A distinctive but intangible quality surrounding a person or thing (4)
23 Short advertisement (2)

Colossal Book of Crosswords

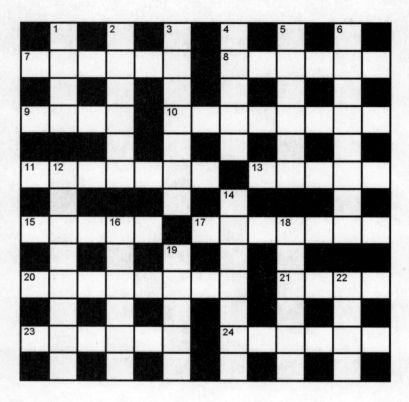

ACROSS

7 Continental sausage (6)
8 Something that baffles understanding (6)
9 Japanese rice wine (4)
10 Capable of being treated by surgical operation (8)
11 A haphazard distribution in all directions (7)
13 The capital and largest city of Japan (5)
15 Effigy - I a gem! (5)
17 A drink credited with magical power (7)
20 A royalist supporter of Charles I (8)
21 Last part of cigarette or american bottom! (4)
23 Come out, emerge (6)
24 Barbarous, cruel, savage (6)

DOWN

1 A ditch that sounds like laughter? (2-2)
2 Of or relating to or supporting Romanism (6)
3 Man whose wife has died (7)
4 Heat in infection or illness (5)
5 A noisy or scolding or domineering woman (6)
6 A person or firm that employs workers (8)
12 Race between candidates for elective office (8)
14 As a result of which - why beer! (7)
16 Rock fragments and pebbles (6)
18 Confinement (6)
19 1st (5)
22 Male monarch or emperor (4)

Colossal Book of Crosswords

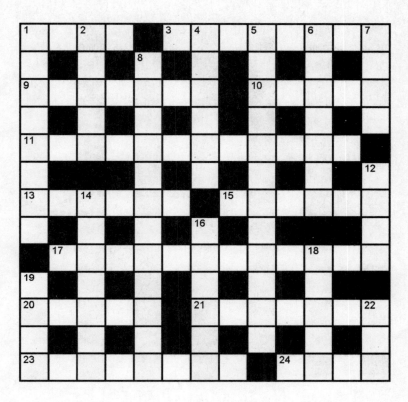

ACROSS

1 Constellation in middle of largos! (4)
3 More disdainful - fires fin! (8)
9 Russian dramatist (7)
10 Push or throw out (5)
11 A short thick jacket; often worn by workmen (6-6)
13 Metallic element used in alloys (6)
15 Musical compositions (6)
17 Bottles with double walls to keep drinks hot (6,6)
20 Not telling the truth (5)
21 Fleshy rooted plant, source of tapioca (7)
23 Fancy woman (8)
24 Strip the skin off (4)

DOWN

1 A mishap (8)
2 Gather, as of as crops (5)
4 A member of an Athapaskan people (6)
5 A furniture varnish (6-6)
6 Make a deep and indelible impression on someone (7)
7 Have confidence or faith in, swear by (4)
8 A hamburger with melted cheese on it (12)
12 Sister and wife of Osiris (4)
14 Loonies, nutters... (7)
16 Loose overalls, sometimes stitched in patterns (6)
18 Not large (5)
19 Oval smooth-skinned fruit with a single pit (4)
22 Girl's name (3)

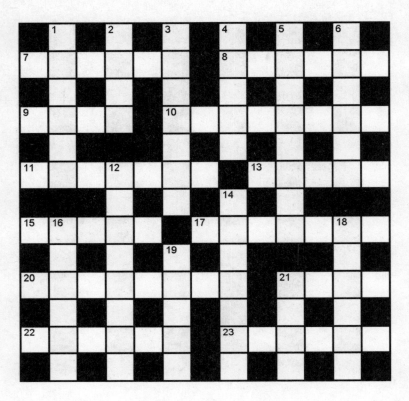

ACROSS

7 To do with cats (6)
8 A major South American river (6)
9 6 balls in cricket! (4)
10 A dark shade of blue (4-4)
11 Where sea meets fresh water (7)
13 Bunk on a ship (5)
15 Fit and active, flexible (5)
17 Reflexive form of "her" (7)
20 Boot worn by German soldiers in wartime (8)
21 Grudging admiration (4)
22 All together, as a group, en masse (2,4)
23 Hug romantically (6)

DOWN

1 The main organs of photosynthesis (6)
2 A coffin along with its stand (4)
3 Man's name (7)
4 Invertebrate in growth stage (5)
5 People who are no longer popular (3-5)
6 Talk or behave amorously, chat up (6)
12 Has little chance of being the case or coming about (8)
14 Any of various plants of the genus Lactuca (7)
16 Granular, made up of large particles (6)
18 Full of life and energy (6)
19 Coerce, make someone do something (5)
21 Flow in a circular current, of liquids (4)

Colossal Book of Crosswords

ACROSS

6 Off the beaten track, far away (6)
7 Animal food container (6)
8 Burrowing marine mollusc (4)
9 Passkey for raising or drawing back a latch (8)
10 Silvery-white radioactive metallic element; (7)
12 The amount a salary is increased (5)
14 An impure form of quartz (5)
16 A fabric made from the hair of sheep (7)
19 Sweetened beverage of diluted lemon juice (8)
20 Apartment (4)
21 Bequest (6)
22 Talisman (6)

DOWN

1 Bank clerk or cashier (6)
2 Type of gear, found in garden? (4)
3 Covetous (7)
4 Sphere of camphor used to protect clothing in store (4-4)
5 In accord, goes along with (6)
7 Very short skirt worn by ballerinas (4)
11 Not based on fact or investigation (8)
13 Some unspecified time in the future (7)
15 Baby talk for horse! (3-3)
17 Hard white tooth covering (6)
18 Man with strong sexual desires, forest god (5)
20 A bitter quarrel between two parties (4)

Colossal Book of Crosswords

ACROSS

7 Sputum, lethargy (6)
8 A fortification of earth (6)
9 Narrow strip of land that juts out into the sea (4)
10 Upper side of the thighs of a seated person (3)
11 Long green edible beaked pods (4)
12 Night wear (7)
14 Bright green fabric, used on snooker tables (5)
16 Investigation (5)
18 Capable of reproducing (7)
21 A lightweight handheld collapsible canopy (8)
22 The probability of a specified outcome (4)
23 Say this when asking it's good manners! (6)
24 Flower (6)

DOWN

1 Rough sea with small waves (6)
2 A hole for the escape of gas or air (4)
3 Dental filling material (7)
4 Alter and reuse in another way (5)
5 Not having the facts or knowledge (8)
6 Mineral - used in watches? (6)
13 Of or relating to or formed by trees (8)
15 A member of a senate (7)
17 Disturb the smoothness of something - lumper! (6)
19 A male child (6)
20 Any of various church officers (5)
22 One time (4)

Colossal Book of Crosswords

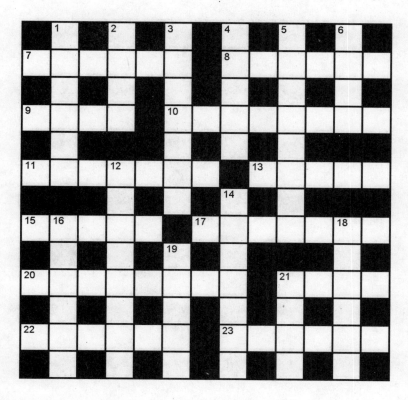

ACROSS

7 Dress down, tell off (6)
8 A cart that is drawn by an ox! (6)
9 The basic unit of money on Malta (4)
10 By air mail - in French (3,5)
11 Clear and certain mental apprehension (7)
13 Register formally, perhaps at college (5)
15 To swallow hurriedly, gulp down (5)
17 Noiselessness (7)
20 An introduction to a play (8)
21 (archaic) to (4)
22 Sweet dark purple plum (6)
23 To come to rest, settle or burst into flame? (6)

DOWN

1 Archaic terms for army, could be foreign (6)
2 Type of hoop, for spinning round hips! (4)
3 Lose confidence or hope; become dejected (7)
4 Snake (5)
5 Collect discarded or refused material (8)
6 Group of three (4)
12 Unmarried (8)
14 Matter other than plant or animal (7)
16 Not having been read (6)
18 Likely to attract attention, like a tune? (6)
19 Great pain and, sometimes, aunt? (5)
21 A single undivided natural entity (4)

Colossal Book of Crosswords

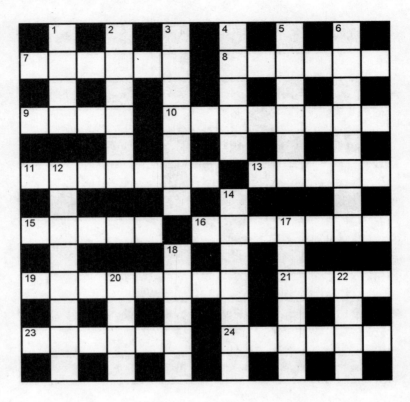

ACROSS

7 Call to mind from an earlier time (6)
8 Drill that is used to enlarge holes - er mare! (6)
9 Turn to liquid through heat (4)
10 Influence or urge by gentle urging (8)
11 Dismount (7)
13 Food that God gave the Israelites (5)
15 Elongated leather strip used to secure things (5)
16 Straight line that touches but does not intersect a curve (7)
19 Inhabitant (of a village)! (8)
21 A light inflated pastry shell (4)
23 Colour (6)
24 Person in religious orders (6)

DOWN

1 An elaborate party (often outdoors) (4)
2 A design on the skin made by pricking (6)
3 Oval (7)
4 A small growth of trees without underbrush (5)
5 Youngest daughter of the prophet Mohammed (6)
6 Linen or cotton articles for a bed (3-5)
12 Providing nourishment - inert nut! (8)
14 A stack of hay (7)
17 Burrowing rodent - pre hog! (6)
18 Inuit home (5)
20 The habitation of wild animals, den (4)
22 Alcoholic drink containing beaten egg (4)

Colossal Book of Crosswords

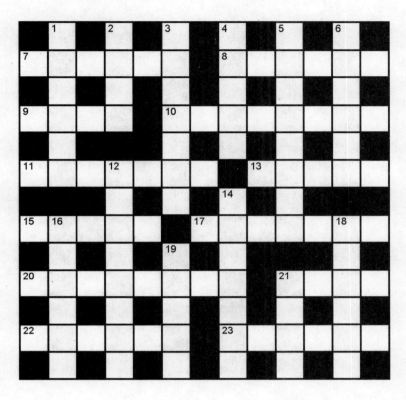

ACROSS

 7 Prepare for strenuous physical activity (4,2)
 8 Having existed from the beginning (6)
 9 Excessive complacency or self-satisfaction (4)
10 Based on or having the nature of an illusion (8)
11 One of the major dialects of Old English (7)
13 Idle or foolish and irrelevant talk (5)
15 A very short time or padded envelope? (5)
17 With great skill - pet lady! (7)
20 Brimless cap fitting the crown of the head (5-3)
21 The act of preventing the opposition from scoring (4)
22 Leaves used for seasoning (6)
23 An edge tool for cutting grass (6)

DOWN

 1 Wealth regarded as an evil influence (6)
 2 Air pollution (4)
 3 Most desirable possible - pilot am! (7)
 4 Enchantment (5)
 5 Landing place for aircraft (8)
 6 Attic or loft room, loved by artists? (6)
12 A crease on the palm (8)
14 Composed of animal fat (7)
16 Type of computer printer - jet kin! (3,3)
18 Full of zest or vigour (6)
19 One of a pair of short-handled oars (5)
21 Dismiss (4)

Colossal Book of Crosswords

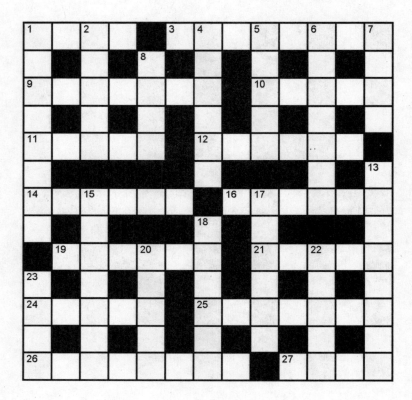

ACROSS

1 Religious ritual (4)
3 Deserving or inciting pity (8)
9 A cry of praise or adoration - has Nona! (7)
10 Make dim or indistinct (5)
11 Toward the future; forward in time (5)
12 Shrewd, sharp (6)
14 Wet with a spurt of liquid (6)
16 City in southwestern Switzerland (6)
19 Join up, get help (6)
21 Small piece of e.g. bread or cake (5)
24 Bush (5)
25 Belief about (or mental picture of) the future (7)
26 11th (8)
27 Make senseless or dizzy (4)

DOWN

1 Try out part to be played on stage (8)
2 Sensing through the mouth (5)
4 A new embodiment of a familiar idea - at vara! (6)
5 An established custom (5)
6 Dramatic art or place to see it (7)
7 A line made of twisted fibers or threads (4)
8 Woman's name - like Blyton! (4)
13 The skin of a lamb with the wool still on (8)
15 Disturb the composure of someone (7)
17 Charge up, arouse, get going (6)
18 The greatest possible degree (6)
20 Permeate (5)
22 Submarine (1-4)
23 Small island (4)

Colossal Book of Crosswords

ACROSS

7 Productive work (6)
8 Having had weeds removed (6)
9 Cause to be annoyed (4)
10 Expressing or given to expressing the truth (8)
11 Produced under conditions involving intense heat (7)
13 Beneath (5)
15 A number of similar things like bananas (5)
17 Formed by forcing molten metal into a die (3-4)
20 Travelling through water (8)
22 Mariner's shout (4)
23 A small handbook (6)
24 Mollusk with a low conical shell, also mine (6)

DOWN

1 Removing, or making photograph? (6)
2 A shaped mass of baked bread (4)
3 Radioactive isotope of hydrogen - trim Tiu! (7)
4 Dreadful, terrible (5)
5 Someone skilled in operating machine tools (8)
6 Induce to have sex (6)
12 European Economic Community (3)
14 A punctuation mark - evil rug! (7)
16 Remove the outer cover of a present (6)
18 Taken without owners consent (6)
19 Edge up to someone - slide! (5)
21 Injure badly by beating (4)
22 Ammunition (4)

ACROSS

7 Inactivity, listlessness - pro rot! (6)
8 A visible symbol for a group (6)
9 Flower (4)
10 Supplementary material added to the back of a book (8)
11 Special device for raising chickens (7)
13 The base part of a tree (5)
15 Die away - a beta! (5)
17 A learned person (7)
20 Oxide with one oxygen atom (8)
21 Successor, inheritor (4)
22 Summerhouse (6)
23 A wispy white cloud (6)

DOWN

1 Painful grief; a poetic term - or ludo! (6)
2 A domed or vaulted recess esp in church (4)
3 Waves breaking on the shore (7)
4 Pace (5)
5 At the beginning - latin (2,6)
6 Atomic number 2, used in balloons (6)
12 Out of fashion, out of date (8)
14 Sharp piercing cry, made by owl (7)
16 Monkey-bread tree (6)
18 A feeling of ill will arousing active hostility - a minus! (6)
19 A young person (5)
21 Damage (4)

Colossal Book of Crosswords

ACROSS

7 A loose robe, possibly japanese (6)
8 Of telephone lines and people, get together (4-2)
9 Cut into cubes (4)
10 Up to the knees (4-4)
11 A medical instrument (7)
13 Confuse (3-2)
15 Rigidly formal, resistant to bending (5)
17 Newspaper with half-size pages (7)
20 Not friendly - min cilia! (8)
21 Destiny (4)
22 Sound control knob (6)
23 A reflex response to sudden pain (6)

DOWN

1 Spread negative information about (6)
2 Knowledge gained through folk tradition (4)
3 A fee charged for a vessel to use a dock - cake dog! (7)
4 Bedding item (5)
5 Business reputation - gild wool! (8)
6 An administrative unit of government (6)
12 Having an exceedingly bad reputation (8)
14 Cancel (4,3)
16 Sinew (6)
18 Entire, undamaged (6)
19 Eightsome (5)
21 Dart, flutter (4)

Colossal Book of Crosswords

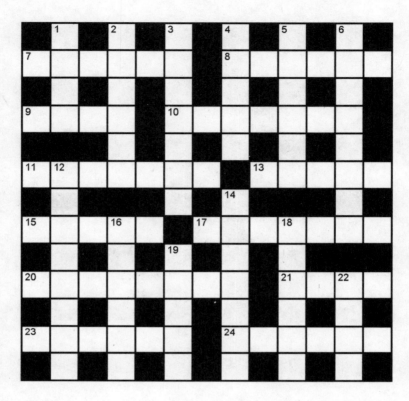

ACROSS

7 Tropical American arboreal lizards (6)
8 Calculating machine with beads (6)
9 Give over; surrender or relinquish (4)
10 The act of imposing a new organisation (5-3)
11 Two wheeled transport device (7)
13 Book of maps (5)
15 Accumulate, stash (5)
17 Short advert for a film (7)
20 Insolvent (8)
21 A toothed wheel (4)
23 Rich and fashionable people (3,3)
24 Excavated remains of animal from the past (6)

DOWN

1 A giant who likes to eat human beings (4)
2 Where bread is made (6)
3 A small container or medicine container (7)
4 Basic, the base of a plant (5)
5 Not presently active (6)
6 A salt or ester of sulphuric acid (8)
12 A person who worships idols (8)
14 Make happy or satisfied (7)
16 Shows carefree unconventionality or disreputableness - shark I! (6)
18 Assimilate (6)
19 Said - old english (5)
22 Amongst, In the middle of (4)

ACROSS

7 (British) colloquial word for look - if shut! (6)
8 A complex of methods or rules governing behavior (6)
9 Thought, concept (4)
10 A transparent purple variety of quartz (8)
11 Exaggerate one's acting, ham up! (7)
13 Bringing death (5)
15 Exactly vertical (5)
17 Having three units or components or elements (7)
20 Inspiring scornful pity (8)
21 Outcry (4)
23 Any ornamental pattern or design (6)
24 Besmirch (6)

DOWN

1 Shrug off coat, garden building (4)
2 Romantic illicit sexual relationship (6)
3 Commercial activity of providing funds (7)
4 Someone employed to conduct others (5)
5 Respiratory disorder (6)
6 Fellow soldier you eat with (8)
12 One who has lived in a village (8)
14 Heavy expensive material with a raised pattern (7)
16 Silky hair of the Angora goat (6)
18 The final payment of a debt (6)
19 Further or added - throe! (5)
22 Green fruit (4)

Colossal Book of Crosswords

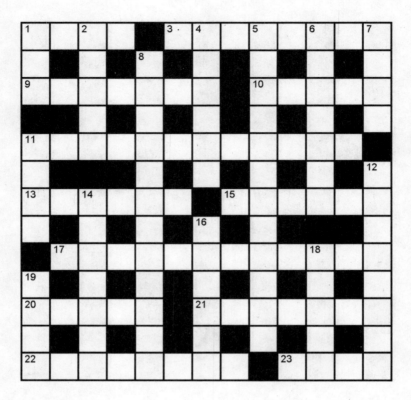

ACROSS

1 Move toward, travel toward something (4)
3 Portable power saw (8)
9 Sexual deviant (7)
10 Sit, as on a branch (5)
11 Money orders - from post office (6,6)
13 Someone who drives a herd (6)
15 To this writing or document - he rote! (6)
17 The second half of the Christian Bible (3,9)
20 A stringed instrument (5)
21 Unit of heat (7)
22 Cause to change ownership (8)
23 Make an etching of (4)

DOWN

1 Headwear (3)
2 Conventions (5)
4 A car modified to increase its speed (3,3)
5 Unreformable - deem blearier! (12)
6 Punish severely (7)
7 A unit of power (4)
8 Three way sexual relationship (6,1,5)
11 What peas come in! (4)
12 Birthday after thirty ninth! (8)
14 A large group of islands (7)
16 A beautiful princess loved by Cupid (6)
18 Any of various usually white herons (5)
19 Lie adjacent to, border, adjoin (4)

Colossal Book of Crosswords

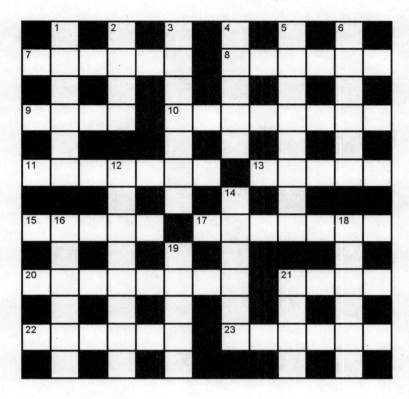

ACROSS

7 Fine cord for sewing (6)
8 In the land of nod (6)
9 500 sheets of paper (4)
10 Commit to memory (8)
11 A prosthesis placed permanently in tissue (7)
13 Question (5)
15 An unforeseen development, 60s dance (5)
17 Membrane in the ear (7)
20 Advertise noisily or blatantly (8)
21 Tablet (4)
22 Example (6)
23 Deprive of food (6)

DOWN

1 Emotionlessness (6)
2 Bug (4)
3 Remainder (7)
4 Informal terms for a mother (5)
5 Many-sided (3-5)
6 One who cuts naughty bits out of films (6)
12 Dispirited, lacking zest (8)
14 Not close or near (3-3)
16 Lessen the strength of (6)
18 If not (6)
19 Call, contact (5)
21 Ceremonial elegance (4)

Colossal Book of Crosswords

ACROSS

7 Part of a dress above the waist (6)
8 Protein that makes dough sticky (6)
9 A dress worn primarily by Hindu women (4)
10 A cut of beef (8)
11 On aglow confused scores against himself! (3,4)
13 Ladies clothing item (5)
15 Array (5)
17 Cut open or cut apart (7)
20 Drop and kick (a football) (4-4)
21 Energy (4)
23 Inventor's document (6)
24 Contemptibly small in amount (6)

DOWN

1 Worn by men in ancient Rome (4)
2 A fragment rubbed off by the use of a file (6)
3 Secreted by honeybees to build honeycombs (7)
4 Softly bright or radiant (5)
5 Heat with sugar and spices, think about (4)
6 Rapid rise to fame or fortune (8)
12 Having extensive information or understanding (4-4)
14 Trucks or record player parts (4-3)
16 Small burrowing animal (6)
18 Make a sound like frying fat (6)
19 The time when life begins (5)
22 4840 square yards is one (4)

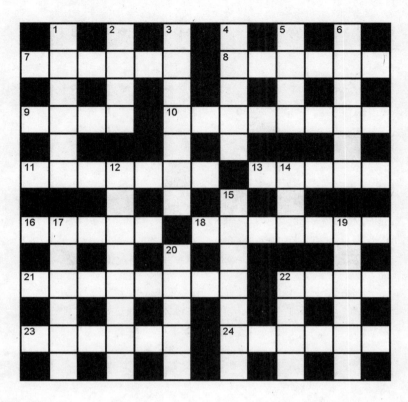

ACROSS

7 Road that takes traffic around the edge of a town (6)
8 Electrical control (6)
9 Appear to be (4)
10 Not very convincing (8)
11 Beg, plead (7)
13 Farm where milk is produced (5)
16 A tiny piece of anything (5)
18 Type of steak (7)
21 Exempt from duty (4-4)
22 Small pond of standing water (4)
23 Self-concern - semi go! (6)
24 The right to enter (6)

DOWN

1 Public hall for lectures and concerts (6)
2 Steadiness of mind under stress (4)
3 Where salt and fresh water mix (7)
4 Sacred song (5)
5 The string in a candle (4)
6 Relating to or using sight - our lac! (6)
12 Bran tub - puck idly! (5,3)
14 A pointed tool (3)
15 Not vegetable or animal (7)
17 Jump in (6)
19 An inflow, usually sudden (6)
20 Smell (5)
22 Spice (4)

Colossal Book of Crosswords

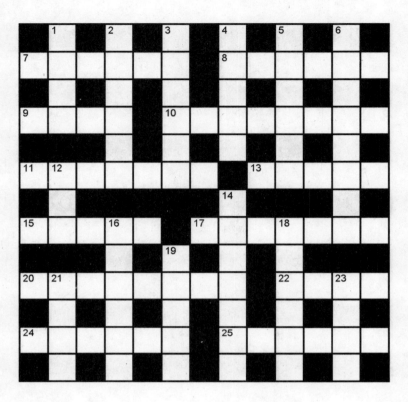

ACROSS

7 Distilled from wine or fermented fruit juice (6)
8 Catchy saying in advertising (6)
9 Drink from bottle (4)
10 Short account of an incident, story (8)
11 The principal bullfighter (7)
13 Loud (5)
15 Knock down with force (5)
17 A major road (7)
20 Someone who is dazzlingly skilled in any field (8)
22 A small island (4)
24 Living quarters reserved for wives in a Muslim household (6)
25 Boredom (6)

DOWN

1 Make beer (4)
2 A difficult problem (6)
3 Generator (6)
4 A useful or valuable quality (5)
5 A practitioner of voodoo (6)
6 A musical composition of a free form (8)
12 Completely (3)
14 Rejoinder, quick witty reply (7)
16 The time at which something begins (6)
18 The arrangement of the hair (6)
19 A punctuation mark (5)
21 The first Czar of Russia (1530-1584) (4)
23 Praise, glorify, or honour (4)

Colossal Book of Crosswords

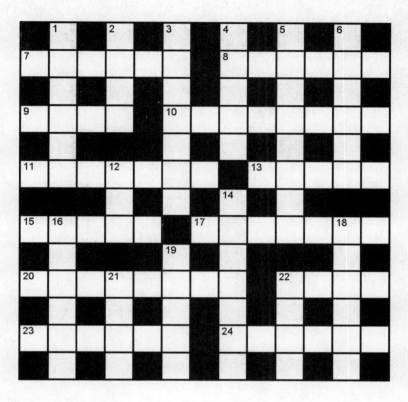

ACROSS

- **7** A ribbonlike strip of pasta (6)
- **8** Beat through cleverness (6)
- **9** A ship's small boat (4)
- **10** Cares wei! - confused smart aleck (8)
- **11** A Greek epic poem (7)
- **13** A crown-like jewelled headdress (5)
- **15** Self Contained Underwater Breathing Apparatus (5)
- **17** A Mid-Atlantic state (3,4)
- **20** Dishonest scheme, fix, fiddle (3-2,3)
- **22** A brief written record (4)
- **23** Decorated with small pieces of coloured glass (6)
- **24** On the golf course where putting is done (6)

DOWN

- **1** In the direction of (6)
- **2** Effigy that is worshipped (4)
- **3** Plant growing in the sea (7)
- **4** Cook with dry heat (5)
- **5** Form layers (8)
- **6** Reflecting surface (6)
- **12** Weep noisily (3)
- **14** Bug that lives in bed! (7)
- **16** Voucher, could be for football (6)
- **18** Rank in a military organisation (6)
- **19** Throw out (5)
- **21** Beehive State (4)
- **22** Requirement (4)

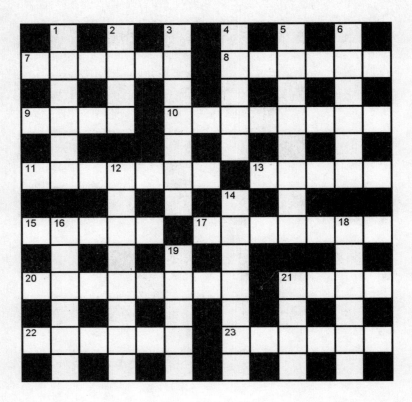

ACROSS

7 Play boisterously, frolic (6)
8 Overweight - fly she! (6)
9 The habitation of wild animals, den (4)
10 Musical composition based on religious text (8)
11 Of or relating to a taxonomic order - I Arnold! (7)
13 Connections (5)
15 Alter or improve (5)
17 Make free (7)
20 A railcar where passengers ride (8)
21 Ocean movement (4)
22 Combination breakfast and lunch (6)
23 Naughtily or annoyingly playful (6)

DOWN

1 A street of small shops (in Orient) (6)
2 IV (4)
3 A low stool (7)
4 Variety meat in USA - of AFL! (5)
5 Knock down (8)
6 Make smaller (6)
12 Not having the facts (8)
14 Constantly present (7)
16 Very small amounts (6)
18 Put money into a scheme (6)
19 Subject at school to do with numbers (5)
21 Rub (4)

ACROSS

7 Powerful and strong - like a mouse? (6)

8 Fix, mend (6)

9 Animal droppings (4)

10 Retaliatory action against an enemy in wartime (8)

11 Love unquestioningly and uncritically (7)

13 Extend in scope or range or area (5)

15 A metal spike with a hole for a rope (5)

17 Coins collectively (7)

20 A narrow street with walls on both sides (8)

21 Cheerful and bright (4)

22 Unwind or untwist (6)

23 Strikingly strange or unusual (6)

DOWN

1 In cash or easily convertible to cash (6)

2 A strong coarse tobacco that has been shredded (4)

3 Any of numerous evergreen conifers (7)

4 Burial chamber (5)

5 Lens maker (8)

6 Fodder harvested while green (6)

12 Someone who looks on (6-2)

14 The smallest sovereign state in the world (4,3)

16 A land mass that is surrounded by water (6)

18 Free of charge (6)

19 Make one's home or live in (5)

21 A small cave - trog? (4)

Colossal Book of Crosswords

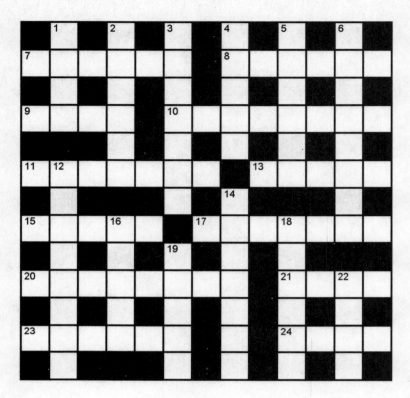

ACROSS

7 Involving financial matters (6)
8 Chamber (6)
9 A film of impurities (4)
10 A long slender cigar (8)
11 Cleanse with a cleaning agent (7)
13 Call up (5)
15 Put up, build, construct (5)
17 Structure at side of house for car (7)
20 A term for food poisoning that is no longer in scientific use (8)
21 Excessively abundant (4)
23 Having talents that are natural (6)
24 Good fortune (4)

DOWN

1 Record (4)
2 Someone who cuts and delivers ice (6)
3 A young woman in the 1920s (7)
4 Harass with persistent criticism or carping, tease (5)
5 Someone you feel sorry for (6)
6 Situated between the earth and the moon (8)
12 An airfield without normal airport facilities (8)
14 A smooth hair style (4-3)
16 Extraterrestrial object (5)
18 In part; in some degree; not wholly (6)
19 Blouse with a sailor collar (5)
22 A concept whose truth can be proved (4)

ACROSS

7 Spectre, spook, ghost (6)
8 Not wide (6)
9 Consideration in dealing with others (4)
10 Recall (8)
11 Being long-lasting and recurrent (7)
13 Creep (5)
15 Cause to move forward with force (5)
17 The act of inventing a word or phrase (7)
20 Disposed or willing to comply (8)
21 A person regarded as arrogant and annoying, snob (4)
22 Lightproof box with a lens at one end (6)
23 Social ethic or propriety (6)

DOWN

1 Flower arrangement at funeral (6)
2 Cloth (4)
3 Gland near the base of the neck (7)
4 Opposing military force (5)
5 Guilty of crime or serious offence (8)
6 Devotion (Roman Catholic) (6)
12 An ornamental but poisonous flowering shrub (8)
14 Land over which rule or control is exercised (7)
16 Vertebrate (6)
18 A festive merry feeling (6)
19 Submarine (1-4)
21 Mark with a scar (4)

Colossal Book of Crosswords

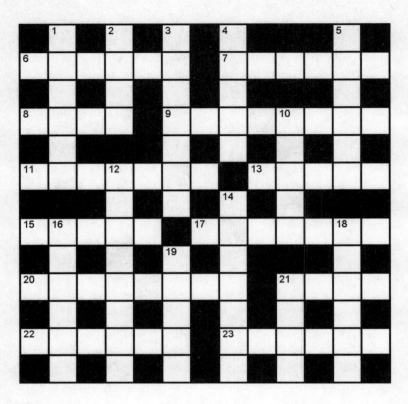

ACROSS

6 Get temporarily (6)
7 Beat-up! confused - cheerful (6)
8 Turn sharply; change direction abruptly (4)
9 A person with the same name as another (8)
11 Produce a mottled effect (7)
13 Leans over to one side (5)
15 Grown up (5)
17 A punctuation mark (7)
20 A common venereal disease (8)
21 Informal or slang terms for mentally irregular (4)
22 4th (6)
23 Disney's famous mouse (6)

DOWN

1 Lavatory (6)
2 Bird (4)
3 Get less or smaller (7)
4 Extremely pleasing to the sense of taste, informal (5)
5 Coat or potato skin (6)
10 Insect bite (5)
12 Small fish (8)
14 Slender, supple (7)
16 A crumbling and drying of timber (3,3)
18 The last of things mentioned (6)
19 Hawaiian greeting (5)
21 Connects the head to the rest of the body (4)

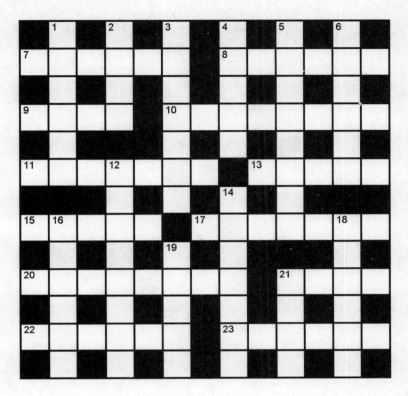

ACROSS

7 Riches (6)
8 Juju - charm from Haiti (6)
9 Upholstered seat for more than one person (4)
10 Make (someone) agree, win over (8)
11 Building (7)
13 Of time long past (5)
15 Any number of entities that work as a unit (5)
17 Narrow platform for fashion show (3-4)
20 Statues collectively (8)
21 A British imperial capacity measure (4)
22 A band worn around the arm for decoration (6)
23 Get back (6)

DOWN

1 Used to draw attention to something, Lo (6)
2 Humble request for help (4)
3 Chocolate coated ice cream block (4-3)
4 Something that happens at a given place and time (5)
5 The husband of your daughter (3-2-3)
6 Knobbly fabric, usually woollen (6)
12 Small insects whose larvae feed on fruits (5-3)
14 A rope for raising or lowering a sail or flag (7)
16 Come back (6)
18 Dried edible flattened lens like pulse (6)
19 Pleasing to the sense of taste (5)
21 One sheet in a book or newspaper (4)

Colossal Book of Crosswords

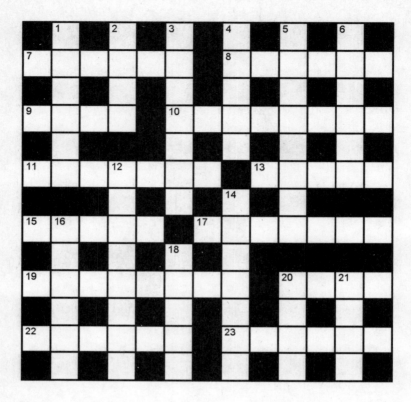

ACROSS

7 1/60 of a minute (6)
8 A male child, diminutive term (6)
9 Good-hearted (4)
10 Uneaten and saved for eating later (4,4)
11 In an opposing direction (7)
13 One who leads a wandering unsettled life (5)
15 Young owl (5)
17 The chief city of ancient Mesopotamia (7)
19 Heater, object that radiates energy (8)
20 The act of delivering a blow with the foot (4)
22 Money returned to a payer (6)
23 Customer (6)

DOWN

1 Fleshy part of the human body you sit on (6)
2 Headdress that protects the head and face (4)
3 Hero-worship (7)
4 At or to great height (5)
5 Political theory (8)
6 Galley with two rows of oars (6)
12 Retired professor's title? (8)
14 A building used to house military personnel (7)
16 A ship engaged in whale fishing (6)
18 A detailed critical inspection (5)
20 Create fabric with needles and wool (4)
21 Coin worth one-hundredth of the value of the basic unit (4)

ACROSS

7 Instruction to go away (6)
8 The froth produced by soaps or detergent (6)
9 A small island in his leg! (4)
10 An artificially produced flow of water (8)
11 Eldest son of the King of France (7)
13 Doughnut-shaped roll (5)
16 (informal) aggravation or aggression (5)
18 Persons who practice law (7)
21 A midday meal (8)
22 A rigid circular band of metal (4)
23 Coolness and composure under strain (6)
24 Transfer to another (6)

DOWN

1 A Japanese woman trained to entertain men (6)
2 A score of zero in tennis or squash (4)
3 An electronic device that amplifies sound (4-3)
4 A target used in archery (5)
5 Proofreading mark - remove or cancel (4)
6 To do with cats (6)
12 Slice of meat from a pig (4-4)
14 Girl's name (3)
15 A flat bread made of oat or barley flour (7)
17 Bad tempered (6)
19 A small stream (6)
20 Type of hat and place in North of England (5)
22 A place to go for ice skating (4)

ACROSS

7 Projectile from gun (6)
8 Smiled brightly (6)
9 A particular geographical region (4)
10 A faction unwilling to accept new ideas (3,5)
11 Goal scored by one of your own team (3,4)
13 A hidden storage space, also in computers (5)
15 The brother of your father or mother (5)
17 Menacing - able flu! (7)
20 Direction (8)
21 Cornmeal boiled in water, call to huskies? (4)
22 Dwarf ornamental indoor tree (6)
23 Fervent believer - to laze! (6)

DOWN

1 Dig hole under ground (6)
2 Blood-sucking parasitic insect (4)
3 Pouffe, footstool (7)
4 Home, place where you live (5)
5 Develop and reach maturity - emu attar! (8)
6 Fireplace (6)
12 Small particles of gold (4-4)
14 Solo passage near the end of a piece of music (7)
16 Nerve cell - no rune! (6)
18 Consequence - to push! (6)
19 Edible terrestrial mollusk (5)
21 Groan, indicate pain (4)

Colossal Book of Crosswords

ACROSS

7 Barroom (6)
8 Hard dark-brown wood (6)
9 Remain where you are (4)
10 Consist of (8)
11 Taken hold of roughly (7)
13 Insert, let into something else (5)
15 British horse race meeting (5)
17 Oratorio for voices and orchestra (7)
20 Not firm or firmly fixed; likely to give way (8)
21 Body powder (4)
22 One who carries the golf clubs for a player (6)
23 Period at bat in cricket (6)

DOWN

1 A person who captures and holds people (6)
2 Blush coloured, optimistic (4)
3 Device on outer door to announce presence (7)
4 Low land that is seasonally flooded (5)
5 Musical instrument (8)
6 Scuffle (6)
12 Supports at each end of row of books (4-4)
14 A spear thrown in competition (7)
16 Famous sailor from Arabian Nights (6)
18 Natural ability (6)
19 Bed cover (5)
21 A portable shelter used in camping (4)

Colossal Book of Crosswords

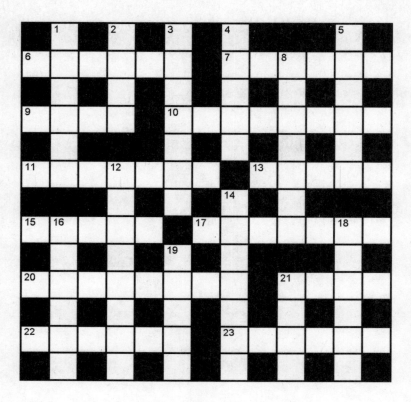

ACROSS

6 A network of intersecting blood vessels (6)
7 Discharge (6)
9 The bill in a restaurant (4)
10 Extricate, possibly from ties? (8)
11 Method of cooking (4-3)
13 A punctuation mark (5)
15 Pop open, like a pricked balloon (5)
17 A difference of opinion (7)
20 Pants (8)
21 Relinquish possession, give way for another (4)
22 Lighthouse (6)
23 Sit or let sit in boiling water (6)

DOWN

1 Out of fashion (3,3)
2 Way out (4)
3 Esq (7)
4 A path or strip cut by mowing (5)
5 Pejorative terms for an insane asylum (6)
8 Rocks produced under great heat (7)
12 Available material (8)
14 State of relatedness (7)
16 Unwind from or as if from a reel (6)
18 The practice of living without clothes (6)
19 A reddish brown dye used especially on hair (5)
21 Coffee bar (4)

ACROSS

7 Bribe (6)
8 Deficient in amount or quality or extent (6)
9 A symptom of some physical hurt or disorder (4)
10 Project over (8)
11 The principal theme in a speech or literary work (7)
13 Bear called Winnie? (4)
16 Put out, as of a candle or a light (5)
18 Skittles (7)
21 The side or slope of a hill (8)
22 Male parent of an animal (4)
23 The contestant who wins the contest (6)
24 Discharge (6)

DOWN

1 Impairment, injury (6)
2 The natural satellite of the Earth (4)
3 Underwear - rosy TNF! (1-6)
4 Fossil resin used for jewelry (5)
5 A thin coat of water-based paint (4)
6 Soak thoroughly (6)
12 Young bird not yet fledged (8)
14 Viscous liquid used in lubrication (3)
15 Type of fungus (7)
17 The place where something begins (6)
19 Conventional, not unusual (6)
20 Jewelled headdress (5)
22 A flight in which the aircraft pilot is unaccompanied (4)

Colossal Book of Crosswords

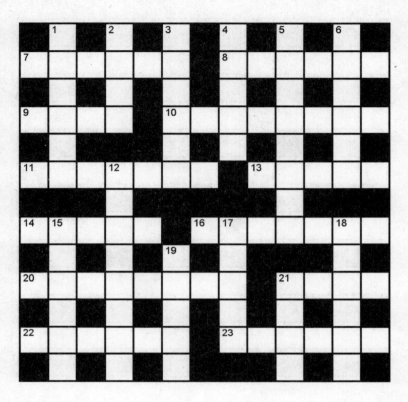

ACROSS

7 Fruit (6)
8 Cunning, like the dodger? (6)
9 Rum cut with water (4)
10 Beautiful mausoleum at Agra (3,5)
11 A toiletry that diffuses a fragrant odour (7)
13 Go along with (5)
14 A church associated with a monastery (5)
16 Alongside each other, in touch with the latest news (7)
20 Soft drink, mainly USA - toe borer! (4-4)
21 The number of seasons (4)
22 Bodyguard, date (6)
23 Sleep lightly or for a short period of time (6)

DOWN

1 A tower with a light that gives warning (6)
2 Snob is just messed up grip! (4)
3 Mysterious person dealing in occult (6)
4 String instrument (5)
5 Lag behind in an untidy group (8)
6 Concern with the alleviation of suffering (6)
12 Vote to select the winner of a political office (8)
15 Used especially of women, colourful (6)
17 Tired of the world (5)
18 Game played in an enclosed court (6)
19 Inferior in rank or status (5)
21 The motion characteristic of fluids (4)

Colossal Book of Crosswords

ACROSS

6 An inclination to approve (6)
8 Did as was bid (6)
9 One item of footwear (4)
10 Butter bean in USA (4,4)
11 Someone in touch with the occult - like Meg? (6)
13 Tool for shaping by turning (5)
15 Noise made by frog (5)
17 Ex-serviceman (7)
20 Agricultural, farming (8)
21 Accompanying (4)
22 Besmirch, slander (6)
23 Express discontent - in peer! (6)

DOWN

1 Humorous or satirical mimicry (6)
2 Civil wrong (4)
3 Weaving machines (5)
4 A thin pliable sheet of material (8)
5 Old material that is slightly reworked (6)
7 Antiquity that has survived from the past (5)
12 A reckless and impetuous person (4,4)
14 Man's name and saintly dog (7)
16 Someone who rigs, thin brush (6)
18 Be present at (6)
19 The circumstances and ideas of the present age (5)
21 Shed tears (4)

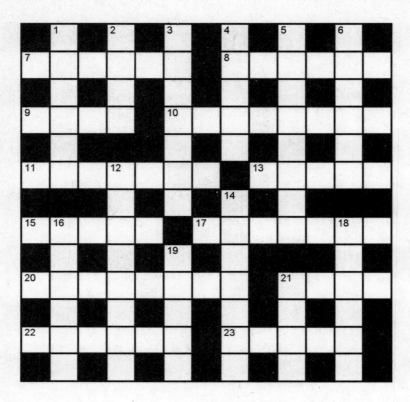

ACROSS

7 Densely wooded area (6)
8 Home for historic artefacts (6)
9 A long dagger with a straight blade (4)
10 The distinct personality of an individual (8)
11 Loose-fitting nightclothes (7)
13 Identification mark on skin, made by burning (5)
15 An illusory feat (5)
17 More decorative or ornamented than others (7)
20 Guidepost (8)
21 Good bye! (2-2)
22 (British slang) very unpleasant or offensive (6)
23 Protective kitchen wear (5)

DOWN

1 Organise into a code or system (6)
2 Pack of cards or part of ship (4)
3 Honourable, with principles (7)
4 To fix or set securely or deeply (5)
5 Understandable by only an enlightened inner circle (8)
6 A round fastener sewn to shirts (6)
12 Arouse hostility or indifference (8)
14 A difficult entangling situation - part tar! (3-4)
16 A shed containing a number of beehives (6)
18 Still in existence (6)
19 A small vascular growth (5)
21 A mountain lake, possibly glacial (4)

Colossal Book of Crosswords

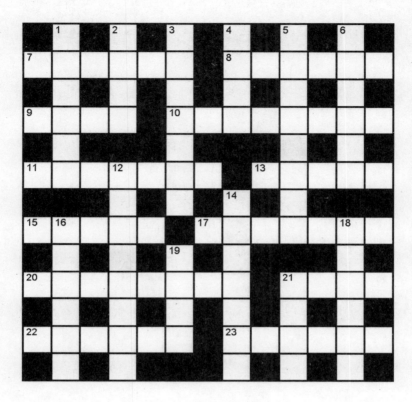

ACROSS

7 Give an account of (6)
8 Instrument used in fighting or hunting (6)
9 An effervescent beverage (4)
10 Badge of quality - kit maker! (4,4)
11 Transfer, dump (7)
13 Continuation of the coat collar (5)
15 Limit in quality or quantity (5)
17 Castrated male horse (7)
20 Forceful and definite in expression or action (8)
21 Bind with a rope (4)
22 A full supply (6)
23 In actual fact (6)

DOWN

1 Any cognitive content held as true - be life! (6)
2 A genre of popular music (4)
3 Day of the week, not Saturday or Sunday (7)
4 Kill fly with quick blow (4)
5 A rural area where agriculture is practised (8)
6 Where something comes from (6)
12 Written in ink on paper with a pen (8)
14 Messenger of Jupiter and god of commerce (7)
16 Go along with without protest (6)
18 A close and affectionate embrace (6)
19 Remain behind (4)
21 A rich soil (4)

Colossal Book of Crosswords

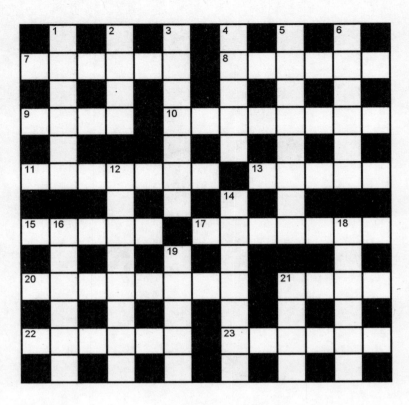

ACROSS

7 How much of something is available (6)
8 Decapitate (6)
9 The act of flipping a coin (4)
10 Tissue layer (8)
11 A speech disorder involving hesitations (7)
13 Hilarity (5)
15 Analyse (chemical substances) (5)
17 An armed thief, bandit (7)
20 Rum and lime or lemon juice (8)
21 Green acidic fruit (4)
22 Open rebellion against constituted authority (6)
23 The central area in a building; open to the sky (6)

DOWN

1 Bring in from a foreign country (6)
2 Usually large hard-shelled seeds (4)
3 Confounded, run out in cricket (7)
4 A nuclear weapon (1-4)
5 Stirring (cream) vigorously to make butter (8)
6 Trees of the genus Juglans (6)
12 Free from disturbance, calm (8)
14 A skilled worker (7)
16 Great meal - up pals! (4-2)
18 A dark grey cloud bearing rain (6)
19 A woman who tells fortunes (5)
21 Knowledge gained through tradition or anecdote (4)

Colossal Book of Crosswords

ACROSS

7 Race on skis around obstacles (6)
8 Deficient in amount or quality or extent (6)
9 Admit openly; make no bones about (4)
10 A person who likes to be active late at night (5-3)
11 In proportion (3,4)
13 The ability to see; the faculty of vision (5)
15 Issue a grunting, low, animal-like noise (5)
17 A very poisonous metallic element (7)
20 Previous lover (3,5)
21 Become quiet or still; fall silent (4)
22 Relating to a recently developed fashion or style (6)
23 Migratory grasshopper (6)

DOWN

1 Shorebird (6)
2 Killed intentionally and with premeditation (4)
3 Proceed or issue forth, as from a source (7)
4 An adult insect produced after metamorphosis (5)
5 For less than the standard number of hours (4-4)
6 Black bird having a raucous call (4)
12 Without paying rent (4-4)
14 Not haphazard (7)
16 A woman's foundation garment (4-2)
18 Beg persistently and urgently (6)
19 Coating to protect or decorate a surface (5)
21 German wine (4)

ACROSS

7 Jewish salutation used at meeting or parting (6)
8 Become used up; be exhausted (3,3)
9 Secluded place, goes with cranny? (4)
10 Religious offering - Latin boo! (8)
11 Pressed together in rows (7)
13 A strong feeling of anxiety (5)
15 Strike with disgust or revulsion (5)
17 Female part of flower (6)
20 Newspaperman (8)
21 Find enjoyable or agreeable (4)
22 A former communist country (6)
23 A person who is deemed to be despicable (6)

DOWN

1 Royal seat (6)
2 Artillery designed to shoot at aircraft (4)
3 Give or delegate power to (7)
4 Fish with a hook and line drawn through the water (5)
5 Excessively suave or ingratiating (8)
6 The quality of being funny (6)
12 Revise or renew one's assessment, reevaluate (8)
14 Dry by spinning (4-3)
16 Go in search of or hunt for (6)
18 Type of computer printer (3,3)
19 Slanderous defamation (5)
21 Thin strip of wood used as backing for plaster (4)

Colossal Book of Crosswords

ACROSS

7 Come out (6)
8 Second book of the Old Testament (6)
9 Female employee in the home (4)
10 Unpatriotic (8)
11 Conveyance that carries skiers up a hill (3-4)
13 One who eats (5)
15 Smell (5)
17 Drum (6)
20 A motley assortment of things, hotchpotch (8)
21 Brusque (4)
22 Boredom (6)
23 Cream mixed with eggs and alcohol (6)

DOWN

1 Go on board, set out on a journey (6)
2 A network of horizontal and vertical lines (4)
3 Bon voyage, farewell party (4-3)
4 Sound practical judgment (5)
5 Driver (8)
6 Caring about suffering (6)
12 Mainstay - holds wheel on to axle (8)
14 The snail-shaped tube in the ear (7)
16 Lavatory (6)
18 Vegetable, sometimes grown overlarge for shows (6)
19 Destiny - am ark! (5)
21 Metal enclosure to keep animals in (4)

ACROSS

6 Give personal assurance; guarantee (5)
8 Permanent polar ice (3-3)
9 Succulent plants whose oil is used in shampoo (4)
10 Brought back together (8)
11 The quality of being polite and respectable (7)
13 A quantity of paper; 24 or 25 sheet (5)
16 Game played with an oval ball (5)
18 Plant part - rid lent! (7)
21 A fighter plane used for suicide missions (8)
22 Not at all or in no way (4)
23 First in order of birth (6)
24 Dry to sweet amber wine from Jerez (6)

DOWN

1 Lithesome - TV eels! (6)
2 Certain (4)
3 Devoutly religious (5)
4 Abominable snowman (4)
5 Move headlong at high speed, towards a job? (6)
7 Roman lyric poet (6)
12 The tide while water is flowing out (3-5)
14 Snakelike marine or freshwater fish (3)
15 Let go (7)
17 Lacking in power or forcefulness (6)
19 Refuse to acknowledge (6)
20 Unpleasant (5)
22 Man's name used at Christmas? (4)

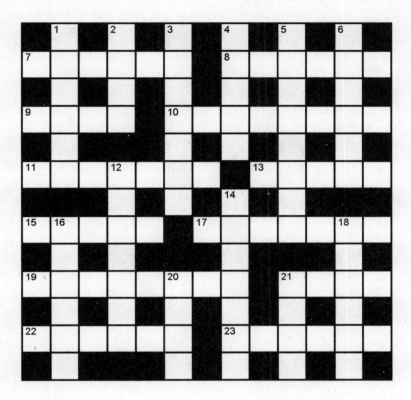

ACROSS

7 French lemon (6)
8 Of or befitting a lord (6)
9 Saclike respiratory organ (4)
10 Text that is typed or printed on paper (4,4)
11 Lasting for ever (7)
13 Woman who was regarded as an oracle (5)
15 Make a groove in wood (5)
17 A rich and spectacular ceremony (7)
19 Bring together parts to make a whole (8)
21 Small or narrow cave (4)
22 Rarely, not often (6)
23 Comfort (6)

DOWN

1 A stately court dance in the 17th century (6)
2 Trigonometry, in short (4)
3 Hold spellbound (7)
4 Warning device (5)
5 Engage in a rehearsal (of) (8)
6 Type of computer disc (6)
12 Ragwort - grade we! (7)
14 The countries of eastern Asia (3,4)
16 Marine mollusk with a rough irregular shell (6)
18 Beginner, learner, tyro (6)
20 Explosive device (4)
21 A brief social visit (4)

Colossal Book of Crosswords

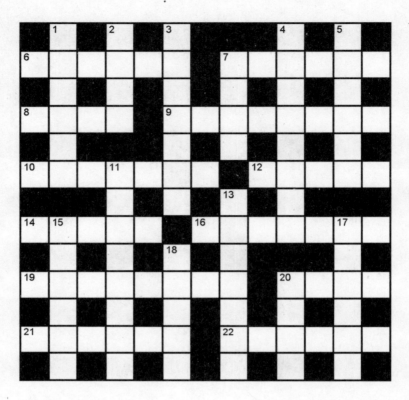

ACROSS

6 Groundnut (6)
7 Affray (6)
8 Lacking sensation (4)
9 A gambling game (8)
10 Eager (7)
12 Accepted or habitual practice (5)
14 Abounding in trees, also cartoon woodpecker (5)
16 Crude iron tapped from a blast furnace (3-4)
19 Emitting light in sudden short bursts (8)
20 Flow in a circular current, of liquids (4)
21 Deliver a sharp blow, as with the hand, fist, or weapon (6)
22 An erect or climbing bean or pea plant (6)

DOWN

1 Examine or consider in detail (6)
2 Cold shoulder (4)
3 Horse rider's foot holder (7)
4 Broad ski for skimming over water (5-3)
5 Riffraff, term for common people (3-3)
7 Act that violates the rules of a sport (4)
11 Title used to address any peeress except a duchess (8)
13 A punctuation mark (/) (7)
15 Pumpkin-shaped (6)
17 Swelling from accumulation of serous fluid (6)
18 An assumption that is taken for granted (5)
20 The boundary of a surface (4)

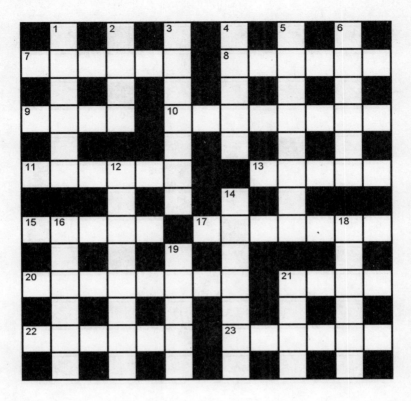

ACROSS

7 Study of moral values and rules (6)
8 Provide evidence for; stand as proof of (6)
9 (of music) characteristic of rural life (4)
10 Mausoleum, built in 1649 by Shah Jahan (3,5)
11 Foul up (4-2)
13 Determine the direction of travel, possibly with a wheel (5)
15 A large ladle (5)
17 Floating leaves of a water lily (4,3)
20 A trial that is invalid or inconclusive (8)
21 A company emblem (4)
22 Toy gun that makes a popping sound (3-3)
23 Ambrosia - trance! (6)

DOWN

1 A reception held in your own house (2-4)
2 Connection (4)
3 Atom - too pies! (7)
4 Cannabis - an jag! (5)
5 Taking pains to avoid being observed (8)
6 Break free from captivity (6)
12 Dearth or deficit (8)
14 Aircraft with two wings (7)
16 Trousers made with chino cloth (6)
18 A coat made of sheepskin (6)
19 Musical instrument (5)
21 Good fortune (4)

Colossal Book of Crosswords

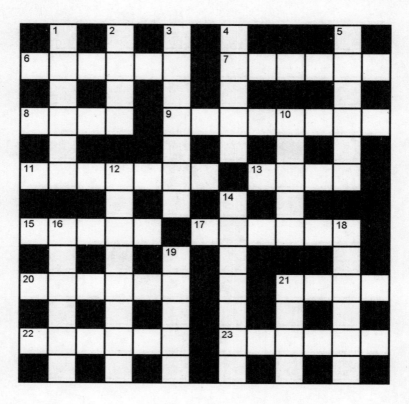

ACROSS

6 Stretches muscles (6)
7 An indulgence rather than a necessity (6)
8 Allow someone through a barrier (4)
9 Recognise someone (8)
11 Add water or moisture (7)
13 Opaque gem (4)
15 Conscious awareness (5)
17 Drawing instrument (6)
20 Breed of dog (6)
21 Sudden sharp painful emotion (4)
22 Urinary organ (6)
23 Metal covering used in ancient combat (6)

DOWN

1 Morally degraded (6)
2 Centre around which something rotates (4)
3 Helps (7)
4 Precipitate as a mixture of rain and snow (5)
5 Not straightforward or candid (6)
10 Subject for discussion (5)
12 Someone who lives in a particular place (8)
14 Taking away (7)
16 Strikingly strange or unusual (6)
18 Identity parade (4-2)
19 Mineral, valued as gemstone (5)
21 Large American feline resembling a lion (4)

437

Colossal Book of Crosswords

ACROSS

7 A state resembling deep sleep (6)
8 A chance at something - no kilo! (4-2)
9 Charge, Act or move at high speed (4)
10 One who writes novels for a living (8)
11 A late afternoon or evening worship service (7)
13 Morally degraded or dubious (5)
15 Harsh or corrosive in tone or smell (5)
17 Chemical compound - ply Rome! (7)
20 Send a signal via a radio (8)
21 Device to block an entrance to a field (4)
22 Malevolence (6)
23 Allegiance or loyalty to a nation (6)

DOWN

1 Game bird or complain (6)
2 Imperial measure of length (4)
3 The official residence of a dean (7)
4 Living (5)
5 Coal mine (8)
6 Traditional Chinese cuisine served in numerous small portions (3,3)
12 A loose dressing gown for women - groin pie! (8)
14 Strengthen (7)
16 A pen for cattle (6)
18 Everything you own (6)
19 Fossil resin used for jewelry (5)
21 The mother of your father or mother, in short (4)

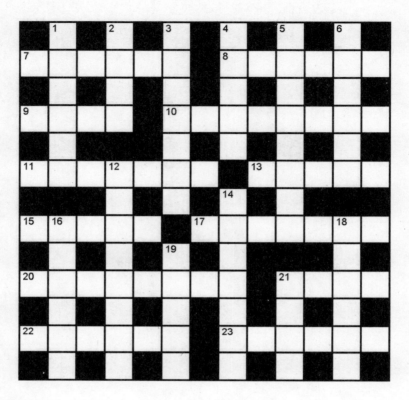

ACROSS

7 Having more than one spouse at a time (6)
8 Adding machine (6)
9 Failed to tell the truth (4)
10 Laws providing support for the poor (4,4)
11 The line at which the sky and Earth appear to meet (7)
13 Forest god (5)
15 An impure form of quartz (5)
17 Singing on the streets for money (7)
20 An enclosed passageway in a building (8)
21 The back side of the neck (4)
22 Title used for a married Frenchwoman (6)
23 Shallow dish to hold a cup (6)

DOWN

1 Sexual desire (6)
2 Magic stick (4)
3 Feeling that sick people have (7)
4 Type of crinkly cabbage (5)
5 Assay-mark (8)
6 Landing strip (6)
12 Happening inside (8)
14 Tall marsh plant (7)
16 Involving the entire earth (6)
18 A son of your brother or sister (6)
19 Mammary gland of bovid (5)
21 A word that can be used to refer to a person or place or thing (4)

ACROSS

7 Destroy with explosive device (4-2)
8 Well-seasoned stew of meat and vegetables (6)
9 Entice (4)
10 Restricted availability (8)
11 Deteriorate in health (7)
13 Stop in one place (4)
15 Seize power, take control (5)
17 Small cake (7)
20 Expressing desire for something (8)
21 Electrical safety wire (4)
22 Large bearing on a car - beg din! (3,3)
23 Someone who drives a herd (6)

DOWN

1 The power to entice or attract through personal charm (6)
2 Affectedly dainty or refined (4)
3 Cause to suffer or keep down people (7)
4 Unruly children (5)
5 A person who doubts truth of religion (8)
6 A guarantee that an obligation will be met (6)
12 Commercial enterprises that provide scheduled flights (8)
14 Exterior (7)
16 Having beautiful natural scenery (6)
18 Fate (6)
19 Expression of delight - do goy! (5)
21 A complete failure (4)

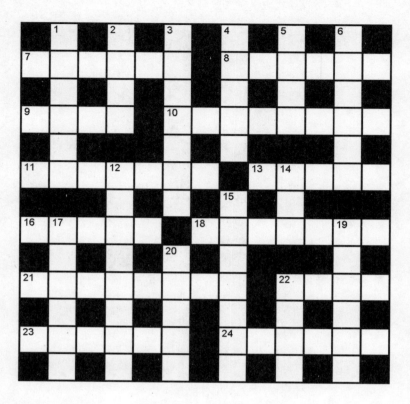

ACROSS

7 Ghost (6)
8 Boat steering mechanism (6)
9 Fault (4)
10 Stringed instrument (8)
11 Extract used in toiletries (7)
13 Dark wood (5)
16 Pry (5)
18 Troglodyte (4,3)
21 Extra large, for a monarch? (4-4)
22 Get up in the morning (4)
23 Church officer looking after sacred objects (6)
24 Unfair (6)

DOWN

1 Fruits (6)
2 People who serve on a ship (4)
3 Digestive organ (7)
4 Bitten by a bee (5)
5 The lowest female singing voice (4)
6 Leave voluntarily; of a job (6)
12 Make longer (8)
14 Honey making insect (3)
15 Forbidding, menacing (7)
17 Fixed by nails (6)
19 Help (6)
20 A stupid foolish person (5)
22 A Hindu prince or king in India (4)

Colossal Book of Crosswords

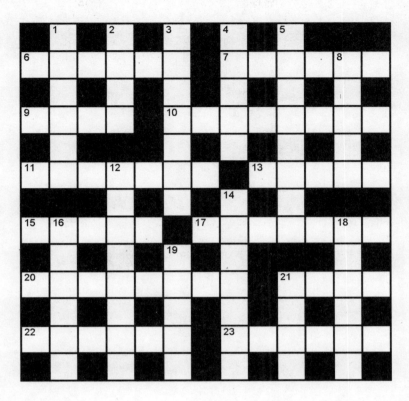

ACROSS

6 Dock for small yachts and cabin cruisers (6)
7 Temper metal by heating and cooling (6)
9 Cause annoyance in (4)
10 Lathyrus odoratus (8)
11 Rodent with large cheek pouches (7)
13 A motorbike that can be pedalled (5)
15 Large black bird, Corvus corax (5)
17 A small container, possibly for drugs (7)
20 Escape (5-3)
21 Villein (4)
22 Arrived at without due care or effort (6)
23 Plant part (6)

DOWN

1 Oxide on the surface of a metal (6)
2 Bee house (4)
3 Colorfull swirled pattern of curved shapes (7)
4 Long legged bird or wellington? (5)
5 Oily - uncut sou! (8)
8 Girl's name (5)
12 An outline or synopsis of a play (8)
14 Administer baptism to (7)
16 Someone who operates an aircraft (6)
18 Food store (6)
19 Produced by occupants of 2 (5)
21 Move back and forth in an unstable manner (4)

ACROSS

7 Light sensitive membrane (6)
8 Shrub (6)
9 A coniferous tree (4)
10 Of the common people of ancient Rome (8)
11 Spare time (7)
13 Bed sheets (5)
15 A region of complete shadow (5)
17 Badly behaved (7)
20 Self-important, with overbearing pride (8)
21 Without, in French (4)
22 From this place, belonging here (6)
23 Small beard (6)

DOWN

1 Complain - nip ere! (6)
2 A style of jazz (4)
3 Dracula was one (7)
4 Tower built by Noah's descendants (5)
5 Gradually narrowed toward a point (8)
6 A shot or scene that is photographed again (6)
12 Disdainfully or ironically humorous (8)
14 Superior or more favourable position (7)
16 Half man and half fish; lives in the sea (6)
18 A hole in the ground made by an animal (6)
19 Front of coat collar (5)
21 Chair (4)

Colossal Book of Crosswords

ACROSS

7 Felt hat with a creased crown (6)
8 Suitors - rose ow! (6)
9 Roster (4)
10 Disappointing less significant event - vent neon! (3-5)
11 Sequence of powerful leaders in the same family (7)
13 Escargot (5)
15 Large carnivorous mammals (5)
16 An aggressive and violent young criminal (7)
19 Small songbird (8)
22 In addition (4)
23 Cause to become loose (6)
24 Place where bread is made (6)

DOWN

1 A tendril-bearing vine (6)
2 First name of soviet gymnast Korbut (4)
3 Young swans (7)
4 Garden toy (5)
5 Formally brought together (8)
6 A sultanate in northwestern Borneo (6)
11 A light touch or stroke, small sea fish (3)
12 An arm of the Mediterranean (8)
14 Negative (2)
17 Not certain (6)
18 Strained (5)
20 Track down (4)
21 A deep and vivid red gem (4)
22 Egyptian symbol (4)

ACROSS

7 Mad (6)
8 Travel in one direction only allowed (3-3)
9 Adjust musical instrument (4)
10 Faith (8)
11 Slide (7)
13 Mark used by author meaning to insert (5)
15 Dispose of as useless (5)
17 A tide in the same direction as the wind (3,4)
20 Being is a worse state than before (5,3)
21 Type of fish (4)
22 Pointless (6)
23 A substance believed to cure all ills (6)

DOWN

1 Happening each year (6)
2 The central area of a church (4)
3 Question someone about a mission after completion (7)
4 A light semitransparent fabric (5)
5 Army rank (8)
6 Early release from jail, on conditions (6)
12 Send a message by wireless (8)
14 Brochure (7)
16 Garden flower (6)
18 Cause train to run off the tracks (6)
19 Pugilist (5)
21 Voucher for a sum of money owed (4)

Colossal Book of Crosswords

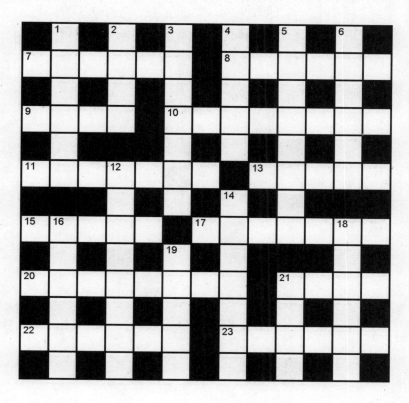

ACROSS

7 A religious doctrine (6)
8 Immeasurably small (6)
9 An urban area with a fixed boundary (4)
10 Permitting (8)
11 People who lead a group (7)
13 Man made waterway (5)
15 Pastry cups with a filling of fruit (5)
17 Bored holes in (7)
20 Accepts as true (8)
21 Two considered together (4)
22 Silvered surface where pictures can be projected (6)
23 Consuming food (6)

DOWN

1 Turn into something (6)
2 Append your signature (4)
3 Secretive or illicit sexual relationships (7)
4 Aroma, pong (5)
5 Accumulate at a rapidly accelerating rate (8)
6 A fixed number of lines of verse (6)
12 Elaborated (8)
14 Hair care implements (7)
16 Bureau (6)
18 Stretch out over a distance (6)
19 Kitchen appliances (5)
21 Sink teeth into (4)

ACROSS

7 Vehicle used to ride on snow (6)
8 The basic unit of money in Russia (6)
9 Direct one's course or way (4)
10 Ground tree material used to make paper (4-4)
11 Lasting for ever (7)
12 Movies (5)
14 Sharp (5)
17 Flower - in agent! (7)
20 Make known, officially (8)
21 Old (4)
22 A mountainous republic of south-central Europe (6)
23 Strong and well built (6)

DOWN

1 Customer (6)
2 Gentle and helpful (4)
3 Promoter, impresario (7)
4 March in a procession (5)
5 Under threat of shooting (8)
6 Race on skis around obstacles (6)
13 Let go (7)
15 Large artillery gun that is usually on wheels (6)
16 A sharp-pointed tip on a stem or leaf (5)
18 To make better; (6)
19 Prowl about furtively (5)
21 Lie adjacent to another (4)

Colossal Book of Crosswords

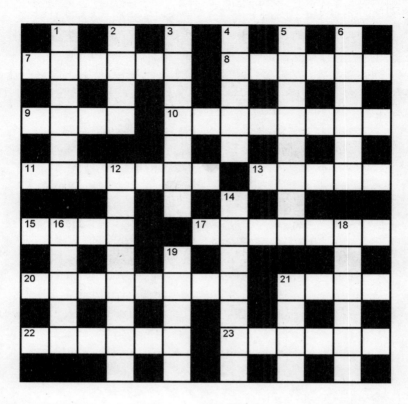

ACROSS

7 A written agreement between two states (6)
8 Meal (6)
9 Resentment at seeing the success of another (4)
10 Lovely (8)
11 Half woman and half fish; lives in the sea (7)
13 Cause to be perplexed or confounded (5)
15 A male monarch or emperor (4)
17 An island in the Persian Gulf (7)
20 Response to an inquiry or experiment (4,4)
21 Fool or hoax (4)
22 Fearful (6)
23 A separate section of a legal document (6)

DOWN

1 At or constituting a border or edge (6)
2 Simple, not difficult (4)
3 Royal tomb in ancient Egypt (7)
4 Sing softly (5)
5 Splash haphazardly (8)
6 Mental home (6)
12 An imaginary great circle on the surface of the earth (8)
14 A large expanse of floating ice (4-3)
16 Several things tied together, historically corn (5)
18 Naughtily or annoyingly playful (6)
19 Humorously vulgar (5)
21 Pull back the string of (a bow) (4)

ACROSS

7 Ought to have done something (6)
8 A woman's top that fastens behind the back (6)
9 Uncomplimentary terms for a policeman (4)
10 Make weak (8)
11 I = E/R - electrical law (4,3)
13 Mineral valued as gemstone (5)
15 Turn away or aside (5)
17 Medical examiner (7)
20 A dissolute character in Shakespeare (8)
22 A small amount of solid food; a mouthful (4)
23 Overwhelming feeling of fear and anxiety (6)
24 Stereophonic, in short (6)

DOWN

1 Bird (6)
2 Sound of rapid vibration or bee (4)
3 Near the kidneys - an alder! (7)
4 Perceive by inhaling through the nose (5)
5 A very close and trusted friend (5,3)
6 Potpourri (6)
12 An inflatable life jacket .... west! (3)
14 Befuddle (7)
16 A frequently visited place (6)
18 The principal dish of a meal (6)
19 Espouse, wed (5)
21 Copied or imitated (4)
22 Cattle that are reared for their meat (4)

ACROSS

7 Marine mammal, with carpenter in literature (6)
8 Someone who leaves one country to settle in another (6)
9 The right to take another's property (4)
10 Precarious, unsound (8)
11 A large mass of ice floating at sea (7)
13 A thin soup (5)
15 A thin flake of dead epidermis (5)
17 Weapons using atomic energy (7)
20 Exterior covering of a bird's egg, dull paint (8)
21 Torture machine (4)
22 Potentially existing (6)
23 Folding a sheet of paper three times to form eight leaves (6)

DOWN

1 Madman (6)
2 Roughage (4)
3 Where a river meets the sea (7)
4 Left-hand page (5)
5 Hearing with two ears (8)
6 Armlet (6)
12 Bird food (8)
14 Part of a window (7)
16 Brandy (6)
18 A small recess or bay (6)
19 Contemptibly narrow in outlook (5)
21 Charge per unit (4)

Colossal Book of Crosswords

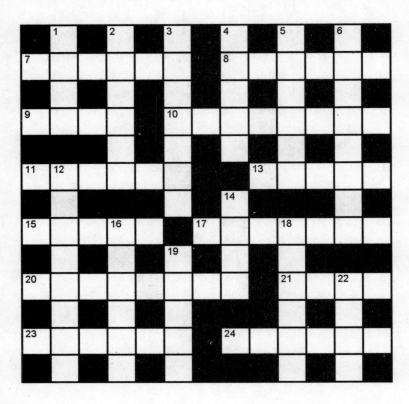

ACROSS

7 Yellow tropical fruit (6)
8 Having removed clothing (6)
9 Wingless blood-sucking parasite (4)
10 Stress, accent (8)
11 Informal, unisex top wear (1-5)
13 (used informally) very small (5)
15 Full of trivial conversation (5)
17 A small wave on the surface of a liquid (7)
20 Dawn (8)
21 Grave (4)
23 Announce (6)
24 Wine bottle (6)

DOWN

1 Shopping centre (4)
2 Sausage (6)
3 Flat board for paint mixing (7)
4 Where you are down in the when unhappy! (5)
5 Period when earth was covered in glaciers (3,3)
6 Good-natured tolerance (8)
12 Sea dog (8)
14 Dog noise (4)
16 Small lynx of North America (6)
18 Total, complete, all of (6)
19 Poised for action (5)
22 Cause to be annoyed (4)

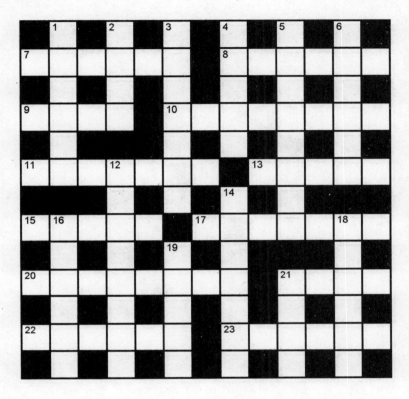

ACROSS

7 Continue after a break (6)
8 Insightfulness, knowledge and ability (6)
9 Touch with the tongue (4)
10 The distinct personality of an individual (8)
11 Comedian - on his feet? (5-2)
13 By surprise, usually taken (5)
15 Cloak (5)
17 Number (7)
20 Extinct terrestrial reptile (8)
21 An associate who provides assistance (4)
22 A handsome youth loved by Aphrodite (6)
23 English admiral (6)

DOWN

1 Fight back (6)
2 Mass (4)
3 Boring (7)
4 The overhang at the lower edge of a roof (5)
5 Appropriate for the desired purpose (8)
6 Feverish, busy (6)
12 Towns planned and built by the government (3,5)
14 Take precedence in military status (7)
16 Arrangement of the hair (6)
18 Bursting into flower (6)
19 Narrowing of the body between the ribs and hips (5)
21 Capable (4)

Colossal Book of Crosswords

ACROSS

7 Smoked herring and tie! (6)
8 Ingratiate oneself to; be difficult (4,2)
9 Start of the day (4)
10 Speculate, conjecture (8)
11 A quantity of no importance, nil (7)
13 Storage space also on a computer (5)
15 An island consisting of a circular coral reef surrounding a lagoon (5)
17 Tedium, ennui (7)
20 Without beauty or charm (8)
21 Wild pig (4)
22 Grievous, very strong or vigorous (6)
23 All together (2,4)

DOWN

1 Emperor of Japan, Gilbert & Sullivan comic opera (6)
2 Rotate (4)
3 Putting words on paper (7)
4 Rapidity, swiftness (5)
5 Figuratively someone crowned with a laurel wreath (8)
6 Coup d'etat (6)
12 Worthy of religious veneration (8)
14 State of the Vatican City (4,3)
16 Proposal to buy at a specified price (6)
18 Public speaker (6)
19 Annoy continually or chronically (5)
21 A very young child (4)

ACROSS

6 Annoy continually or chronically (6)
8 Containing little excess - sky imp! (6)
9 Solid fuel (4)
10 Careful (8)
11 Something very ugly and offensive (7)
13 Keen to get on (5)
15 Famous comic - a bone! (5)
17 Number (7)
20 Lucky clover (4-4)
21 A domed or vaulted recess (4)
22 Climb (6)
23 Type of snow transport and hammer (6)

DOWN

1 A car that is old and unreliable (6)
2 Shoe tie (4)
3 Come forth (5)
4 Engage in legal proceedings (8)
5 A person's partner in marriage (6)
7 Protected (6)
12 Dried naturally by the sun (3-5)
14 Cause to spread or flush or flood through (7)
16 Self-centredness (6)
18 Give an assignment to, allot (6)
19 A low triangular area where a river divides (5)
21 In bed, confused bead! (4)

Colossal Book of Crosswords

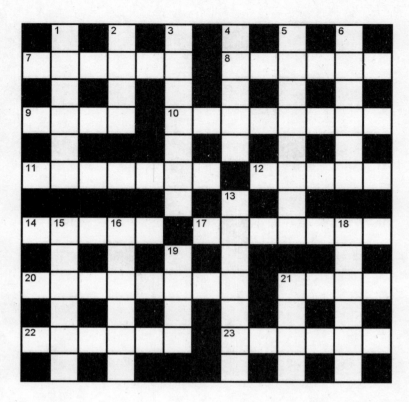

ACROSS

7 Get in the way of - progress? (6)
8 Help (6)
9 Car (4)
10 Turn one's stomach (8)
11 Speak softly; in a low voice (7)
12 Monastery, convent (5)
14 Once more (5)
17 Utter a shrill cry coming to a halt? (7)
20 A sudden unexpected piece of good fortune (8)
21 Gratis, costing nothing (4)
22 Flashing light (6)
23 Made from or covered with gold (6)

DOWN

1 Wait in hiding to attack (6)
2 Roman Emperor (4)
3 Come back into earth's atmosphere (2-5)
4 A Louisianian descended from Acadian immigrants (5)
5 Put together (8)
6 Blood-sucking African fly (6)
13 Environmental science (7)
15 A festive merry feeling (6)
16 Inside (6)
18 Mentally quick and resourceful (6)
19 Head of hair of horse (5)
21 Tumbled (4)

Colossal Book of Crosswords

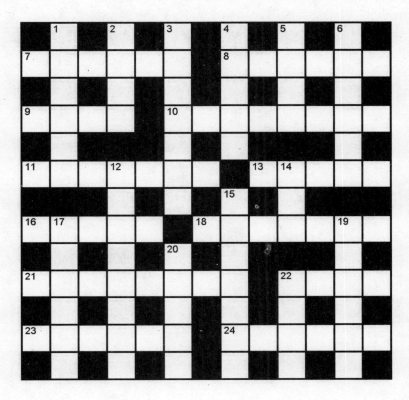

ACROSS

7 Decapitate (6)
8 The countries of Asia (6)
9 Repair by sewing, esp. of socks (4)
10 Saltwater fish (8)
11 Printing plate made with the use of acid (7)
13 A preserve made of the jelled juice of fruit (5)
16 Value (5)
18 Conscript (7)
21 Someone skilled in operating machine tools (8)
22 Adult male chicken (4)
23 Design made of small pieces (6)
24 Moving toward a position ahead (6)

DOWN

1 Bookworm - tap den! (6)
2 Pulse (4)
3 Something unusual -- perhaps worthy of collecting (7)
4 Informal terms for a human head - con be! (5)
5 Conceal oneself - perhaps to watch birds? (4)
6 Remove the cover from (6)
12 An entrance equipped with a hatch (8)
14 Gremlin (3)
15 Someone who supervises (an examination) (7)
17 Nocturnal wildcat (6)
19 Call for additional performance (6)
20 Garment neckline in a V shape (1-4)
22 Protective covering (4)

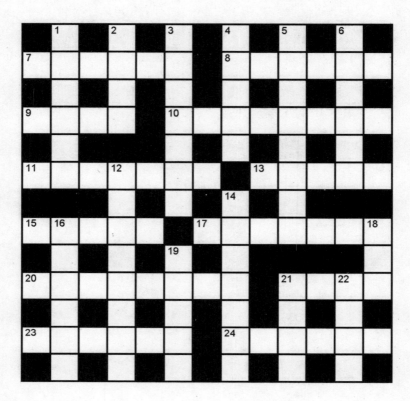

ACROSS

7 Movie theatre (6)
8 Slacken off (6)
9 Exchange one item for another (4)
10 Breed of large wiry-coated terrier (8)
11 Lasting forever (7)
13 Tired (5)
15 A condensed but memorable saying (5)
17 Scary spooks - bone gym! (4-3)
20 Person who takes a position in the political centre (8)
21 Blood-sucking insect parasites (4)
23 Being three in one - true in! (6)
24 Raise the price of something after agreeing on a lower price (6)

DOWN

1 Fool (6)
2 Small sound or quick look (4)
3 Island country in the Atlantic (7)
4 Extremist (5)
5 Ribbed fabric (8)
6 Storage space where wines are stored (6)
12 Legally valid (8)
14 Stamp (7)
16 Depressing in character or appearance (6)
18 Used to indicate the maiden name of a married woman (3)
19 Bee houses (5)
21 Be idle; exist in a changeless situation (4)
22 State of deep and often prolonged unconsciousness (4)

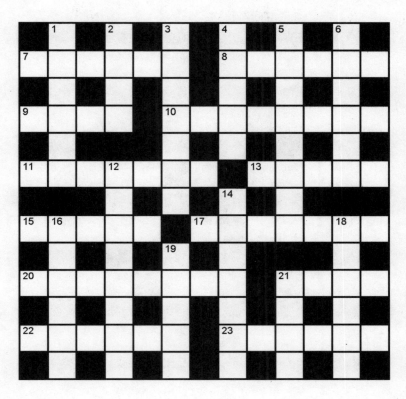

ACROSS

7 Need for food (6)
8 Hind portion of a side of bacon (6)
9 A unit of military aircraft and bird (4)
10 The act of turning yourself away (8)
11 Serious infection (7)
13 Planet (5)
15 Something believed to bring good luck (5)
17 A rope for raising or lowering a sail or flag (7)
20 The lines spoken by characters in drama (8)
21 Tear or be torn violently (4)
22 Need for water (6)
23 A heart condition (6)

DOWN

1 In a busy manner (6)
2 Highly excited, awestruck (4)
3 Fertiliser derived from vegetable matter (7)
4 Concur (5)
5 Envoy, sent to represent another person (8)
6 A group people (6)
12 The tracing of genealogies (8)
14 The feast day of a saint whose name one bears (4-3)
16 Distance from the base of something to the top (6)
18 A deep narrow steep-sided valley (6)
19 Quartz used in pestles and mortars (5)
21 Great anger (4)

ACROSS

7 A father or mother (6)
8 Covered with growing trees and bushes etc (6)
9 Travel in a boat propelled by wind (4)
10 Volcanic glass - Ido basin! (8)
11 An indefinite number more than 2 or 3 (7)
13 Very recently, perhaps born? (5)
16 Choose and follow (5)
18 Laid back (7)
21 Three wheeled bicycle (8)
22 Bird watcher's tent (4)
23 Take into confinement or custody (6)
24 In entirety - onto it! (6)

DOWN

1 Martial art form (6)
2 Back of foot (4)
3 Old empire (7)
4 (informal) elegant and fashionable - hi SSW! (5)
5 Provoke into doing something (4)
6 Become of; happen to, bechance (6)
12 Surpassing what is common or usual or expected -a eclipse! (8)
14 The conscious mind (3)
15 A small fireproof dish used for baking (7)
17 Weedy annual grass - larned! (6)
19 Cause something to happen (6)
20 Sugary cake covering (5)
22 Dislike intensely; feel antipathy or aversion towards (4)

Colossal Book of Crosswords

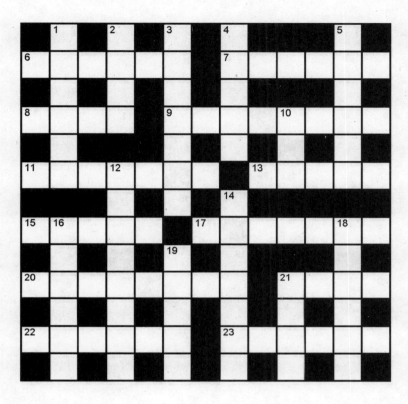

ACROSS

6 Plot a map of (land) (6)
7 Protect by insurance (6)
8 Person who divines the future (4)
9 A woman aviator (8)
11 Violating principles of right and wrong (7)
13 A lineage or race of people (5)
15 The basic unit of money in Poland (5)
17 Witty language used to convey insults (7)
20 Showing an exaggerated opinion of your importance (8)
21 Design (4)
22 Taxonomic group - enrage! (6)
23 A long chair; for reclining (6)

DOWN

1 Building housing historical artefacts (6)
2 To declare or affirm as true, avow, swear (4)
3 Loose bed wear (7)
4 Applying to ordinary citizens (5)
5 Cook in liquid (6)
10 A man who serves as a sailor (3)
12 Old-fashioned (8)
14 Fretwork (7)
16 Move heavily or clumsily (6)
18 Thinly populated (6)
19 A closed litter for one passenger (5)
21 Fruit (4)

Colossal Book of Crosswords

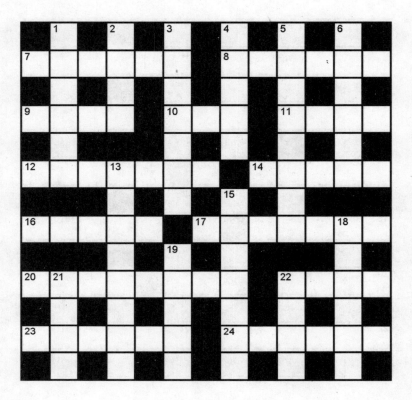

ACROSS

7 Hat and canal (6)
8 Sloping letterform (6)
9 Sudden rush (4)
10 Head wear (3)
11 Part of a hospital (4)
12 Refrain from harming (7)
14 Mammal having webbed and clawed feet (5)
16 Soft creamy toffee (5)
17 Flattery used to gain favour, from the stone? (7)
20 Uncastrated adult male horse (8)
22 A hexahedron with six equal squares as faces (4)
23 An enveloping bandage (6)
24 Go over the limit (6)

DOWN

1 Accept a higher offer on property after selling to a previous bidder (6)
2 Money in the form of bills or coins (4)
3 Lively and spirited, with a smoothing iron? (7)
4 Unclean (5)
5 Water from a tap - obvious but true! (3-5)
6 Ferocious (6)
13 Bring under control (8)
15 Unburnt remains of a coal or wood fire (7)
18 Badge (6)
19 Body of water (5)
21 Pulls along with a rope (4)
22 South American shrub whose leaves are chewed (4)

Colossal Book of Crosswords

ACROSS

6 A protective covering for a knife or sword (6)
8 Quantity of something (6)
9 Beat with a cane or whip (4)
10 Early flowering white plant (8)
11 As you would expect (7)
13 Cap worn by some armed forces (5)
16 An actor forgetting his lines (5)
18 Man's name (7)
21 Intact, still in one piece (8)
22 Alcoholic drink (4)
23 Document giving inventor control over invention (6)
24 Instrument for cutting holes in skull (6)

DOWN

1 Cold (6)
2 Sound of explosion (4)
3 Shaving tool (5)
4 Small body of water - for ducks? (4)
5 Cries meaning 'more' at theatre (6)
7 Cavalryman known for elegant dress code - rush as! (6)
12 In the know (8)
14 The capital and largest city of Japan (3)
15 Between peat and bituminous coal - tingle I! (7)
17 Along a path or line (6)
19 Braying characteristic of donkeys (6)
20 Large fish and wheeled footwear item (5)
22 Round red root vegetable (4)

Colossal Book of Crosswords

ACROSS

7 Humorously vulgar - bridal! (6)
8 Liquid cosmetic (6)
9 Cloth sheet to propel boat (4)
10 Oxford or Cambridge Universities (8)
11 State clearly, good from abroad? (7)
13 Annoy continually or chronically (5)
15 Bad tempered (5)
17 Talk noisily and about nothing important (7)
20 A high boot made of rubber - bogus MOT! (8)
21 French for black - in film genre (4)
22 Ski race around poles (6)
23 Yellow bird kept as pet (6)

DOWN

1 Countenance (6)
2 Fixing device found at end of finger (4)
3 Break from a meeting or trial (7)
4 Legal defence - you were somewhere else (5)
5 Unpleasantly loud and harsh (8)
6 Move to and fro - gel jog! (6)
12 Ring of buoyant material used on ship (8)
14 One of the sciences - shy pics! (7)
16 Russian currency (6)
18 Someone who leaves one country to settle in another (6)
19 A punctuation mark (5)
21 Quantity of zero (4)

Colossal Book of Crosswords

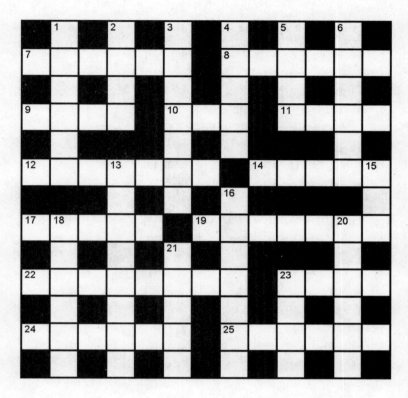

ACROSS

7 Hairdressing consisting of a perfumed oil (6)
8 Ask someone to one's house (6)
9 A connecting point - done! (4)
10 Precious stone (3)
11 North Atlantic Treaty Organisation (4)
12 Add water or moisture (7)
14 Part of staircase (5)
17 Useful (5)
19 Platinum metal - used in alloys - atomic number 77 (7)
22 Marked by excessive self-indulgence (8)
23 A person who inherits some title or office (4)
24 Elaborate and systematic plan of action (6)
25 All together, en masse (2,4)

DOWN

1 Another name for Bologna sausage (6)
2 Look at with mouth open wide (4)
3 Heavy (7)
4 Gadget (5)
5 Cooking device (4)
6 Carved stone figure (6)
13 Blushing (3-5)
15 Computer chip and sheep! (3)
16 Creature (7)
18 Bureau (6)
20 Occurring together or simultaneously (6)
21 Nut chewed by people in SE Asia (5)
23 Tramp, mainly used in USA (4)

Colossal Book of Crosswords

ACROSS

7 A feeling of pleasure and enjoyment (6)
8 At no charge (6)
9 Near, about to happen (4)
10 Inside (8)
11 Self-importance (7)
13 Normal (5)
15 Thread for cleaning the spaces between the teeth (5)
17 In the middle of (7)
20 The members of a male religious order (8)
21 Laugh or scoff at (4)
22 Make possible (6)
23 Out of control (6)

DOWN

1 The state of being alive (6)
2 Angle (4)
3 In opposition to (7)
4 Chalcedony - gemstone (5)
5 A fortified military post (8)
6 Grasshopper (6)
12 Glass tube closed at one end - for babies? (4-4)
14 Presaging ill-fortune, foreboding (7)
16 Part of throat, voice box (6)
18 According with custom or propriety (6)
19 Wicker basket used by anglers to hold fish (5)
21 A body of citizens sworn to give a true verdict according to the evidence presented in a court of law (4)

ACROSS

7 Storage space where wines are stored (6)
8 Hard hat - metal version (3,3)
9 The longest division of geological time; two or more eras (4)
10 Pyrotechnic device (8)
11 Sea captain (7)
13 Late (5)
15 A smooth fabric of silk or rayon (5)
17 Make use of (7)
20 Escape without punishment (4-4)
21 Leave out (4)
22 Jump on - like a hunting animal (6)
23 Plating - shiny (6)

DOWN

1 Decorate (6)
2 Scale drawing of a structure (4)
3 Offer (7)
4 Look at with fixed eyes (5)
5 Precipitation in the form of ice crystals (8)
6 A very strong feeling of dislike (6)
12 Reproduction by applying ink to paper (8)
14 Extend beyond the ordinary limit (7)
16 Fix firmly and stably (6)
18 A symbol of disgrace or infamy (6)
19 Put to the test (5)
21 Ladies' fingers (4)

Colossal Book of Crosswords

ACROSS

7 Natural endowment (6)
8 Belonging to or lasting from times long ago (3-3)
9 A coil of rope or wool or yarn (4)
10 Any of numerous small long-tailed parrots (8)
11 An efficient incentive (7)
13 Inferior in rank or status, small crime (5)
15 Called elk in Europe (5)
17 The seed of flax used as a source of oil (7)
20 Practicable, workable (8)
21 Terminate someone's employment (4)
22 Dull and slow-moving and stolid; like an ox (6)
23 Not fully prepared, green (6)

DOWN

1 Earnings (6)
2 Root vegetable sounds like escaping water? (4)
3 Check bleeding by contracting the tissues (7)
4 A return punch (5)
5 Not fit to assume responsibility (8)
6 Someone who pays for goods or services (6)
12 A murderer, sometimes hired (8)
14 So extremely ugly as to be terrifying (7)
16 Nocturnal wildcat of Central and South America (6)
18 Get away, break free from bondage (6)
19 A slender double-reed instrument (4)
21 Place into groups or categories (4)

Colossal Book of Crosswords

ACROSS

7 Dance by spinning round and twisting hips (6)
8 Conspicuously and tastelessly indecent (6)
9 A small tuft or lock (4)
10 A landowner who leases to others (8)
11 Second childhood (6)
13 Viscera and trimmings of an animal (5)
15 Take over, seize (5)
17 Historical soldier - British (7)
20 A plant of southern Europe thought magical (8)
22 Fringe benefit (4)
23 Lithesome (6)
24 Yearly event (6)

DOWN

1 A large indefinite number (6)
2 Struggle for breath (4)
3 Study of rocks (7)
4 Denim trousers (5)
5 Intellectually productive (8)
6 Himalayan mountaineer (6)
12 Cover roads with asphalt (3)
14 Various - leavers! (7)
16 Die of food deprivation (6)
18 In a foreign country, out and about (6)
19 Belly button (5)
21 Child's plaything (4)
22 Open flat-bottomed boat (4)

Colossal Book of Crosswords

ACROSS

7 Small grotesque supernatural creature (6)
8 Dye after knotting the fabric (3-3)
9 A refusal to recognise someone you know (4)
10 Elementary particle with negative charge (8)
11 After the expected or usual time; delayed (7)
13 Coating to protect or decorate a surface (5)
15 Put out, as of a candle or a light (5)
17 A bar that serves only wine (4,3)
20 Occurring or payable twice each year (8)
21 Flying plaything (4)
22 Act nervously; be undecided; be uncertain (6)
23 The solid part of the earth's surface (6)

DOWN

1 Rebound (6)
2 Block - thick piece of something (4)
3 Whole number (7)
4 Not the same one already mentioned (5)
5 A period of unusually hot weather (4,4)
6 A very wealthy or powerful businessperson (6)
12 French drink (8)
14 Steal goods; take as spoils (7)
16 Where something comes from (6)
18 Playing a part on stage (6)
19 Indian food (5)
21 Be cognizant or aware of (4)

ACROSS

7 Burning, fervent, with a passion (6)
8 Derive by reason (6)
9 An insect in the inactive stage of development (4)
10 Kiss (8)
11 Impressive country house in France (7)
13 A disrespectful laugh (5)
15 Go along with (5)
17 Slang for 'drunk' (3-4)
20 Heated cooking surface (3,5)
21 Additional (4)
22 A period of the year (6)
23 Maintain (6)

DOWN

1 Animal feeding device (6)
2 Greek cheese (4)
3 Footstool (7)
4 To gain with effort - a goal? (5)
5 An act of aggression (8)
6 Pass through to remove impurities (6)
12 Enter another's property without permission (8)
14 Den, hiding place (7)
16 A retail merchant who sells foodstuffs (6)
18 An upright tripod for displaying something (5)
19 Cause to lose courage - dun at! (5)
21 Persistence of sound after its source has stopped (4)

Colossal Book of Crosswords

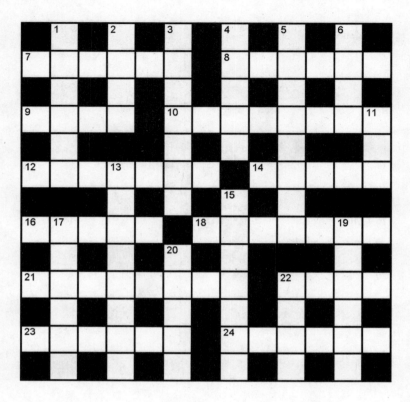

ACROSS

7 An authoritative rule of conduct (6)
8 A feeling of pleasure and enjoyment (6)
9 Dull, dingy, dismal (4)
10 Concentrate on a particular place (8)
12 Small explosive bomb thrown by hand (7)
14 Sweet or savoury small bakery item (5)
16 Wheeled vehicle drawn by horse (5)
18 Behavior that makes your feelings public (7)
21 Pasta in the form of slender tubes (8)
22 Bathroom powder (4)
23 Carnivorous freshwater fish (6)
24 Consequence (6)

DOWN

1 German leader (6)
2 A soft thick wormlike larva (4)
3 Block passage through (7)
4 Timepiece (5)
5 Rounded brimless cap fitting the crown of the head (5-3)
6 Onerous or difficult, burden of proof (4)
11 First lady (3)
13 During the first month after birth (8)
15 Relating to or containing bile (7)
17 A musical composition played slowly and with grace (6)
19 Bursting into flower (6)
20 An ore of boron used in cleaning (5)
22 Diagnostic assay (4)

Colossal Book of Crosswords

ACROSS

7 The second sign of the zodiac (6)
8 Not able to transmit light (6)
9 Nocturnal insect (4)
10 Not smooth (5)
11 Ancient hawk-headed Egyptian sun god (2)
12 Clear and certain mental apprehension (7)
14 Any break in the skin or an organ (5)
16 Strong and sharp (5)
18 Being under the control of another person (7)
21 Formalwear for men (4-4)
22 Compass point (4)
23 Tastelessly showy (6)
24 Call forth; of emotions, feelings, and responses (6)

DOWN

1 Bar or car (6)
2 Curved shape over an opening (4)
3 The wife or widow of a czar (7)
4 Appear suddenly or unexpectedly (3-2)
5 Fine rope inside window (4-4)
6 Long distance race for amusement (3,3)
13 Injury to the neck due to car accident (8)
15 Necktie - sometimes called dicky (3,3)
17 A baby bed with sides and rockers (6)
19 Light conversation for social occasions (6)
20 Young kangaroo (5)
22 Make editorial changes (in a text) (4)

Colossal Book of Crosswords

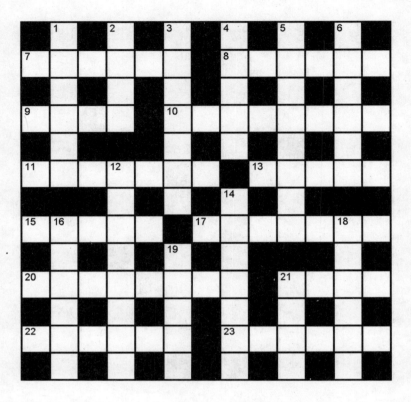

ACROSS

7 Pitching dangerously to one side (6)
8 A cart that is drawn by an ox (6)
9 Doomed to extinction or going under water? (4)
10 Amphitheatre (8)
11 Turned red, as if in embarrassment (7)
13 Tastelessly showy (5)
15 Dismal (5)
17 A symbol used to represent a number (7)
20 A drug that produces numbness or stupor (8)
21 Prod with finger (4)
22 Any group of human beings (6)
23 Small shallow dish for holding a cup (6)

DOWN

1 Dressed down, in a relaxed manner (6)
2 Humble in spirit or manner (4)
3 Unfasten by rotating (7)
4 A stupid mistake (5)
5 Travel on ice by foot (3-5)
6 Reduced to small pieces by pounding (6)
12 A painting of the sea (8)
14 Excluded from a society (7)
16 Darkened with overcast sky (6)
18 An ornament worn around the ankle (6)
19 Sit in boiling water to extract the flavour (5)
21 Fruit (4)

Colossal Book of Crosswords

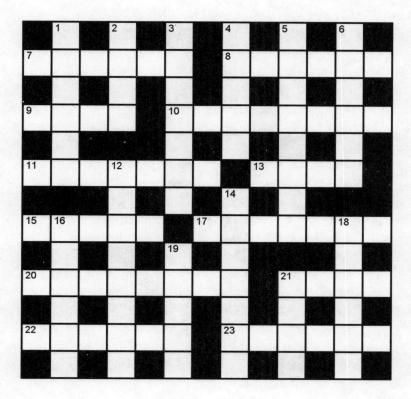

ACROSS

7 Past events to be put aside (6)
8 A cue given to a performer who has forgotten lines (6)
9 Give food to (4)
10 The rational and systematic study of religion (8)
11 Innumerable but many - meet pun! (7)
13 Hit swiftly with a violent blow (4)
15 Someone who is skilled in any field (5)
17 Wooden prop used to support the roof of a mine (3-4)
20 A club used as a weapon (8)
21 Very short skirt worn by ballerinas (4)
22 A cowboy of the South American pampas (6)
23 Draw off liquid through a tube (6)

DOWN

1 A public hall for lectures and concerts - me Lucy! (6)
2 A deep yellow colour (4)
3 A rock group from Liverpool (7)
4 Knocked over (5)
5 A second (or subsequent) examination (6-2)
6 A plug for a bunghole in a cask (6)
12 Electronic item for playing magnetic tapes (4,4)
14 A close observer, possibly of a crime (7)
16 American monetary unit (6)
18 Possible choice (6)
19 Wooden projection to fit in mortise (5)
21 Write by means of a typewriter (4)

Colossal Book of Crosswords

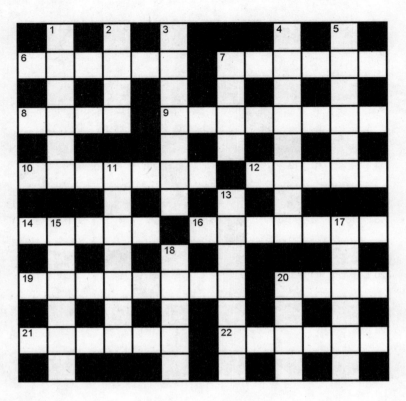

ACROSS

6 Mix with water before use (6)
7 Track, or walk behind to observe (6)
8 French for at the home of goes with nous? (4)
9 Non digital - ale guano! (8)
10 Speech organ - lot gist! (7)
12 Marked by or arising from malice, from felines (5)
14 A cordial disposition (5)
16 A recurrent rhythmical series (7)
19 Vigorously active (8)
20 Derogatory term for papers or documents (4)
21 Underground tunnels occupied by rabbits (6)
22 Love unquestioningly and uncritically (6)

DOWN

1 French man's name (6)
2 Sound of rapid vibration, fly low over (4)
3 Jelly from animal tissue (7)
4 Apportion (8)
5 Talk or behave amorously, without serious intentions (6)
7 Anti aircraft fire (4)
11 Nominal (7)
13 Childcare during the day while parents work (3,4)
15 Common to or shared by two or more parties (6)
17 Photographic equipment (6)
18 Rock (5)
20 A group of girls or young women (4)

Colossal Book of Crosswords

ACROSS

7 Someone who pays rent (6)
8 Become larger in size or volume or quantity (6)
9 The act of losing (4)
10 A wooden board on which food is carved (8)
11 Break up a meeting until another time (7)
13 Very overweight (5)
15 Malevolence (5)
17 Argument (7)
20 Small rodent (8)
21 A stack of hay (4)
22 Not dense (6)
23 Excused from payment or duty (6)

DOWN

1 Before third (6)
2 French for without (4)
3 High level of respect, height (7)
4 Cover with drops, as with dew (5)
5 Typewriter key that creates a space (5-3)
6 If not -sun els! (6)
12 Beat through cleverness and wit (8)
14 At a lower volume (7)
16 On time (6)
18 Prevent from being included (6)
19 Located outside, external wrapping (5)
21 Fishing line holder (4)

Colossal Book of Crosswords

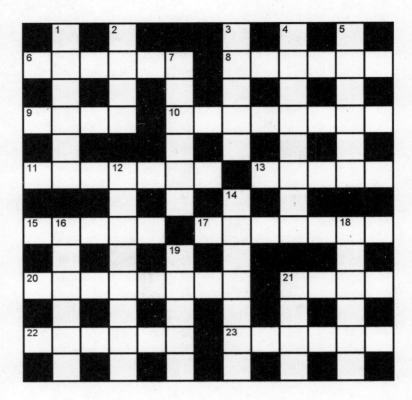

ACROSS

6 Direction of crossword clue (6)
8 From earliest times - arm lip! (6)
9 Make the burden less (4)
10 Drivers who take up the whole road (4-4)
11 Make believe (7)
13 Of high moral or intellectual value - to fly! (5)
15 The ground in a house? (5)
17 Beaver-like aquatic rodent - sam Turk! (7)
20 An early Christian church (8)
21 Twelve midday (4)
22 Spanish currency (6)
23 Free from disease - resistant (6)

DOWN

1 Oblong cream puff (6)
2 A small inlet (4)
3 Small fatty European fish (5)
4 A barbed hook for catching 3 above? (4-4)
5 Hooked! (6)
7 South Pacific loose skirt (6)
12 Person who has relationships with two people at the same time (3-5)
14 Madman (7)
16 Organs of photosynthesis (6)
18 Bless with oil or ointment (6)
19 A roll of tobacco for smoking (5)
21 Mention and identify, possibly to shame? (4)

Colossal Book of Crosswords

ACROSS

7 Man of the church - now also woman! (6)
8 Full of life (6)
9 Horizontal timber in a framework (4)
10 Blue aromatic herb, used to calm (8)
11 Gallantry (7)
13 Water course (5)
15 A small farm (5)
17 Old people (7)
20 A soft grey ductile metallic element - atomic number 41 (7)
22 Skin disorder (4)
23 Small beard (6)
24 Snow always on top of mountain (3-3)

DOWN

1 Solidified carbon dioxide, used as a refrigerant (3,3)
2 Exchange for money (4)
3 Make use of something (7)
4 Handwear: covers the hand and wrist (5)
5 The latter part of the day - even diet! (8)
6 Report or maintain, accuse someone (6)
12 Clumsy fool! (3)
14 An elderly unmarried woman (3,4)
16 Selected haphazardly (6)
18 A four-wheel covered carriage - an auld! (6)
19 Someone who files! (5)
21 Swearing the truth of a statement (4)
22 Assert is a rave returned! (4)

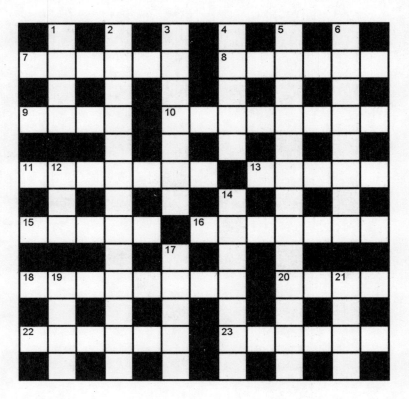

ACROSS

7 Liquid of life (6)
8 An armed thief or brigand (6)
9 A magician or sorcerer of ancient times (4)
10 Practicing complete abstinence from alcohol (8)
11 One who betrays his country (7)
13 Savoury jelly (5)
15 Two items of the same kind (5)
16 Medicine used in to relieve pain - annoyed! (7)
18 The act of slapping on the bottom (8)
20 Tear down to make flat with the ground (4)
22 Decisive change of government illegally or by force (6)
23 Writer (6)

DOWN

1 Insect (4)
2 Showing off (13)
3 An instance of oratory (7)
4 Church building (5)
5 Thoughtless (13)
6 An official award - it action! (8)
12 Uncooked (3)
14 Word formed by jumbled letters (7)
17 Electromagnetic radiation (5)
19 Decant liquids (4)
21 Rapid climb, also type of camera lens (4)

Colossal Book of Crosswords

ACROSS

7 Helical (6)
8 The period of greatest prosperity (6)
9 Burden (of proof) (4)
10 Regretted strongly (8)
11 Word - same spelling different meanings (7)
13 Speak of yourself in superlatives (5)
15 Oppose or stop something (5)
17 Cut of steak (7)
20 Concealed motive for action (8)
21 Small and remote and insignificant, dingy (4)
23 The one who gets the goal! (6)
24 B vitamin that aids in body growth (6)

DOWN

1 Rotate (4)
2 Wall painting (6)
3 Network of school chums?- sly doob! (3,4)
4 Words that are similar in sound in poetry (5)
5 Generator (6)
6 Ride across the water on pair of skis (5-3)
12 A film of oil floating on top of water (3,5)
14 Get undressed (7)
16 Fruit with a single hard stone (6)
18 Portable computer (6)
19 Joint in wood cut at angle of 45 degrees (5)
22 Tie or link together (4)

ACROSS

7 Detachable compartment of a spacecraft (6)
8 A blood vessel (6)
9 A single undivided whole (4)
10 Disintegrate as a result of excess soaking (8)
11 Device to help the hard of hearing (4-3)
13 Fortune teller or Basil Fawlty's wife (5)
15 Flowed out - like the tide (5)
17 Look after young children when parents go out for evening (4-3)
20 Inspiring scornful pity (8)
21 The goddess of youth and spring; (4)
22 A full supply, lots of (6)
23 Take the mickey, imitate (4-2)

DOWN

1 Jump on by surprise (6)
2 Fair (4)
3 Female sea dweller (7)
4 Wood tipped with combustible chemical (5)
5 For ever (8)
6 Rather down market and grubby (6)
12 Drawn without mechanical aids (4-4)
14 Extreme right wing political standpoint (7)
16 A minor parish official (6)
18 Permeate or impregnate - be muir! (6)
19 Corsets (5)
21 Sharpen with a fine gritstone (4)

Colossal Book of Crosswords

ACROSS

7 Acquire by one's efforts or actions (6)
8 Shelf that projects out above fireplace (6)
9 The protruding part of the lower jaw (4)
10 A long slender cigar (8)
11 Gun that is held and fired with one hand (4,3)
13 Escargot (5)
16 A daily written record (5)
17 Someone who controls resources (7)
19 Costing less than standard price (3-5)
20 Not difficult (4)
22 A number of uniform projections on a gear (5)
23 Nuts or fruit pieces in a sugar paste (6)

DOWN

1 Clean with soap and water (4)
2 Continuous, without disturbance (13)
3 Hanging cloth used as a blind - dare pry! (7)
4 Make good, make better, heal breach (5)
5 Happening without delay (13)
6 The abode of Satan (4)
12 Morally objectionable behavior (8)
14 Belligerence aroused by a real or supposed wrong (3)
15 Elaborate representation of scenes from history (7)
18 Suspicious, to do with sea creatures! (5)
21 Aquatic bird (4)

Colossal Book of Crosswords

ACROSS

6 Spanish wine shop (6)
7 Domesticated llama with long silky fleece (6)
9 A feeling of deep, bitter anger and ill-will (4)
10 A baroque musical composition (7)
11 Unshaven facial hair (7)
13 A garment hanging from the waist (5)
15 Bright (5)
17 A strong north wind that blows in France (7)
20 Of heaven or the spirit (8)
21 Strong cord (4)
22 Walk quietly (6)
23 Picture made up of many small pieces (6)

DOWN

1 A genre of modern art (3,3)
2 A deep hole dug to obtain water (4)
3 Producing a sensation of touch (7)
4 Comedy involving satire and silly situations (5)
5 Designed for high-income consumers (2-6)
8 Something you sit in (5)
12 A pin for holding women's hair in place (8)
14 Certificate (7)
16 Things set out in rows and columns (6)
18 A young foreigner who lives with a family in return for doing light housework (2,4)
19 Regenerate (5)
21 Formation of reddish-brown ferric oxides (4)

ACROSS

7 Appropriate to or befitting a god (6)
8 Very strong dislike (6)
9 Hang about, waiting for someone (4)
10 Punishment for one's actions (8)
11 Plate for printing made with the use of acid (7)
13 Ruffle (5)
15 Minute two-winged mosquito-like fly (5)
17 Give information or notice to (7)
20 Snuggest, most comfortable (7)
21 Microbe (4)
22 Mostly tropical songbird (6)
23 Part of a flower (6)

DOWN

1 A card game (6)
2 A fabric (4)
3 Having close kinship and appropriateness (7)
4 Censure severely or angrily (5)
5 Disciplinarian, martinet (8)
6 Rupture in smooth muscle tissue (6)
12 The most interesting or memorable part (4,4)
14 An inscription on a tombstone (7)
16 Receives a specified treatment (6)
18 A painful injury to a joint (6)
19 Chewed nut (5)
21 A strong current of air (4)

Colossal Book of Crosswords

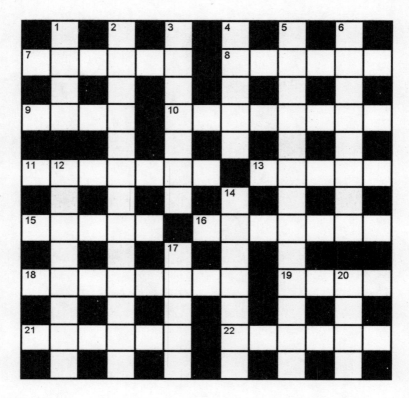

ACROSS

7 Payment or reward for catching criminals (6)
8 Mate of peacock (6)
9 Flat carrier for food or drink (4)
10 Obtains from a substance, parts of a larger work (8)
11 Clap (7)
13 Bird with red breast (5)
15 Small dog (5)
16 Material thrown away, could be natural? (7)
18 Of heaven or the spirit (8)
19 Projections used to assemble something (4)
21 Someone who makes written copies of document (6)
22 Scots dish (6)

DOWN

1 Rain heavily (4)
2 Book of factual information (13)
3 In a state of anxious agitation (5,2)
4 A sudden forceful flow (5)
5 Study of fossils (13)
6 Arranging oneself in a comfortable and cozy position (8)
12 Heated material applied to skin as cure (8)
14 Hunting cry (5-2)
17 Intense nervous anticipation (5)
20 Smooth-tongued (4)

ACROSS

7 An act of travelling by water (6)
8 Of or relating to or comprising atoms (6)
9 Small cubes with 1 to 6 spots on the faces (4)
10 Dash a liquid upon or against (8)
11 Not deep (7)
13 As normal, nothing unusual (5)
15 Musical instrument, body part (5)
17 Rational motives for a belief or action (7)
20 The latter part of the days (8)
21 A set of two similar things considered as a unit (4)
22 Type of wood from nut tree (6)
23 Bicycle for 2 people (6)

DOWN

1 Clean and shine by rubbing (6)
2 Trucks with an enclosed cargo space (4)
3 Period of time (7)
4 Goes in a boat (5)
5 Is made up of (8)
6 Where you go to watch a moving film (6)
12 Acquiring knowledge or skill (8)
14 Room with bed and sitting room in one (6)
16 Show (6)
18 Sound, usually unwanted (5)
19 Makes from wool and needles (5)
21 Cooking utensils (4)

ACROSS

7 Continental sausage (6)
8 Tool used for putting in nails (6)
9 Follow command or instruction (4)
10 Funny (8)
11 Challenge, competition (7)
13 A special set of circumstances (5)
15 Blacksmith's block (5)
17 Thing that is made or sold (7)
20 People who move into new country (8)
21 A prison for forced labourers (4)
22 Choose (6)
23 Send abroad for sale (6)

DOWN

1 Woody grasses used in furniture making (6)
2 Be subject to change (4)
3 Most wealthy (7)
4 Words that sound similar in poetry (5)
5 Made better (8)
6 Go back (6)
12 The decade from 1930 to 1939 (8)
14 Swept across or over (7)
16 Required (6)
18 Photographic device that holds the film (6)
19 Used to catch fish (4)
21 Headwear given to national team player (3)

Colossal Book of Crosswords

ACROSS

7 Previous (6)
8 Thicknesses laid one on the other (6)
9 Simple boat (4)
10 The result of parcelling out or sharing (8)
11 Education imparted in a series of lessons (7)
13 The boundaries of a surface (5)
15 Aptitude (5)
17 Travel upon or across (7)
20 Camouflage (8)
21 Successful pop records (4)
22 Surpassing the ordinary especially in bravery (6)
23 Astonished, finding it hard to believe (6)

DOWN

1 Salad bowl component (6)
2 Leave out (4)
3 Grabbed hold of (7)
4 Stare at with contempt (5)
5 A chamber within which piston moves (8)
6 European nation (6)
12 Belief in a divine power (8)
14 Some unspecified time in the future (7)
16 Item of cutlery (5)
18 One or the other (6)
19 Dance club (5)
21 Lead teacher in a school (4)

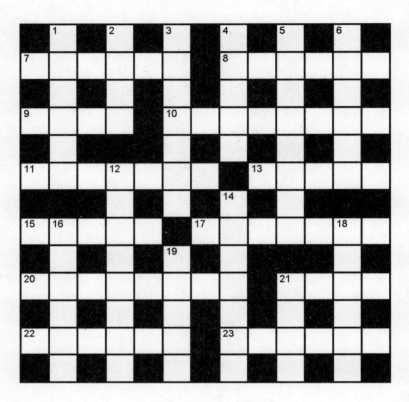

ACROSS

7 Skin decoration (6)
8 Number (6)
9 Month (4)
10 Month (8)
11 Given office by vote (7)
13 Opposing military force (5)
15 Fish (5)
17 Pushed aside (7)
20 Number (8)
21 Rodents (4)
22 Sport played with racquets (6)
23 Natural ability (6)

DOWN

1 Marked by blithe unconcern (6)
2 Remain (4)
3 Hunting dog (7)
4 Cooking device (5)
5 Parts of a whole, like orange pieces (8)
6 Moving body of water (6)
12 Breaking into small pieces (8)
14 Plutonic igneous rock (7)
16 Brought up (6)
18 Level, magnitude (6)
19 Animal, creature (5)
21 Depend upon (4)

ACROSS

7 Sock with a diamond-shaped pattern (6)
8 Plumbing fixture that sprays water over you (6)
9 Tall annual cereal grass (4)
10 Consider as ideal (8)
11 Portion, assisting (7)
13 Crispy top of loaf of bread (5)
15 Striped animal (5)
17 Spear thrown in competition (7)
20 Remote places (3-5)
21 Money owed (4)
22 Earthquake - me sis! (5)
23 Showing a natural aptitude for something (6)

DOWN

1 Channel or furrow, as in a record (6)
2 A song of praise (4)
3 Markedly different from an accepted norm (7)
4 Organic compound is Esther less H! (5)
5 Road on which no charge is paid (4-4)
6 A periodic count of the population (6)
12 Heating oil (8)
14 Suitcases and the like (7)
16 Pass by, as of time (6)
18 Feature produced by inbreeding (6)
19 A body embalmed and dried and wrapped (5)
21 Quick and skillful in movement (4)

Colossal Book of Crosswords

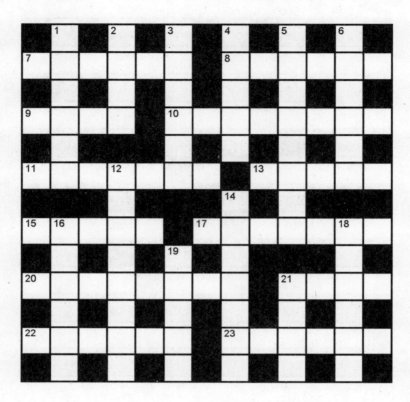

ACROSS

- **7** Separate or cut with a tool (6)
- **8** Battle cry and magazine? (3-3)
- **9** Be exposed (4)
- **10** Circle (8)
- **11** Maybe, possibly (7)
- **13** Make reference to (5)
- **15** Not large (5)
- **17** A small measure (usually of food) (7)
- **20** Representative or envoy (8)
- **21** Eat (4)
- **22** A sale of miscellany; often for charity (6)
- **23** Device that prevents a ship from moving (6)

DOWN

- **1** Give pleasure to; be pleasing to (6)
- **2** Job (4)
- **3** Create disorder, make a muddle (4-2)
- **4** Turn in a twisting or spinning motion (5)
- **5** Of or relating to or formed by trees (8)
- **6** An alloy of copper and tin (6)
- **12** The man who steers a ship (8)
- **14** Imitator, possibly feline? (7)
- **16** Warm-blooded vertebrate (6)
- **18** Gear with a small number of teeth (6)
- **19** A mound of stones (5)
- **21** An enclosed conduit (4)

Colossal Book of Crosswords

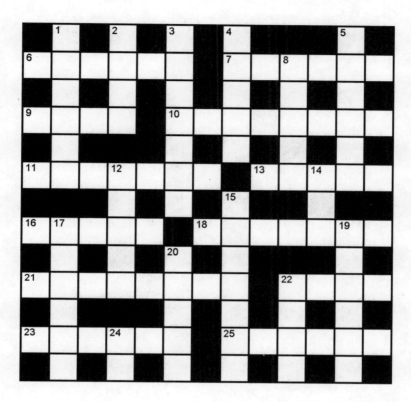

ACROSS

6 Go over the limit (6)
7 Very pleasing to the eye (6)
9 The central meaning or theme (4)
10 Not having form or shape (8)
11 Science of rock study (7)
13 Express in speech, completely (5)
16 Cake topping (5)
18 Attract; cause to be enamoured (7)
21 The quality of unselfish concern (8)
22 An inn in some Eastern countries - hank confused! (4)
23 Careless (6)
25 Close at hand, not far away (4-2)

DOWN

1 Act as a stimulant (6)
2 Immediately following in time or order (4)
3 Declare to be - jag dude! (7)
4 Showing your contempt by derision (5)
5 The wool of a sheep or similar animal (6)
8 Any admirable quality or attribute (5)
12 A large commercial passenger ship (5)
14 A small amount, A young child (3)
15 Appearing as such but not necessarily so (7)
17 In an unemotional manner (6)
19 Perversely irritable (6)
20 Plastic used to make floor coverings (5)
22 Cut off (4)
24 Doctor (2)

ACROSS

7 Long strip of cloth for decoration or advertising (6)
8 Sloping letters (6)
9 Dull colour (4)
10 A source of oil and food (4,4)
11 In a perfect situation (7)
13 A special lineage (5)
15 Effigy (5)
17 Late comedian, Tony, had half hour! (7)
20 A parallelogram with adjacent sides of unequal lengths (8)
21 The highest point of something (4)
22 A conical shape used to pour liquid (6)
23 Street with only one direction (3-3)

DOWN

1 Used to push charge into muzzle loading gun (6)
2 Exclusively (4)
3 A supporting tower (7)
4 A military dictatorship in North Africa (5)
5 Without civilising influences (8)
6 Someone who robs at sea (6)
12 Debate (8)
14 Happy seaside dweller - any bods! (7)
16 (India) the driver and keeper of an elephant (6)
18 Conqueror of Gaul and master of Italy (6)
19 Expresses possibility (5)
21 Again but in a new or different way, afresh (4)

493

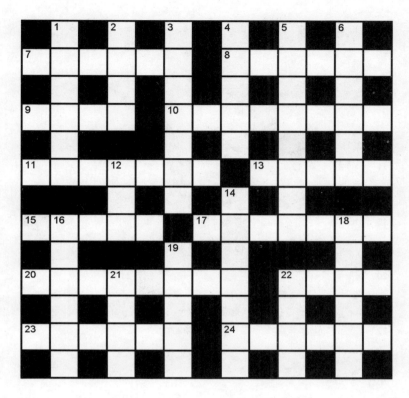

ACROSS

7 A city in southern England (6)
8 Belonging to one by birth (6)
9 The story that is told in a novel (4)
10 An imaginary place of great wealth (8)
11 Incapable of functioning usefully (7)
13 Mark placed over some Spanish words (5)
15 Place where you live, humble maybe? (5)
17 Drinking mug in the shape of a seated man (4-3)
20 A town enjoying sudden prosperity (8)
22 Tramp (4)
23 Candlestick hanging on wall (6)
24 Go to something (6)

DOWN

1 People expelled from home or country (6)
2 Just about, almost all, mainly (4)
3 In an opposing direction (7)
4 A positively charged electrode (5)
5 Forever (8)
6 Avoided capture, eluded (6)
12 Pan cover (3)
14 Soft cover on sports car (7)
16 A decorative pin worn by women (6)
18 Straighten up or out; make straight (6)
19 Extraterrestrial object travels round the sun (5)
21 Semiaquatic mammal used for fur (4)
22 Intense dislike (4)

Colossal Book of Crosswords

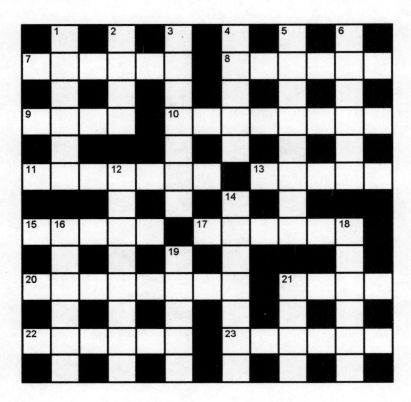

ACROSS

7 A person who announces important news (6)
8 A small informal restaurant; serves wine (6)
9 A person who is not very bright (4)
10 Unbranded range animal (8)
11 Vicar's salary (7)
13 The beginning or early stages (5)
15 Great pain (5)
17 A raucous musical gathering - up aver! (4-2)
20 Important in history (8)
21 An impact (as from a collision) (4)
22 Goods carried by a large vehicle (6)
23 A person of no influence (6)

DOWN

1 A quick reply (6)
2 Component (4)
3 Not capable of being swayed (7)
4 In a higher place (5)
5 Alienate (8)
6 Child care centre (6)
12 A hair style (8)
14 The act of taking something unlawfully (7)
16 Stringed instrument (6)
18 Hairdressing (6)
19 Sediment (5)
21 A very young child (4)

Colossal Book of Crosswords

ACROSS

7 Dress down (6)
8 Extreme mental retardation (6)
9 Any of several small graceful hawks (4)
10 Part of egg used in meringues (3-5)
11 The secret state police in Nazi Germany (7)
13 An audible warning signal (5)
15 Say something (5)
17 Fully ripened sweet red pepper (7)
20 The edge of a garment around the neck (8)
21 The cry of a goose (4)
22 A victim of ridicule or pranks (6)
23 Pudding or sweet course (6)

DOWN

1 To do with cats (6)
2 Favourable public reputation (4)
3 Written acknowledgment of payment (7)
4 Drinking spree (5)
5 Vertical housing development (4-4)
6 An edge tool for cutting grass (6)
12 A conversational expression of gratitude (5-3)
14 Small carrier attached to side of motorcycle (7)
16 Lots of (6)
18 A vast treeless plain in the arctic regions (6)
19 Assisted, helped (5)
21 Small crude shelters used as a dwelling (4)

ACROSS

7 A theatre where films are shown (6)
8 A high-pitched howl (6)
9 Lazy (4)
10 The framework of a bed (8)
11 Attractive or reasonable (4)
12 Characterised by dignity and propriety (5)
14 Explosive device (4)
15 Show to be invalid (7)
18 Take person against his will to work on ship (8)
19 Protein molecule, unit of heredity (4)
20 A wide street or thoroughfare (6)
21 If not - sun els! (6)

DOWN

1 Deprive of by deceit - lidded! (6)
2 With out - administer or bestow (4)
3 A finely woven white linen (7)
4 In reserve; not for immediate use (5)
5 The final aggregate (3,5)
6 An overland journey by hunters (6)
11 Associated with women and not with men (8)
13 Marked by extreme anger (7)
14 Be appropriate or necessary (6)
16 The place designated as the end (6)
17 A person who is in charge (5)
19 A gay festivity (4)

Colossal Book of Crosswords

ACROSS

6 Kind and tender (6)
7 A jar made of glass or plastic for chemistry (6)
8 Tranquil silence (4)
9 The main cavity of the ear (8)
10 Edge or road or pavement (4)
11 Located outside, like space? (5)
13 Singing range (4)
14 Triumph over enemies (7)
17 A condition of great disorder (8)
19 Wild goat (4)
20 A clergyman (6)
21 A farewell remark (5)

DOWN

1 Cause to be confused emotionally (6)
2 Something that produces a desire to scratch (4)
3 Parsonage (7)
4 Plaything used to propel stones (8)
5 Examine or consider in detail (6)
7 Backside (3)
10 Set of parts to build something (3)
12 A male relative (7)
13 For a short time (6)
15 Of southern Asia; used in medical research (6)
16 A simple valve with a hinge on one side (5)
18 Female equine animal (4)
19 Wading bird (4)

ACROSS

7 Coffee (4)
8 Pleasing by delicacy or grace (6)
9 The colour of the clear sky in the daytime (4)
10 One of the four countries that make the UK (8)
11 Keep from happening (7)
13 To go stealthily or furtively (5)
15 A measuring instrument for weighing (5)
17 Grounds for doing something (7)
20 Vehicles that can fly (8)
21 A collection of facts (4)
22 Come to rest (6)
23 Not able to (6)

DOWN

1 Greater in height (6)
2 A large bundle as of hay or straw (4)
3 Touching with the lips (7)
4 A piece of cutlery (5)
5 Grows worse (8)
6 Number of lines of verse (6)
12 Speed (8)
14 Any of various plants of the genus Lactuca (7)
16 Wound around something (6)
18 The people who live in a country (6)
19 Signalled with the hands (5)
21 A ridge of sand (4)

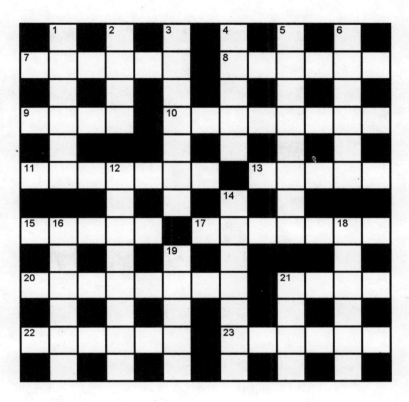

ACROSS

7 Grinding teeth (6)
8 Astonished (6)
9 Confine a wild animal (4)
10 From the USA (8)
11 Looked up to (7)
13 Ingested, as medicine (5)
15 Heaps (5)
17 Be composed of (7)
20 Funny drawings, sometimes moving (8)
21 Oceans (4)
22 Water boiler (6)
23 Placed or arranged at intervals (6)

DOWN

1 In the direction of (6)
2 A special set of circum stances (4)
3 Breaks free from captivity (7)
4 Founded (5)
5 Upper case letters (8)
6 Opposite to male (6)
12 Characteristics by which a thing is recognizable (8)
14 Own (7)
16 Pictures (6)
18 Said clearly (6)
19 Place of lodging for holiday (5)
21 Mark left after healing of would (4)

Colossal Book of Crosswords

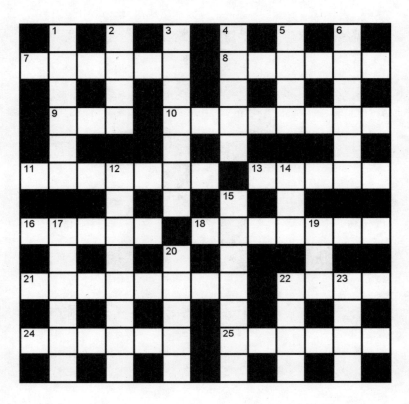

ACROSS

7 Cut of pork (6)
8 Remorseful (6)
9 3 or 4-wheeled motor vehicle (3)
10 Title for peeress (8)
11 Of little substance or significance (7)
13 A republic in eastern Africa (5)
16 Unable to move or resist motion (5)
18 Considered or looked at in detail (7)
21 Briefly giving the gist of something (8)
22 Place a bet on a horse (4)
24 Relating to or promoting digestion (6)
25 Excessive self-indulgence and moral decay (6)

DOWN

1 A cavalryman armed with a lance (6)
2 African ruler or chief (4)
3 Uncertain, muddy (7)
4 The commercial exchange of goods (5)
5 Elongated fish found in fresh water (4)
6 In a busy manner, actively (6)
12 Truthfulness (8)
14 Finish (3)
15 Speech impediment (7)
17 Make sexually inactive (6)
19 Woman's name (3)
20 Play out a scene from a drama (5)
22 Polish to a shine (4)
23 Felines (4)

Colossal Book of Crosswords

ACROSS

7 Part of the eye (6)
8 A canopy or sunshade (6)
9 Pleasant (4)
10 Dish baked in pastry-lined pan (3)
11 An opening that permits escape (4)
12 Capable of being shaped or bent (7)
14 A measuring instrument (5)
16 A fixed look with eyes open wide (5)
18 Christen (7)
21 Expecting a child (8)
23 Make children (4)
24 Of or relating to or supporting Romanism (6)
25 A set of china or silverware for serving tea (3-3)

DOWN

1 Spread negative information about (6)
2 Journey in a vehicle driven by someone else (4)
3 Decorated post for dancing round (7)
4 Gentleman's gentleman (5)
5 Underplay (8)
6 Conclusion (6)
13 Term of address for a man (3)
15 Oratorio (7)
17 Declaration of an intention to harm another (6)
19 Dock (6)
20 Fry briefly over high heat (5)
22 Take a firm hold of (4)
23 Rise rapidly, as of a current or voltage (4)

Colossal Book of Crosswords

ACROSS

7 A source of danger (6)
8 Completely devoid of wisdom or good sense (6)
9 Discharge, dismiss (4)
10 Make used (to something) (8)
11 Protection from harm (7)
13 Carving in low relief on a stone on brooch (5)
16 Game played with oval ball (5)
18 Looked after child while parents went out (7)
21 Splash with water or paint - prattles! (8)
22 Intense dislike - enough to do harm (4)
23 Native-born persons of French descent in Louisiana (6)
24 Hand tool used to get into cans (6)

DOWN

1 An appetizer (6)
2 Reverse (4)
3 Money given before book is written (7)
4 Move in a graceful and rhythmical way (5)
5 Goddess of fertility, Egyptian deity (4)
6 American songbird (6)
12 Decorate with heraldic arms or colours (8)
14 Appropriate shortly (3)
15 Barroom (7)
17 Referee in a cricket match (6)
19 Horn of a member of the deer family (6)
20 Early anaesthetic (5)
22 Back of shoe (4)

Colossal Book of Crosswords

ACROSS

7 Compelling immediate action (6)
8 Hind cut of meat from pig (6)
9 Precipitation of ice pellets (4)
10 Paragon - chose nun! (8)
11 Royal tomb in ancient Egypt (7)
13 Very thin (5)
15 Approximately 1.76 pints (5)
17 Deathless (7)
20 City of gold in fables? (8)
21 Made on a loom (4)
22 Sunshade (6)
23 Stiffener (6)

DOWN

1 Written agreement between two states (6)
2 Experience (4)
3 Cut out used in printing (7)
4 Great pain or aunt? (5)
5 Envoy (8)
6 Modern convenience (3,3)
12 Missile launched by one 'plane at another (3-2-3)
14 Training, for example, delivered by your own people (2-5)
16 Relatives by marriage (2-4)
18 Beginner (6)
19 Tropical fruit (5)
21 A raised mark on the skin (4)

Colossal Book of Crosswords

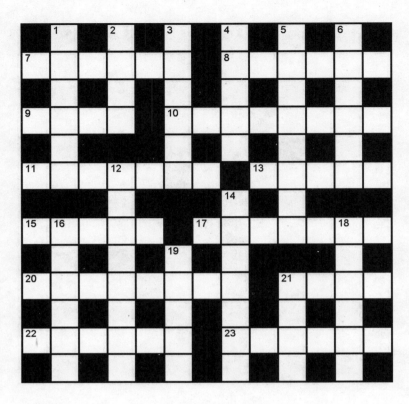

ACROSS

7 Legendary creature, like little old man with pointed hat (6)
8 (formal) by means of this (6)
9 Angel's head wear? (4)
10 Offending against sexual codes - mot deism! (8)
11 Bring back together (7)
13 Thicket (5)
15 Hit with fist, party drink (5)
17 Incorrect ignition in engine (7)
20 Of the blackest black (3-5)
21 Loose flowing garment (4)
22 Aromatic herb (6)
23 Acid squirted by ants (6)

DOWN

1 Make very angry (6)
2 Ammunition, in short (4)
3 Help, lend a hand (6)
4 Hit someone (5)
5 An exchange that occurs as a compromise (5-3)
6 Improper or excessive uses (6)
12 A band around the collar of a garment (8)
14 Start of football match (7)
16 Lumpy (6)
18 Long eared animal that burrows (6)
19 Eating surface (5)
21 Not often seen (4)

ACROSS

7 Desire strongly, long or yearn for (6)
8 Make attractive or lovable (6)
9 Failure (4)
10 Over a short time (8)
11 List everything (7)
13 Christmas plant used in decorations (5)
16 Taxi driver (5)
18 Before anything else, foremost (7)
21 Something that covers an entire page (4-4)
22 Possess or own (4)
23 A rational motive for a belief or action (6)
24 Consequence (6)

DOWN

1 Wooden lattice used on lorries (6)
2 Leave something out, bypass (4)
3 Claim to be proficient (7)
4 Less than (5)
5 Make editorial changes in a newspaper (4)
6 Of or relating to the body or flesh (6)
12 Ready for war (8)
14 Roman deity and short operations (3)
15 Hand held firearm -misread! (4,3)
17 Shrewdness shown by keen insight (6)
19 Full of life and energy (6)
20 A public announcement (in church) of a proposed marriage (5)
22 Become quiet or quieter (4)

ACROSS

7 Bookworm, obsessed by words (6)
8 Take off a hook (6)
9 A complete failure (4)
10 Inflammatory disease in the lungs (8)
11 Small cucumber pickled whole (7)
13 Put forward for consideration (5)
16 Have young - animals (5)
18 Remove all clothing (7)
21 An epic poem adapted for recitation (8)
23 Drag (4)
24 On land (6)
25 The right to enter (6)

DOWN

1 The state of being rich and affluent (6)
2 Lighting unit (4)
3 Astringent used to heal shaving cuts (7)
4 Finely ground food (5)
5 Norse god of thunder (4)
6 A light creamy dessert (6)
12 Type of flour (3)
14 Type of tree (3)
15 Home of frog? (4,3)
17 Rework old material (6)
19 Discoloured injury (6)
20 Not drunk (5)
22 A secret scheme or area of land (4)
23 A mediocre and disdained writer (4)

Colossal Book of Crosswords

ACROSS

7 Small powered vehicle used for fun (2-4)
8 Not having been read (6)
9 That which is responsible for one's thoughts (4)
10 A swift cursory examination or inspection (4-4)
11 Conforming to a type (7)
13 Large luggage carrier (5)
15 A mistake resulting from inattention (5)
17 Bombardment (7)
20 Causes pain or suffering in (8)
21 Let something be known (4)
22 Sealed in a can or jar (6)
23 A small piece of cloth (6)

DOWN

1 A sermon on a moral or religious topic (6)
2 Having no hair on the head (4)
3 Lost empire (7)
4 Covering round plant roots to keep in moisture (5)
5 One who makes armour (8)
6 A cotton fabric with a satiny finish (6)
12 Barefaced (8)
14 Oxford and Cambridge Universities (7)
16 Noisy quarrel (6)
18 Passage between the pharynx and the stomach (6)
19 Liquid that corrodes or burns (4)
21 Good bye! (2-2)

ACROSS

7 French boat (6)
8 Colouring stick (6)
9 Poke (4)
10 A long and mournful complaint - amid jeer! (8)
11 Unfasten, sometimes horse and cart (7)
13 Loading bay for boats (5)
16 Any light downy material (5)
18 Not making the grade (7)
21 Without interruption (8)
22 A shade of blue tinged with green (4)
23 Keep in custody (6)
24 Have a wish or desire to know something (6)

DOWN

1 Underground rabbit home (6)
2 Listen to, take note of (4)
3 The topic of the conversation (7)
4 Dandruff or skin flakes (5)
5 Relaxed (4)
6 Yarn from Angora goat (6)
12 Characteristic of or resembling hell (8)
14 Temperature of 12 above? (3)
15 Bird (4,3)
17 A surgical knife (6)
19 Disgust so strong it makes you feel sick (6)
20 Having no cash! (5)
22 Woman's name (4)

Colossal Book of Crosswords

ACROSS

6 Not there, away (6)
8 Come out (6)
9 Cloth (4)
10 Person living in a place (8)
11 A thorough physical examination (7)
13 A person or animal that is markedly unusual (5)
15 Bring together (5)
17 A rope for raising or lowering a sail or flag (7)
20 Defeat (oneself) by going too far (8)
21 Expression of open-mouthed astonishment (4)
22 Involuntary expulsion of air from the nose (6)
23 A gripping hand tool (6)

DOWN

1 Force or compel somebody to do something (6)
2 Words on paper (4)
3 The limit of capability (5)
4 A party for women only (3-5)
5 A list of matters to be taken up at a meeting (6)
7 Part of insect that carries the wings (6)
12 A person who is interned (8)
14 A wind instrument, typically scots (7)
16 Devotion - prayers over nine days (6)
18 A sharp explosive sound (6)
19 Hold back to a later time (5)
21 A person's manner of walking (4)

Colossal Book of Crosswords

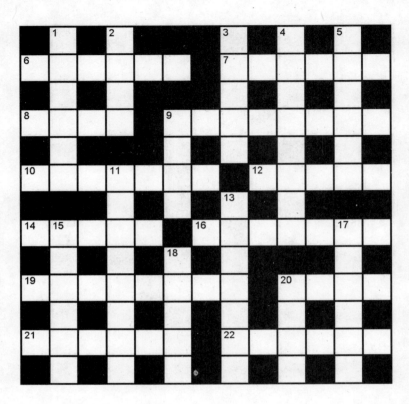

ACROSS

6 Highest part of an orbit away from planet (6)
7 A new embodiment of a familiar idea (6)
8 Number of holes on a short golf course (4)
9 Gown worn by the clergy (8)
10 Serve as the inciting cause of (7)
12 Ability (5)
14 German undersea craft (1-4)
16 The domain controlled by an emir (7)
19 Sell cheaper than one's competition (8)
20 Append your signature (4)
21 The 2nd longest European river (6)
22 Worthy of trust or belief (6)

DOWN

1 Alternative (6)
2 A giant who likes to eat human beings (4)
3 One chap's arbitrary assertion (3-2)
4 A farm machine, a hard punch (8)
5 Of the flesh! (6)
9 Doing word! (4)
11 Gradually take out of use (5,3)
13 Play the part of, copy, simulate (7)
15 Any of various small breeds (6)
17 Skintight knit hose (6)
18 Sloping mass of rocks at the base of a cliff (5)
20 Ignore on purpose (4)

ACROSS

6 Chronological records (6)
8 Mean to do (6)
9 American slang for dollar (4)
10 Associated with an empire, also beard! (8)
11 Give to, in marriage (7)
13 Firearm with a long barrel (5)
15 Reach the highest point of a mountain (5)
17 Half way through the year (3-4)
20 Bag to take home uneaten food (5,3)
21 The 9th letter of the Greek alphabet (4)
22 Disinherit (6)
23 In the area or vicinity (6)

DOWN

1 Harm (6)
2 Position in armed forces (4)
3 Quick and energetic, also to do with fastener? (5)
4 For ever (8)
5 Mean (6)
7 Travel across snow on planks? (3)
12 Faith (8)
14 Illustration to show how something works (7)
16 Composer (6)
18 Go to a function (6)
19 Dark hardwood (5)
21 Religious picture (4)

ACROSS

7 Running race (6)
8 On land, as opposed to water (6)
9 Pottery item (4)
10 Able to read and write (8)
11 Honourable (7)
13 Point around which something rotates (5)
15 Name from metal worker? (5)
17 A punctuation mark, diagonal (7)
20 Cycle wheel cover to protect rider (3-5)
21 Discover (4)
22 Become bony (6)
23 Batsman in cricket deemed to be safe? (3-3)

DOWN

1 Produce buds, also green vegetable (6)
2 Occupy the whole of (4)
3 Astral, to do with stars (7)
4 Our planet (5)
5 Captivating (8)
6 A small cave (6)
12 Depressed engraving or carving on a stone or gem (8)
14 The front and back covering of a book (7)
16 Whipped dessert (6)
18 Make a connection - sometimes over the airwaves (4-2)
19 Woman's name (5)
21 Destiny (4)

Colossal Book of Crosswords

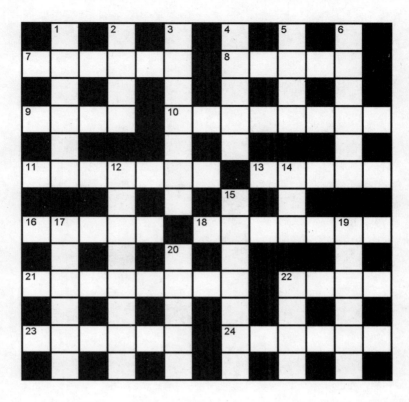

ACROSS

7 Get back together with others (6)
8 Diving gear (5)
9 Any division of quantity - singular (4)
10 Gates in a toll road (8)
11 Attractively old-fashioned (3-4)
13 Unit of currency in UK (5)
16 The immediate descendants of a person (5)
18 Long pillow (7)
21 Pay out (8)
22 Accompanying (4)
23 Exercises involving pulling up from a lying position to a seated one (6)
24 Type of lithographic printing (6)

DOWN

1 Dog house (6)
2 Drink (4)
3 On one occasion (3,4)
4 Take control of; take as one's right or possession (5)
5 Device to draw water from the ground (4)
6 Serviette (6)
12 Marked by unswerving loyalty (4-4)
14 Short military operations (3)
15 Ennui, tedium (7)
17 Ghost or strong liquor (6)
19 Main course (6)
20 Income before any deductions are made (5)
22 Blow gently (4)

ACROSS

7 Securely in position; not shaky (6)
8 A purging medicine (6)
9 Suggestive of sexual impropriety (4)
10 Line marking the upper limit of tree growth (4-4)
11 Move forward (7)
13 Submarine (1-4)
15 Die away (5)
17 Edge of a way or road or path (7)
20 Collection of statues (8)
21 Fill to satisfaction (4)
22 Angrier (6)
23 Pass by, as of time (6)

DOWN

1 A very slender natural or synthetic fibre (6)
2 Change, alter (4)
3 Occult (6)
4 Rapidity, velocity (5)
5 Course of study (8)
6 Old maid flower (6)
12 Height above sea level (8)
14 Idle (4)
16 Comic book hero and military orderly (6)
18 Hate (6)
19 Wed (5)
21 Washing bar (4)
23 Extra Terrestrial! (2)

Colossal Book of Crosswords

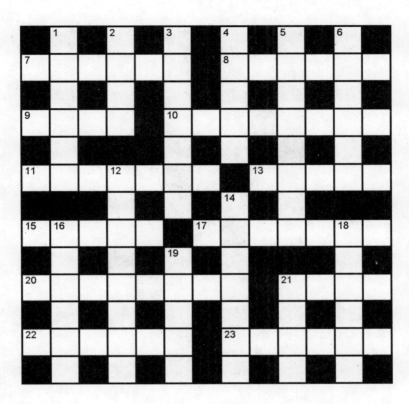

ACROSS

7 Draw back - possibly in repulsion (6)
8 Bead based adding machine (6)
9 Hang about, suspiciously (4)
10 To do with veins (8)
11 Somewhat hungry (7)
13 Fully loaded (5)
15 Rub through a strainer (5)
17 Solo passage near the end of a piece of music (7)
20 Cause to go into a solution (8)
21 Sections of wood for burning on a fire (4)
22 Eat up! (4-2)
23 An invasion or hostile attack (6)

DOWN

1 Affectedly modest or shy (6)
2 A strand or cluster of hair (4)
3 Blindly imitative (7)
4 A mistake resulting from inattention (5)
5 Arrange in tabular form (8)
6 Humanistic, caring for animals maybe (6)
12 Something of sentimental value, souvenir (8)
14 A small fireproof dish (7)
16 One of a kind (6)
18 Having short sharp turns or angles (6)
19 With a forward motion (5)
21 Anything that serves as an enticement (4)

Colossal Book of Crosswords

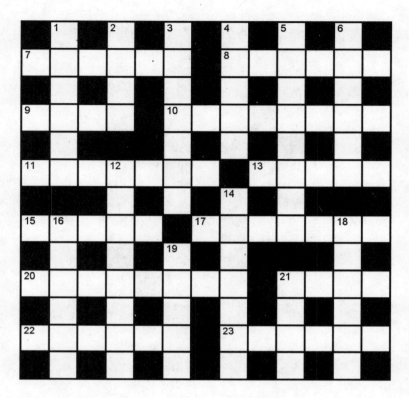

ACROSS

7 Someone who wilfully destroys property (6)
8 In accordance with truth or fact or reality (6)
9 Close (4)
10 In the centre of a boat (8)
11 Bearing great pain without complaint (7)
13 Not real (5)
15 Alter (5)
17 A tide in the same direction as the wind (3,4)
20 Lasting for just a moment (8)
21 Male hen (4)
22 Sell or offer for sale from place to place (6)
23 Go back, like hair? (6)

DOWN

1 A small soft bag (6)
2 Cut text to fit space in a magazine (4)
3 An annual publication (7)
4 Pipe to take away waste water (5)
5 Rotating shaft in car engine that lifts valves (8)
6 Braided or twisted hair (6)
12 An indirect (and usually malicious) implication (8)
14 A state of extreme poverty or destitution (7)
16 Wooden hammer used in carpentry (6)
18 10 years (6)
19 Bee houses (5)
21 Prepare gun for firing (4)

ACROSS

6 A heavy rain (6)
7 Lacking experience of life (6)
8 Wood heaped for funeral (4)
10 Anticipated event that turns out to be far less significant than was expected (3-5)
11 Artists following the school of cubism! (7)
13 Belligerence aroused by a real or supposed wrong (5)
16 Increasing the size of a bet (5)
18 Line on map indicating height (7)
21 A meeting of elected or appointed representatives (8)
22 A musical work is mixed soup! (4)
23 Not similar to (6)
24 Intelligent (6)

DOWN

1 Stringed instrument (4)
2 The principal theme in a speech - keen toy! (7)
3 Very little - possibly clothing? (5)
4 Slavonic language speaker? (4)
5 Rebound from an impact (6)
6 A brief swim in water (3)
9 Second person pronoun; the person addressed (3)
12 A badge worn to show official position (8)
14 Fishing device (3)
15 A loosely woven coarse fabric of cotton (7)
17 Administer an oil to, embrocate (6)
19 Not yet used or soiled (6)
20 Put someone off something (5)
22 Not closed (4)

Colossal Book of Crosswords

ACROSS

6 Fish from the sea (6)
7 Looking glass (6)
8 Look quickly (4)
10 A search for knowledge (8)
11 Do away with (7)
13 A smooth surface in a cut diamond (5)
16 Soreness and warmth caused by friction (5)
18 A knight of a religious military order (7)
20 Being in good health - grill hat! (3,5)
21 Get better (4)
23 A fortification of earth (6)
24 A noisy fight (6)

DOWN

1 Ice skating arena (4)
2 Pledge in marriage (7)
3 Break into pieces (5)
4 An elaborate song for solo voice (4)
5 Knobbly wool - cub Leo! (6)
6 Vim, vigour, pizzazz! (3)
9 The outward flow of the tide (3)
12 Of lower quality (8)
14 Egyptian cobra (3)
15 Having no personal preference (7)
17 Gas (6)
19 Gemstone (5)
21 The handle of a weapon or tool (4)
22 A mythical Greek hero (4)

ACROSS

5 Valuable source of caviar (6)
6 Type of chair and 60s teenager! (6)
7 Water supply (4)
9 Indian plant used as dye and in cooking (8)
10 Scent (7)
12 Black bird (5)
15 March or homeless person (5)
17 Poorness (7)
18 Books for stamps, photographs, etc (6)
20 The persistence of a sound, resound (4)
22 In truth - all rye! (6)
23 Send or sell abroad (6)

DOWN

1 Throw (4)
2 Time after sunrise and before sunset (7)
3 A dull persistent pain (4)
4 Obtain from (6)
5 Weapon, could be long or cross! (3)
6 Not easily found, undercooked meat? (4)
8 The organ of sight (3)
11 In a superlative manner - of asylum! (8)
13 Beer (3)
14 Scary chaps? - bony Meg! (4-3)
16 Hair curler (6)
19 River in Hades (4)
20 Catch sight of (4)
21 The present location; this place (4)

ACROSS

7 Envelop - fondle! (6)
8 Three legged camera stand (6)
9 Payment for release of accused pre trial (4)
10 A journey or flight over a long distance (4,4)
11 Give a speech to (7)
13 One who fights in gloves (5)
15 Any distracting manouver, dummy (5)
17 Small fish (7)
20 Female ogres! (8)
21 A strong restless desire (4)
22 Woman's equivalent of male shirt? (6)
23 Not subject to - taxation for example (6)

DOWN

1 Going forward, like Christian soldiers? (6)
2 Work hard, labour, slog (4)
3 Love unquestioningly and uncritically (7)
4 Hold one's ground; maintain a position (5)
5 Keep back, information maybe? (8)
6 Small rounded wartlike protuberance on a plant (6)
12 The competitor who finishes second (6-2)
14 Stumble - spits me! (7)
16 Flow over or cover completely (6)
18 Leave out (6)
19 Someone employed to conduct others (5)
21 In the Roman calendar: the 15th of March (4)

ACROSS

7 Well-seasoned stew of meat and vegetables (6)
8 Of or relating to or resembling the eye (6)
9 Any small compartment (4)
10 Surpassing what is common or usual or expected (8)
11 Hero-worship (7)
13 Break (5)
15 Unit of weight, imperial (5)
17 Slender and supple (7)
20 Footwear to get you across snow (4-4)
21 A typeface with thick heavy lines (4)
22 Type of hedge (6)
23 Place of work (6)

DOWN

1 Butt of cigarette (3-3)
2 Sheep covering (4)
3 Non believer (7)
4 Flower (5)
5 Gives in to desire (8)
6 Annoy persistently (6)
12 A frequency less than 300 kilohertz (4,4)
14 Part of aircraft wing controls lateral motion (7)
16 Vast treeless plain in the arctic (6)
18 Malevolence, spite (6)
19 Photograph in short! (5)
21 Polish or expert (4)

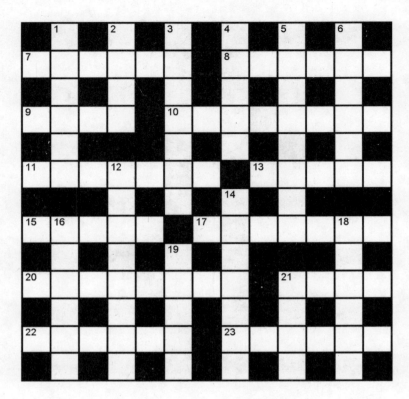

ACROSS

7 Take up or begin anew (6)
8 A plot of ground where plants are cultivated (6)
9 Single channel sound (4)
10 Get started (8)
11 A small globe or ball (7)
13 Not the same one (5)
15 Liquid holder (5)
17 A long, formal letter, sometimes biblical (7)
20 Strip of cloth for decoration or advertising (8)
21 Cipher (4)
22 System of measurement, weight, etc (6)
23 Large deep serving dish with a cover (6)

DOWN

1 Spot, stain, or pollute (6)
2 Monetary unit in Europe since 1999 (4)
3 A sudden and violent collapse (7)
4 Used as a gemstone and for making mortars and pestles (5)
5 Formality in bearing and appearance (8)
6 Grow teeth; cut the baby teeth (6)
12 The craft of basket making (8)
14 Direct or control; projects, businesses, etc. (7)
16 The last one in a list (6)
18 Climbing device (6)
19 Hit, or have a hint of (5)
21 Rope, string, line (4)

Colossal Book of Crosswords

ACROSS

7 Flatten the ends (of nails and rivets) (6)
8 A retail merchant (6)
9 The first light of day (4)
10 Tree fluid (3)
11 A booking for musicians (4)
12 Family (7)
14 A small mallet used by a judge (5)
16 Overgrown, thin and weak (5)
18 Herb used with dandelion to make drink (7)
21 You (8)
22 Morally reprehensible (4)
23 A room in a church (6)
24 Engage or engross wholly (6)

DOWN

1 Water-soluble compounds that turn litmus blue (6)
2 Unknown author (4)
3 Grim, macabre (7)
4 Wide open (5)
5 Written in pen or pencil on paper, not typed! (8)
6 Dog breed (6)
13 United under a central government (8)
15 A person who amuses others by ridiculous behavior (7)
17 A tactical missile (6)
19 The civil and religious leader of a Muslim state (6)
20 The chief source of beryllium (5)
22 Workshop gripping device (4)

Colossal Book of Crosswords

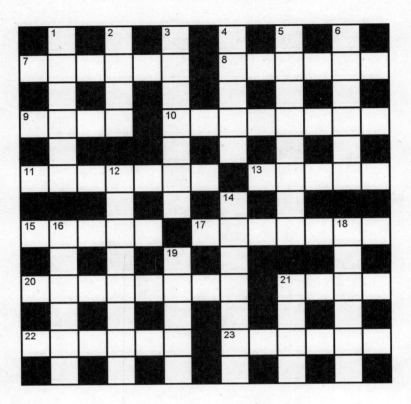

ACROSS

7 Response to order from ship's captain (3-3)
8 Insightfulness (6)
9 Flower (4)
10 Post for flag (8)
11 Building - dice fie! (7)
13 Express strong disapproval of (5)
15 Literary composition (5)
17 Support oneself, survive (7)
20 Unable to appreciate music, hearing problem (4-4)
21 A short light gust of air (4)
22 The back side of the neck (6)
23 Wrench, twist (6)

DOWN

1 Produced by crossbreeding (6)
2 Erratic deflections from an intended course (4)
3 Cannot be made better or improved (7)
4 Causing or resulting in death (5)
5 Hold back or suppress (8)
6 An official appointed to count votes (6)
12 Change from a waking to a sleeping state, quickly through exhaustion (5,3)
14 Cause to spread or flush or flood through (7)
16 A surface burn (6)
18 Added to the end of a word (6)
19 Muscular and heavily built (5)
21 Break up (4)

ACROSS

7 Whine in a tearful manner (6)
8 Cream puff (6)
9 A unit of length equal to 3 feet (4)
10 Female equivalent of a count or earl (8)
11 Something that baffles (7)
13 Fasten a boat to a bitt, pin, or cleat (5)
16 Pastime (5)
18 Hypersensitivity reaction to a particular allergen (7)
21 A person who worships idols (8)
22 The rounded seed-bearing capsule of cotton (4)
23 A city on the Zhu Jiang delta (6)
24 Untie or unfasten, unwrap (6)

DOWN

1 Anxious (6)
2 Marked by active interest and enthusiasm (4)
3 A sign posted in a public place as an advertisement (7)
4 Worked up emotionally by anger (3,2)
5 Plentiful supply, too many of (4)
6 Unhealthy vapour (6)
12 Arrange in table form (8)
14 Organ of sight (3)
15 Erupt or intensify suddenly (5-2)
17 Old fashioned (3,3)
19 Soft blue-grey mineral; lead sulphide (6)
20 Bad smell (5)
22 Small child (4)

Colossal Book of Crosswords

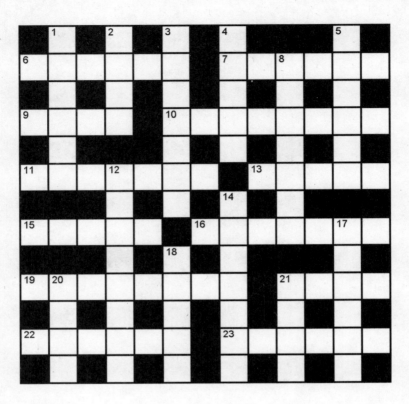

ACROSS

6 Tree (6)
7 Open, break seal (6)
9 Plant of the genus Linum grown to make cloth (4)
10 A metal post supporting an outdoor lamp (8)
11 Matching skirt and cardigan (7)
13 Very tired (5)
15 The mass of eggs deposited by fish (5)
16 Throwing spear (7)
19 Cloth with grooves (8)
21 A sleeveless garment like a cloak (4)
22 Throat - voice box (6)
23 Disturb the smoothness of (6)

DOWN

1 A large sea wave (6)
2 A flow or discharge (4)
3 Suffer from intense heat (7)
4 Extremely pleasing to the sense of taste (5)
5 German emperor (6)
8 Greatest in status or authority or power (7)
12 The period of time that is happening now (8)
14 Cord worn round the neck to hold a whistle (7)
17 Pierce with a sharp stake or point (6)
18 A person authorised to act for another (5)
20 Rounded like an egg (4)
21 Search thoroughly (4)

ACROSS

7 Remove carbon from engine (6)
8 Fruit (6)
9 Ceremonial elegance and splendour (4)
10 Turned or twisted toward one side (8)
11 Saboteur - demolition expert (7)
13 An acute but unspecific feeling of anxiety; (5)
15 Acquire or gain knowledge or skills (5)
17 Move with slow, sinuous movements (7)
20 Make useful again (7)
22 The motion characteristic of fluid (4)
23 The position of professor (5)
24 Loudspeaker system (6)

DOWN

1 Heavy fabric that resembles velvet (6)
2 A rigid circular band of metal or wood (4)
3 Properly nourished (4-3)
4 A car with two doors and front seats (5)
5 A large estate in Spanish-speaking countries (8)
6 Come out of, exit (6)
12 Motor vehicle (3)
14 Reduce to ashes (7)
16 Make richer (6)
18 Bring back luck; be a source of misfortune (6)
19 A fencing sword (5)
21 Cajole (4)
22 Canine tooth of a carnivorous animal (4)

ACROSS

6 Possible choice (6)
8 Brought together (6)
9 An enclosure in a court of law (4)
10 A game invented by American indians (8)
11 A leisurely walk (6)
13 Causing death (5)
15 The skin that covers the top of the head (5)
17 A native or inhabitant of Russia (7)
20 Having a sophisticated charm (8)
21 Make an etching of (4)
22 Security, money held as bond (6)
23 Drag (4)

DOWN

1 Begin to grow, brussels? (6)
2 Take a chance on (4)
3 Rabbit house (5)
4 Spectacles with 2 lens powers (8)
5 A Japanese woman entertainer (6)
7 No score (3)
12 Bystander who observes (8)
14 Supreme head (7)
16 The cavity in which the large intestine begins (6)
18 Grow by addition, as of capital (6)
19 Forest god, lecher (5)

ACROSS

3 Head gear (3)
7 Group of three (4)
8 Sponge (6)
9 Sac or bladderlike structure (4)
10 Happen simultaneously (8)
11 Identical or non identical sibling (4)
13 Short company, as in web URL? (2)
14 Flower (5)
16 The ermine in its brown summer coat (5)
18 The arch of hair above each eye (7)
21 A liquid mixture containing pesticides used on farms (5-3)
22 Hard work (4)
24 Pet bird (6)
25 Unequivocally detestable (6)

DOWN

1 A wild gathering involving promiscuity (4)
2 Make softer (6)
3 Dream up, as a plan (7)
4 Ordinary, unflavoured (5)
5 Fencing term (6)
6 A provocative Spanish courtship dance (8)
12 Vigilant (8)
15 Indication of an illness (7)
17 Take revenge for a perceived wrong (6)
19 Become active, rouse (6)
20 Milk gland of cow (5)
23 Egg cell (4)

Colossal Book of Crosswords

ACROSS

7 Horizontal sculptured band (6)
8 The first or preliminary coat of paint (6)
9 The least powerful chessman (4)
10 Gold vaults in Goldfinger (4,4)
11 An idea accepted as a demonstrable truth (7)
13 An organisation of military naval forces (4)
16 An inquiry (5)
19 With no fixed direction (7)
22 Hopefully looking forward (8)
23 Wood (4)
24 A chessman (6)
25 Male feline (3-3)

DOWN

1 Flower arrangement for christmas (6)
2 Angle, incline (4)
3 An extract of beef in liquid drink (4,3)
4 Style of abstractionism popular in the 1960s (2,3)
5 Colour (4)
6 A succession of notes (6)
12 The capital and largest city of Japan (3)
14 A pointed tool for making holes (3)
15 Say out loud for the purpose of recording (7)
17 Complain, moan (6)
18 Card game (6)
20 A lane at sea (6)
21 A spotted or calico horse or pony (5)
23 Overcome the wildness of an animal (4)

ACROSS

7 Money paid out (6)
8 A forceful forward attack (6)
9 Adhesive (4)
10 Water (8)
11 A word formed from the initial letters of a multi-word name (7)
13 Identifying sticker (5)
15 Group of eight (5)
17 Time for sleep (7)
20 Surround (8)
21 Ceramic wall cover (4)
22 Agree, come together (6)
23 Rub away, sand down (6)

DOWN

1 Community (6)
2 Evidence that helps to solve a problem (4)
3 What You See Is What You Get (7)
4 Goods vehicle (5)
5 Show off, loudmouth (8)
6 Deadly fly (6)
12 Clothing item fashioned in a single piece (3-5)
14 Old soldier (7)
16 A ravine formed by a river (6)
18 Illness (6)
19 Neckwear (5)
21 Rubber car wheel cover (4)

Colossal Book of Crosswords

ACROSS

7 A body of people who settle far from home (6)
8 Covered with growing trees (6)
9 Characteristic of a man (4)
10 Idol worshipper (8)
11 Feathers (7)
13 Frequently (5)
15 Relative magnitude (5)
17 Complacently or inanely foolish (7)
20 Soldiers collectively (8)
22 Blow gently (4)
23 Earlier (6)
24 Sour (6)

DOWN

1 Unlawfully delivered ball in cricket (2-4)
2 The underside of footwear or a golfclub (4)
3 A medical instrument used to inject (7)
4 Pounce (5)
5 Traditional French stew (3-2-3)
6 Become faint or more distant (6)
12 Shortened form of Melanie or Melvin (3)
14 A rope for raising a flag (7)
16 Cupboard (6)
18 Biased (6)
19 Make reference to (5)
21 When this shuts, will another open? (4)
22 Part of bird (4)

ACROSS

7 Type of sleeve (6)
8 Groups of fighting forces (6)
9 An involuntary intake of breath when tired (4)
10 Coordinate (8)
11 One word that means the same as another word (7)
13 Mindless (5)
15 Clean with one's bill, of birds (5)
17 Number (7)
20 From where magicians get things? (4,3)
21 One twelfth part of a foot (4)
22 Fruit (6)
23 Be more cunning than (6)

DOWN

1 A sudden desire, impulse - a gravy! (6)
2 Kin (4)
3 Word that expresses opposite of another word (7)
4 Feature that is regarded as a sign of status (5)
5 Distinction (8)
6 English admiral (6)
12 Dutifully complying with commands (8)
14 Opening in car to allow sun to shine in (3-4)
16 Give up working (6)
18 Device to hold boat in position (6)
19 Face in gemstone (5)
21 Smallest amount possible (4)

ACROSS

7 French cheese (4)
8 Number (6)
9 Torture device (4)
10 Excessively greedy and grasping (8)
11 Throw into great confusion or disorder (7)
13 Normal (5)
15 Decree (5)
17 Top of stairs leading to bedrooms (7)
20 Container top fastened by turning (5,3)
21 A slow pace of running gets pole mixed up! (4)
22 Lack of agreement or harmony (6)
23 Brilliancy (6)

DOWN

1 A covered passageway (6)
2 An incidental benefit (4)
3 Bravery (7)
4 Drag (5)
5 Suffered anguish (8)
6 Lines of verse (6)
12 Grant credentials to (8)
14 Traditional post for dancing round (7)
16 Social grace (6)
18 Linens for the dining table - pre any! (6)
19 Freshwater carnivorous mammal (5)
21 Gradual decline in amount or activity (4)

ACROSS

7 Selection (6)
8 Lock away in jail (4,2)
9 Shatter or smash (4)
10 Give the final details for (8)
11 Valve having five electrodes - not deep! (7)
13 Begin, commence (5)
15 Famous Churchill signal! (1-4)
17 An encampment of huts (7)
20 Soccer (8)
21 Yobbo (4)
22 Spanish currency (6)
23 Desk or office (6)

DOWN

1 Breathe with difficulty (6)
2 A sharp bend in a line (4)
3 An act of deliberate betrayal (7)
4 Black wood (5)
5 Character in a novel by Harriet Beecher Stowe (5,3)
6 Financial officer (6)
12 In collaboration (8)
14 Song sung to baby to help it sleep (7)
16 Digger (6)
18 Of or relating to the nervous system (6)
19 Radio detection and ranging (5)
21 A harp used by ancient Greeks (4)

ACROSS

7 Move to and fro (6)
8 Mariner (6)
9 Large sweet juicy fruit (4)
10 Grow weak and thin (8)
11 Under (7)
13 Jewelled headdress (5)
15 Make available for sale (5)
17 Seer, oracle (7)
20 Cookies (8)
22 Near in space or time (4)
24 Come up with a new idea (6)
25 Of or relating to the sea (6)

DOWN

1 Male monarch (4)
2 Set light to (6)
3 Number (7)
4 Analyze (5)
5 Large North American deer (6)
6 Wine from around Bordeaux in France (8)
12 Fairies that are somewhat mischievous (3)
14 Wearisome (7)
16 Go over the limit (6)
18 Larder (6)
19 Land that is worked by ploughing (5)
21 Hotel providing overnight lodging (3)
23 Metal plate that is struck with a soft-headed drumstick (4)

Colossal Book of Crosswords

ACROSS

7 Summerhouse (6)
8 Not straightforward or candid (6)
9 An acrobatic feat (4)
10 A state of diffused or dim illumination (8)
11 Taken out (4,3)
13 Strange (5)
15 Any of various small plant-sucking insects (5)
17 A native or inhabitant of Russia (7)
20 Anise-flavored Greek liquor (4)
21 Resinlike substance secreted by certain insects (3)
22 Amount of medication to take (4)
24 Bring sound up gradually (4-2)
25 Home appliance that cleans by suction (6)

DOWN

1 Bucket (4)
2 A dictator or dictatorial person (6)
3 Strengthen against attack (7)
4 Conjuring (5)
5 Exert much effort or energy (6)
6 Elation (8)
12 Betrothal - pauses lo! (8)
14 Russian principality in the 13th to 16th centuries (7)
16 Pressed with a hot tool (6)
18 Lure or entice away from duty (6)
19 Put firmly in the mind (5)
23 Refuse to acknowledge (4)

Colossal Book of Crosswords

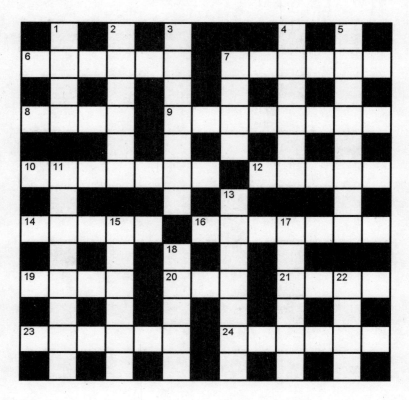

ACROSS

6 Earnest (6)
7 Causing suffering and pain (6)
8 Voluntary contributions to aid the poor (4)
9 Make longer (8)
10 Someone who cuts or beautifies hair (7)
12 Optical glass block (5)
14 From that time (5)
16 Largest city and financial centre of Israel (3,4)
19 Animal shelter (4)
20 Fish (3)
21 A characteristic state or mode of living (4)
23 Plague (6)
24 A source of danger (6)

DOWN

1 The rind of a fruit (4)
2 Lymphatic tissue one on the side of the oral pharynx (6)
3 Fashionable (7)
4 A man who courts a woman (6)
5 Ride over water on skis (5-3)
7 Group of musicians (4)
11 Three wheeled cycle (8)
13 Rich (7)
15 Priesthood (6)
17 Well alight (6)
18 Bunk on ship or train (5)
22 Eating implement with prongs (4)

539

Colossal Book of Crosswords

ACROSS

7 Small wolf (6)
8 Carefree and happy and lighthearted (6)
9 Not short! (4)
10 Letter container (8)
11 Make milk (7)
13 Wind or electric powered instrument (5)
15 A woman who has recently been married (5)
17 Having an agreeably pungent taste (7)
20 A toiletry designed to beautify the body (8)
21 Any uninterrupted stream or discharge (4)
23 An elaborate and systematic plan of action (6)
24 Grand Turk (6)

DOWN

1 Game played on horseback (4)
2 Be unable to remember (6)
3 A reminder of past events, souvenir (7)
4 Higher than (5)
5 Boat steering device (6)
6 A clergyman ministering to some institution (8)
12 An organisation of military air forces (3,5)
14 Formed by forcing molten metal into a mould (3-4)
16 Moisten (6)
18 Open to the view (6)
19 Allow to soak (5)
22 Flattened square, egg shape (4)

Colossal Book of Crosswords

ACROSS

6 Dull and uninteresting (6)
7 An offensive against an enemy (6)
9 A strand or cluster of hair in a coil shape (4)
10 Major items of military weaponry (8)
11 Narrowly restricted in outlook or scope (7)
13 Look forward to the probably occurrence of (5)
15 Tobacco powder inhaled through nose (5)
17 Human powered vehicle (7)
20 For ever (8)
21 A persistently annoying person (4)
22 Choose (6)
23 At rest (6)

DOWN

1 Text block in newspaper (6)
2 Herb (4)
3 An intellectual (who is bald?) (7)
4 Wed (5)
5 Passenger hiding aboard ship, not paying! (8)
8 Breed of dog (5)
12 Lacking in development, immature (8)
14 Half way through the year - me dairy! (3-4)
16 Crackpot - ten rut! (6)
18 Hear with intention (6)
19 Filled or abounding with light fog (5)
21 Pallid (4)

Colossal Book of Crosswords

ACROSS

7 Put into words or an expression (6)
8 Exceedingly harmful (6)
9 Rotate, like political doctor? (4)
10 A periodic paperback publication (8)
11 General fear or worry (7)
13 Era (5)
15 Cutting device (5)
17 Inexpensive showy collectible (7)
20 Runaway (8)
21 A challenge to do something dangerous (4)
22 A slight wind (6)
23 Make equal, uniform (6)

DOWN

1 Composer (6)
2 Early morning light (4)
3 Ant-like social insect that feeds on wood (7)
4 Condensed but memorable saying (5)
5 Almond paste and egg whites (8)
6 Health facility (6)
12 During a flight, like the movie? (2-6)
14 Free from tears (3-4)
16 Sickness (6)
18 A mistake in printed matter (6)
19 A daily written record, usually personal (5)
21 Musical percussion instrument (4)

Colossal Book of Crosswords

ACROSS

7 Interment (6)
8 Borne on the water (6)
9 A sudden impact (4)
10 Volunteer cavalry force organised in 1761 (8)
11 Smug self-serving earnestness (7)
13 There you are - from the french (5)
15 Great pain (5)
17 Strike in which workers refuse to leave the workplace (7)
20 Of imposing height (8)
21 Metropolis (4)
22 Having the properties of glue (6)
23 Serviette (6)

DOWN

1 Incite to commit a crime - or buns! (6)
2 Mud or clay deposited by a river (4)
3 A man devoted to the pursuit of pleasure (7)
4 A priest (5)
5 Organic compound - dial kola! (8)
6 Small individual study area in a library (6)
12 Leaning, disposition, propensity (8)
14 Formation of masts, spars, sails, etc (7)
16 Development (6)
18 On the inside (6)
19 Shiny and tough and flexible plastic (5)
21 A strip of land projecting into a body of water (4)

Colossal Book of Crosswords

ACROSS

7 Money returned to a payer (6)
8 Drink made with eggs and alcohol (6)
9 Small parasite (4)
10 Outside (8)
11 Contained within (7)
13 Saint (5)
15 Art gallery (5)
17 Confused (5-2)
20 Pigs' feet (8)
21 Let or cause to fall in drops (4)
22 Make hard or harder (6)
23 Nerve cell - on rune! (6)

DOWN

1 Madhouse (6)
2 Large American feline resembling a lion (4)
3 In an opposing direction (7)
4 Contemptibly narrow in outlook (5)
5 Break the heart of; cause to feel sorrow (8)
6 Showing a brooding ill humour, glum (6)
12 High noon - at sea? - intone do! (8)
14 A difference of opinion (7)
16 Antenna (6)
18 Occurring together or simultaneously (6)
19 Flower (5)
21 Showing a brooding ill humour (4)

ACROSS

6 Depart (6)
7 Relating to or associated with flowers (6)
8 A fastener that serves to join (4)
9 Instrumentalities (tools or implements) made of metal (8)
11 In progress (7)
13 Cloth - I sell! (5)
15 Old saying (5)
17 Cautiously attentive (7)
20 At the start - ion tibia! (2,6)
21 Throw - pancakes? (4)
22 Dishevel (6)
23 Untie or unfasten (6)

DOWN

1 Archaic terms for army, possibly foreign? (6)
2 Adult male chicken (4)
3 In a casually inconsiderate manner (7)
4 Burning (5)
5 Half of the Stanley and Oliver duo (6)
10 Dispense with (5)
12 Musician (8)
14 17th century decorative art and architecture (7)
16 One who owes money (6)
18 Of or relating to similar to bears - insure! (6)
19 Metal (5)
21 Wind instrument (4)

ACROSS

1 A long walk (4)
3 Showed submission or fear (7)
8 A person who is deemed to be despicable (2-3-2)
9 A hard kind of stone used by cave people (5)
10 Defence used to establish whereabouts (5)
11 Adornment consisting of an ornamental ribbon (6)
13 Glacial period (3,3)
15 Fault (6)
18 Decent, right and proper (6)
20 A long pointed rod used as a weapon (5)
23 With frutti gives an ice cream! (5)
24 (Japanese) very thinly sliced raw fish - is Amish? (7)
25 Nautical (8)
26 Printed characters (4)

DOWN

1 An American whose first language was Spanish (8)
2 Colour of military uniform (5)
3 Selection (6)
4 Thin disk of unleavened bread (5)
5 A horizontal plant stem (7)
6 A meeting arranged in advance (4)
7 Advancing slowly, as if by inches (6)
12 Anaesthetise with ether (8)
14 A citizen who has a legal right to vote (7)
16 Sign up to join the armed forces (6)
17 A common white mineral used in plaster of paris (6)
19 Damp (5)
21 Loud (5)
22 The tube of a tobacco pipe (4)

Colossal Book of Crosswords

ACROSS

7 Calf bone (6)
8 Holy man (6)
9 Heave, pant, puff (4)
10 Early morning moisture (3)
11 Raise money by working (4)
12 Move forward (7)
14 Bird song (5)
16 Seize power (5)
18 Missile launched from submarine (7)
21 Merchant vessels (8)
22 Lie adjacent to another, adjoin directly (4)
23 Feel grief; eat one's heart out, mourn (6)
24 Sufficient (6)

DOWN

1 Reptile (6)
2 Something that bulges out (4)
3 Sea fish (7)
4 Fish eggs (5)
5 Building that would be hard to get out of in a fire (8)
6 To do with the stars in the sky (6)
13 Velocity travelled in an aircraft (8)
15 Place where dead bodies are kept (6)
17 A particular environment or walk of life (6)
19 One who works hard at boring tasks (6)
20 A cord or band of inelastic tissue (5)
22 One who is away or absent without leave (4)

ACROSS

6 Spittle (6)
7 Temper (6)
9 Speck (4)
10 Enclosed, as of a knife or sword (8)
11 Gnawing animal (7)
13 Small crude shelter used as a dwelling (5)
15 Rubber-based paint (5)
17 A small container (7)
20 Go crazy - out faker! (5-3)
21 Fit and nimble (4)
22 A member of the United States Marine Corps (6)
23 Part of a flower (6)

DOWN

1 Head (6)
2 A tubular wind instrument (4)
3 Screaming ghost (7)
4 Made public, shown - like teeth? (5)
5 Smarmy (8)
8 Woman's name (5)
12 Scene, situation (8)
14 Sacrament for entry into church (7)
16 Antenna (6)
18 Food store, pantry (6)
19 A small flock of grouse or partridge (5)
21 Submerge in a liquid and leave there (4)

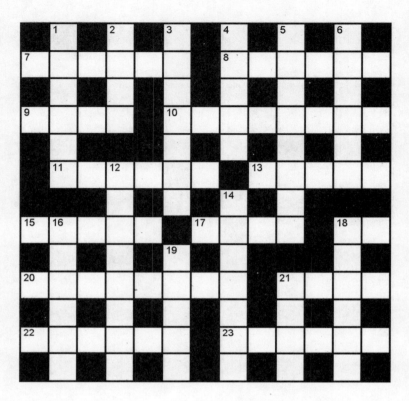

ACROSS

7 Respectful deference (6)
8 Colour of bananas (6)
9 Look with amazement; look stupidly (4)
10 Wedged or packed in together, like teeth? (8)
11 A native of ancient Troy (6)
13 The combined stakes of the betters (5)
15 Brief description given for purposes of identification (5)
17 Reflecting optimism (4)
18 Out of bed (2)
20 Filled with or evoking sadness (8)
21 A polite name for any woman (4)
22 Grating that admits cooling air to car's radiator (6)
23 A slight movement of the air (6)

DOWN

1 Atomic number 27 and a dark blue paint (6)
2 Be behind; approve of (4)
3 Numbered by tens; based on ten (7)
4 Thin coagulable fluid containing white blood cells (5)
5 Briskness (8)
6 Annoy continually or chronically (6)
12 Rule against, overturn previous decision (8)
14 Seeking advancement or recognition (5-2)
16 On a ship, train, plane or other vehicle (6)
18 Bring to the latest state of technology (6)
19 Make available for sale (5)
21 Plant related to onions (4)

ACROSS

7 Salad fruit (6)
8 Not moving (6)
9 Remain (4)
10 Attaining a goal (8)
11 Tooth doctor (7)
13 Yearbook (5)
15 Evidence (5)
17 Expectorated (7)
20 Stone carver (8)
21 Goes hard like concrete (4)
22 Participated in games or sports (6)
23 The dark part of the diurnal cycle considered a time unit (5)

DOWN

1 Glass or plastic vessel (6)
2 Be subject to change (4)
3 Someone who travels for pleasure (7)
4 Written composition (5)
5 Water travel for pleasure (8)
6 The contestant who wins the contest (6)
12 Tram (7)
14 Raining heavily (7)
16 Bring back to mind (6)
18 Everything you own (6)
19 A detailed critical inspection (5)
21 Affix your signature (4)

ACROSS

3 Drinking vessel (3)
7 The general condition of body and mind (6)
8 Male red deer (4)
9 Verse form (4)
10 Travel to or penetrate into (8)
11 Breaks away from captivity (7)
13 6th (5)
15 Of superior grade (5)
17 Instructions that a computer can execute (7)
20 Reflected brightly (8)
21 Animal pelts (4)
22 Derived benefit from (6)
23 Consuming food (6)

DOWN

1 Someone who fights for a cause (6)
2 Slender (4)
3 Given encouragement to (7)
4 Flower (5)
5 Selecting (8)
6 Take into custody (6)
12 Showing or feeling admiration (8)
14 Baby beds with sides and rockers (7)
16 Do over again (6)
18 Protective clothing items (6)
19 Move smoothly and effortlessly (5)
21 Sudden uncontrollable attacks of bad temper (4)

Colossal Book of Crosswords

ACROSS

7 Try out (6)
8 Shown to be true through evidence (6)
9 Most important part (4)
10 Falling, bird waste? (8)
11 The front and back covering of a book (7)
13 Conformity to reality or actuality (5)
15 With sincerity; without pretence (5)
17 In a punctual manner (7)
20 Frozen dessert (3-5)
21 Unfreeze (4)
22 Glass or plastic vessel for liquid (6)
23 Producing exhaustion (6)

DOWN

1 Overland journey by hunters (6)
2 A clear or unobstructed space (4)
3 Giving food to (7)
4 Paved surface where aircraft stand while not being used (5)
5 Examined and noted the similarities or differences of (8)
6 Underground pod of the peanut vine (6)
12 To be handled with care, breakable (8)
14 Protective head gear for motorcyclists (7)
16 Expect, believe, or suppose (6)
18 Gained knowledge or skills (6)
19 Put off (5)
21 Rotate (4)

Colossal Book of Crosswords

ACROSS

7 Outdoor meal (6)
8 Repeated each week (6)
9 A being of great strength and courage (4)
10 Bring back to mind (8)
11 Dried grapes (7)
13 Wrath (5)
15 Sand sloping down to the water of a sea (5)
17 Cooked by radiant heat (7)
20 Men of war (8)
21 Woman married to her husband (4)
22 Middle (6)
23 Consider reasonable or due (6)

DOWN

1 Place to see films (6)
2 Cause to become loose (4)
3 Frightening (7)
4 Low land that is seasonally flooded (5)
5 Final station (8)
6 Part of garment containing arm (6)
12 Protection (8)
14 In clothes (7)
16 Rubber item used to remove pencil lines (6)
18 Cause to happen or occur (6)
19 Long rods used in vaulting (5)
21 Cried (4)

Colossal Book of Crosswords

ACROSS

7 People who can fly aircraft (6)
8 The body of citizens of a state or country (6)
9 Travel on the surface of water (4)
10 Beer (3)
11 Grand Duke of Muscovy (1440-1505) (4)
12 Exposed or shown briefly (7)
14 Narrowing of body between ribs and hips (5)
16 Emblem (5)
18 Be composed of (7)
21 Small book for notes! (8)
22 Hammer god (4)
23 Involving the joint activity of two or more (6)
24 Cause to move around or rotate (6)

DOWN

1 Metallic element used in alloys (6)
2 Weaving machine (4)
3 Gets away (7)
4 Velocity (5)
5 Days off (8)
6 Remains on the surface of a liquid (6)
13 Drop a hint; intimate by a hint (8)
15 A small pouch in a garment (7)
17 In the area or vicinity (6)
19 Digging tool (6)
20 Lines made of twisted fibers or threads (5)
22 Ripped (4)

Colossal Book of Crosswords

ACROSS

7 Nyasaland (6)
8 Capital of England (6)
9 Fit to do the job asked (4)
11 Bearings (8)
12 Cavities where a pieces of equipment fit in (7)
14 In the middle of (5)
16 Space in roof void of house (5)
18 Which ever person (7)
21 Foreign travel document (8)
22 Segments of the trunk of a tree (4)
23 Rubble left after destructive event (6)
24 Be in charge of, act on, or dispose of (6)

DOWN

1 Jane Austin heroine (4)
2 Cost of travel (4)
3 Angling (7)
4 Coat that goes with dagger when secret! (5)
5 Going on forever (8)
6 Clears throat (6)
10 Scary shout! (3)
13 Hinged cutters (8)
15 Beats (7)
17 Go from one place to another (6)
19 Mesh, as in a gearbox (6)
20 Drink to the health of someone (5)
22 Lasting for a prolonged period (4)

555

ACROSS

7 Torn strips of cloth - leading to riches? (4)
8 Do without food (6)
9 Incline head in agreement (3)
10 Compass point (4)
12 Pulling along the floor, taking a long time (8)
13 Parts of garment (7)
15 Push down hard on (5)
17 Group featuring Paul McCartney after The Beatles split up (5)
19 Reverse the winding or twisting of (6)
22 In a resentful manner (8)
23 Grabbed between teeth (3)
24 Takes a rest, nods off (6)
25 Latest, most recent (6)

DOWN

1 Tall perennial woody plant (4)
2 Is not! (4)
3 Horse riding seat (6)
4 Written piece (5)
5 Australian marsupial (8)
6 happenings (6)
11 Everyone or everything (3)
14 Number (8)
16 Unfastening bonds (7)
18 Frozen ice drip (6)
20 Most recent (6)
21 Glass refraction block (5)
23 Archery items (4)

ACROSS

6 One time (4)
7 A feeling of friendship and esteem (6)
9 Rodent (3)
10 Plus, in addition (4)
12 Meant (8)
13 Work, as a machine (7)
15 Presents (5)
18 Type of window, uses cord to pull open (4)
19 Plaything that is ridden up and down (6)
22 Starsign (8)
23 Posses (3)
24 Dealers in stolen property (6)
25 Bigger (6)

DOWN

1 Physical exercises leading to mental well being (4)
2 Quantity of none (4)
3 Painter or sculptor (6)
4 Statement than can be proven or verified (5)
5 Holy man or woman (6)
8 Alcoholic drink with juniper berries (3)
11 Once around a race course (3)
14 Investigation, search for knowledge (8)
16 It is, in short (3)
17 Number of watercraft (7)
18 Follow up story (6)
20 Person in first place (6)
21 Slightly drunk (5)
23 Wooden devices for propelling boats (4)

Colossal Book of Crosswords

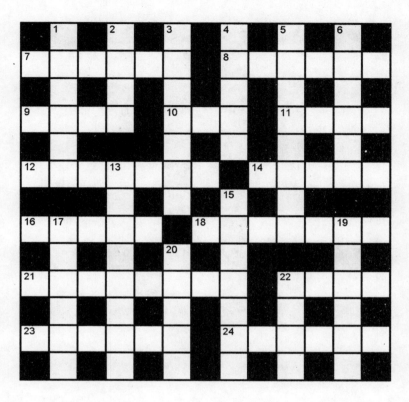

ACROSS

7 Detachment used for security (6)
8 Highest ranking or oldest (6)
9 Having no hair (4)
10 Drink from India and China (3)
11 Naked (4)
12 Large coarse fern (7)
14 Log tossed by a scot? (5)
16 Sound of striking clock (5)
18 From another country (7)
21 Extra vehicle lights used in foggy weather (3-5)
22 Enclosed armoured military vehicle (4)
23 A straight sword and quick wit! (6)
24 Pass on information (6)

DOWN

1 A sale of miscellany; often for charity (6)
2 A small nail (4)
3 A rattling noise (7)
4 State in India where 10 across comes from (5)
5 Fill beyond capacity, deluge (8)
6 Walk unsteadily, as of small children (6)
13 Moan about something (8)
15 The layer of soil on the surface (3-4)
17 Hubble-bubble, water pipe for cooling smoke (6)
19 Scaffolding or framework (6)
20 A region of complete shadow (5)
22 The finishing line for a foot race (4)

ACROSS

5 Descend down vertical surface with ropes (6)
7 Come up with a new idea (6)
9 Resist a trend (4)
10 Time signal (3)
11 Hairstyle popular in the 60s (4)
12 Speak in a small quiet voice (7)
14 The basic unit of money in Algeria (5)
16 Archery target (5)
17 Wander aimlessly - manured! (7)
20 Pouched mammal (8)
22 Take note of, listen to (4)
23 Tell the police in advance about a crime (3-3)
24 Instructions and ingredients for cooking (6)

DOWN

1 Wood (4)
2 Applauded or worn out? (7)
3 Quick and energetic - yzpip! (5)
4 To do with aeroplanes (8)
6 Go red with embarrassment (5)
8 John Major's wife (5)
13 Fish that gives caviar (8)
15 Piquant (7)
18 Let off, fee from certain charges or taxes (6)
19 Small remote farm (5)
21 Waterless (4)
22 German white wine (4)

Colossal Book of Crosswords

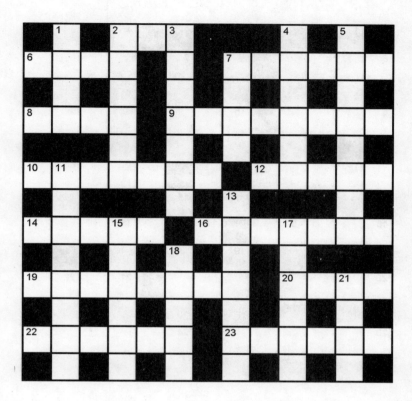

ACROSS

2 Naughty fairy (3)
6 Baby lions (4)
7 Element from sea water (6)
8 Woman's name mistaken for dean? (4)
9 Mixed up (8)
10 A feeling of aversion or antipathy (7)
12 Had or maintained a position (5)
14 Come forth (5)
16 Stupid (7)
19 Breaking out (8)
20 Japanese fighter plane (4)
22 Amount of money you have (6)
23 The nations of the European continent (6)

DOWN

1 Furnish money for a project (4)
2 Jewish republic formerly part of Palestine (6)
3 Thin cake of fried batter (7)
4 Alter or amend (6)
5 In a large quantity (8)
7 Kitchen fitting (4)
11 Asserted (8)
13 Eye protectors (7)
15 Not capable of doing something (6)
17 Reptile or man in lounge? (6)
18 Closely constrained, packed firmly together (5)
21 Ready to pick and eat (4)

ACROSS

6 Deep and often prolonged unconsciousness (4)
7 In an evenhanded manner (6)
8 Feline (3)
9 Swearing to the truth of a statement (4)
10 Make bigger, more or more efficient (8)
11 Internet site (7)
13 Step that goes up on a case (5)
15 Lorry, wagon (5)
17 Collection of things wrapped together (7)
20 Took a court case to a higher court for review (8)
21 At any time (4)
23 Moved with sudden speed (6)
24 Required, wanted (6)

DOWN

1 One-piece cloak worn in ancient Rome (4)
2 Sailing boats (6)
3 Creative people (7)
4 Making no sound (6)
5 Emitting a repeated brief burst of light (8)
7 Thing which can be proven (4)
12 From Europe (8)
14 Intermediate platform in a staircase (7)
16 Boxes with lids (6)
18 Custodian (6)
19 Fly in a non engine powered aircraft (5)
22 Windows of the soul, holes in needles (4)

ACROSS

7 A stately court dance in the 17th century (6)
8 Marine mollusks with rough irregular shell (6)
9 2nd largest city of Brazil (3)
10 Fine ravellings of cotton or linen fibers (4)
11 Whisky, gin or vodka (6)
12 Green vegetable (7)
14 Noisy tower (5)
16 Bare (5)
18 Time during which some action is awaited (4-3)
21 A decorative strip (8)
22 Superfluity of something (4)
23 A tube through which a bullet travels (6)
24 Feeling or showing love and affection (6)

DOWN

1 Colourless vitreous insoluble solid (6)
2 An enclosed conduit for a fluid (4)
3 Lean and sinewy (7)
4 Not tight (5)
5 An approximate calculation (8)
6 Next to, at the side of (6)
13 Entering a building unlawfully (8)
15 Part of bird or flying machine (4)
17 The middle part of insect's body (6)
19 A person who has received a degree (6)
20 Male goat (5)
22 Offer in good faith (4)

Colossal Book of Crosswords

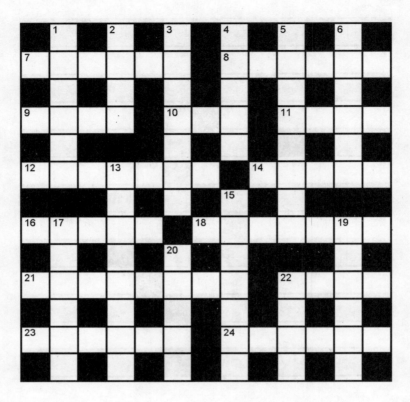

ACROSS

7 Accompany (6)
8 Insect (6)
9 Instrument (4)
10 Idiot (3)
11 Porridge (4)
12 Warm-water seabird (7)
14 Assisted (5)
16 Conjuring (5)
18 Roman magistrate (7)
21 Doodle (8)
22 Travel by horse (4)
23 Modernise (6)
24 Call forth (6)

DOWN

1 Operable (6)
2 Learning by repitition (4)
3 Footstool (7)
4 Astern (5)
5 Bleaching agent (8)
6 Dress (6)
13 Unfriendly (8)
15 Tearless (3-4)
17 Live with (6)
19 Consecrate (6)
20 Church building (5)
22 Precipitation (4)

Colossal Book of Crosswords

ACROSS

7 Bushy (6)
8 On a ship (6)
9 Address God (4)
10 Frozen water (3)
11 Clenched hand (4)
12 Equivalent word (7)
14 Plaything (3)
16 Die away (5)
17 Ladies garment (5)
20 Supplementary material (8)
22 Thug (4)
23 Sausage (6)
24 Lacking enthusiasm (6)

DOWN

1 Drink (6)
2 Unattractive (4)
3 What You See Is What You Get (7)
4 Keen (5)
5 Thrown paper (8)
6 Trustworthy (6)
12 Ocean (3)
13 Be heavier than (8)
15 Not having or involving sex (7)
18 Irritable (6)
19 Dress up (5)
21 Vegetable (3)
22 Soft metal (4)

Colossal Book of Crosswords

ACROSS

7 Art movement (4)
8 Reverberated (6)
9 Set of parts to make something (3)
10 Cite a person (4)
11 Envisaged (8)
12 More cheerful (7)
14 Pleasant facial expression (5)
16 Twenty percent (5)
18 The state of being in operation (7)
21 Motion (8)
22 Place where something is put (4)
23 Game (6)
24 Take out or take away (6)

DOWN

1 Yellow fruit (6)
2 Construct (4)
3 Subject (7)
4 Started (5)
5 Man in charge of meeting (8)
6 Breakfast food (6)
13 Designs (8)
15 People who search for game (7)
17 Pressed (6)
19 Indigenous (6)
20 Banquet (5)
22 Not different (4)

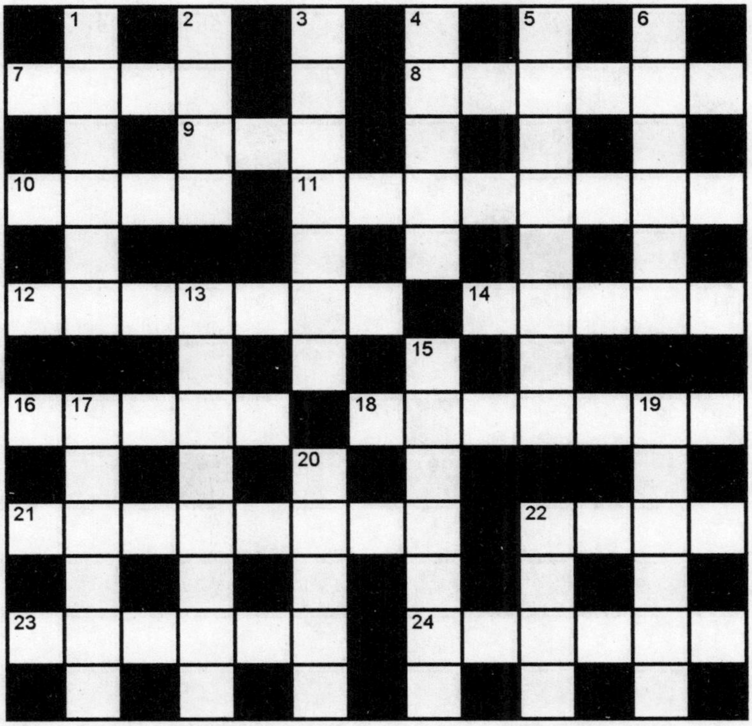

ACROSS

7 Cab (4)
8 Continent (6)
9 Coop (3)
10 Plays the part of (4)
11 The event of giving birth (8)
12 Filled beyond capacity (7)
14 Combined or joined (5)
16 Pile up (5)
18 Railway bridge over valley (7)
21 Brolly (8)
22 Soften through heat (4)
23 Go to (6)
24 Cultivated by growing crops (6)

DOWN

1 Package (6)
2 Pelvis (4)
3 Century (7)
4 A masonry fence (5)
5 Given or furnished with (8)
6 Rare (6)
13 Happened (8)
15 Long necked animal (7)
17 Salad fruit (6)
19 Young of domestic cattle (6)
20 A leaf of grass (5)
22 Planet (4)

Colossal Book of Crosswords

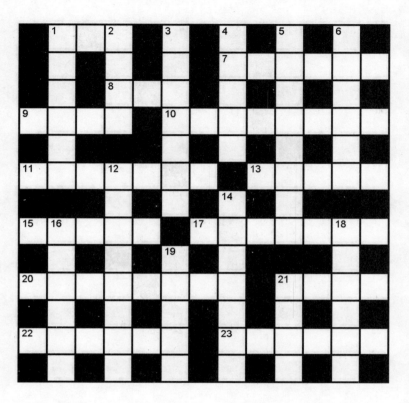

ACROSS

1 Feline (3)
7 Fasten or fix to (6)
8 Carrying container (3)
9 Eat (4)
10 Done more than once (8)
11 Graphite drawing
   implements (7)
13 Broker (5)
15 Book of world maps (5)
17 Bright talking bird (7)
20 Instructors (8)
21 Rip (4)
22 Organ levers (6)
23 Having been got the better
   of (6)

DOWN

1 Selection (6)
2 Underground railway (4)
3 With anger (7)
4 Sources of illumination (5)
5 Unknown person (8)
6 Film viewing surface (6)
12 Burnt wood for drawing (8)
14 Pill (7)
16 Subjects (6)
18 Dealer (6)
19 Conscious awareness (5)
21 Parasite (4)

ACROSS

7 Outermost region of the sun's atmosphere (6)
8 Cut teeth (6)
9 A strong sexual desire (4)
10 Trebuchet (8)
11 Covetous (7)
13 A mutual promise to marry (5)
15 Enter a computer (3,2)
17 Small or medium-sized kangaroo (7)
20 Herbaceous plant (8)
21 Strains to vomit (4)
22 Decapitate (6)
23 Wealthy and privileged person (3,3)

DOWN

1 Newspaper article (6)
2 Cry of an owl (4)
3 A sacred place of pilgr image (7)
4 Say clearly (5)
5 Of or relating to or limited by time (8)
6 Swiss house (6)
12 Idol worshipper (8)
14 Ear covering (7)
16 Followed orders (6)
18 A pauper who lives by begging (6)
19 Breezy (5)
21 Movable barrier in a fence or wall (4)

Colossal Book of Crosswords

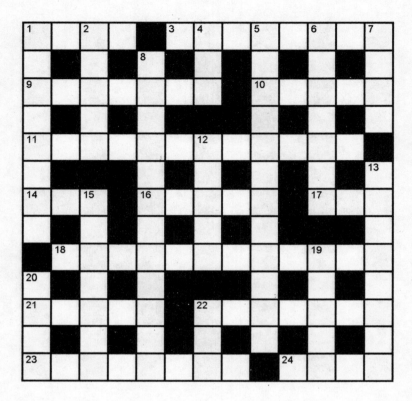

ACROSS

1 Completed (4)
3 The most, the highest (8)
9 Less tense, at ease (7)
10 Routes, tracks (5)
11 Established way of doing things (12)
14 Aged (3)
16 Effigy (5)
17 Number (3)
18 In spite of that (12)
21 Confess to doing something (5)
22 Brings back (7)
23 Average (8)
24 Weapons (4)

DOWN

1 Someone who controls resources (8)
2 Synthetic fabric (5)
4 Top (3)
5 Betterment, advances - primmest oven! (12)
6 Appeal, draw in (7)
7 Not difficult (4)
8 In the development phase - mix plane-tree! (12)
12 Cooked bread (5)
13 Is made up of (8)
15 Saw in sleep (7)
19 Mistake (5)
20 Agricultural work place (4)
22 Controlled a company (3)

ACROSS

2 Gets better (5)
7 Remedy (4)
8 Number (6)
9 Capable (4)
10 Sinking to a lower level (8)
11 Gift (7)
13 Beams of light (4)
15 Separate, away from (5)
17 Fresh fruits and vegetables (7)
20 Calling (8)
21 Fasten shut (4)
22 United by being of the same opinion (6)
23 Models of excellence (6)

DOWN

1 Wood (6)
2 In this place (4)
3 Funny (7)
4 Printing deletion mark (4)
5 Announced officially (8)
6 Spread in equal thickness (6)
12 Planes (8)
14 Excessively agitated (7)
16 Farming implement (6)
18 A baby bed with sides and rockers (6)
19 Sorts (5)
21 Perceived by sight (4)

ACROSS

6 Place of pilgrimage (6)
7 Land surrounded by water (6)
9 The main stem of a tree (4)
10 Contacting (8)
12 Cast a spell over someone (7)
14 Small dog (5)
16 Controller on trumpet (5)
18 Beg (7)
21 Cuckolded (3-5)
22 Get better (4)
23 A young swan (6)
24 Close to this place (4-2)

DOWN

1 Royal seat (6)
2 Grains used as food (4)
3 Lactuca leaves in salad bowl (7)
4 Sudden outburst of anger (5)
5 Pub (3-5)
8 Turn over soil with spade (3)
11 Short sleep (3)
13 Attractive and tempting (8)
15 Cul de sac (4,3)
17 For ever (6)
19 Bad tempered (6)
20 Horse shoe maker (5)
22 A person who is in charge (4)

Colossal Book of Crosswords

ACROSS

7 Self-improvement (6)
8 Confirm the truth of (6)
9 Search for (4)
10 A fortified military post (8)
11 The dead body of a human being (7)
13 Body politic (5)
15 Rapid sliding up or down (5)
17 Use again after processing (7)
20 Disease of the skin (8)
21 Fool or hoax (4)
22 A mixture of soluble salts (6)
23 Conference of native americans (6)

DOWN

1 Withdraw from an organisation (6)
2 Meat from a domestic hog or pig (4)
3 Conceive of (7)
4 Each and all (5)
5 A superior skill (8)
6 Endeavour (6)
12 Better than average - at golf? (5,3)
14 A vote that blocks a decision (4)
16 Headdress from medieval times (6)
18 Portable computer (6)
19 Fairy (5)
21 Soft fine feathers (4)

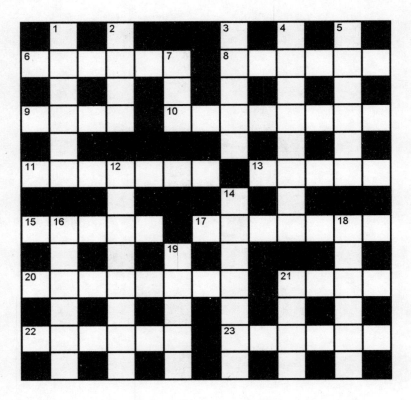

ACROSS

6 The act of wiggling (6)
8 Come to the end of a supply, leave room (3,3)
9 Home in rock (4)
10 A gauze fabric, very fine (8)
11 Money paid to ex-spouse (7)
13 Complacently or inanely foolish (5)
15 A hidden storage space (5)
17 Candy made of a thick creamy sugar paste (7)
20 Derived from or containing glass (8)
21 A subdivision of a larger religious group (4)
22 Covered with unclean things - egg run! (6)
23 A young eagle (6)

DOWN

1 Sudden violent wind (6)
2 Prevent from being seen or discovered (4)
3 Put on clothes (5)
4 Lacking a crew, remote-controlled (8)
5 Large deep serving dish (6)
7 Drinking vessel (3)
12 A princess in India or the wife of a maharaja (8)
14 A sled pulled by dogs (7)
16 A shed containing a number of beehives (6)
18 A US coin worth one twentieth of a dollar (6)
19 A small spiked wheel at the end of a spur (5)
21 A mentor, a herb (4)

Colossal Book of Crosswords

ACROSS

7 White sheep (6)
8 Hot water spring (6)
9 Bottle stopper (4)
10 Lacking nothing (3,5)
12 School (7)
14 Platter (5)
16 A sandwich (5)
18 Larger than average (7)
21 Bristly rodent (8)
22 Partially open (4)
23 Liveliness of mind or spirit (6)
24 Reverent petition to a deity (6)

DOWN

1 Not first (6)
2 Join together (4)
3 Feelings of allegiance (7)
4 Mentally quick (5)
5 Belonging to me (2)
6 Feel remorse for some deed done (6)
11 Wrecked and abandoned ships (5)
13 Family, class (8)
15 A dark cell (7)
17 Marked by a lack of quiet (6)
19 Fervent and even militant proponent (6)
20 Sloping channel, sloping trough (5)
22 Amongst, In the middle of (4)

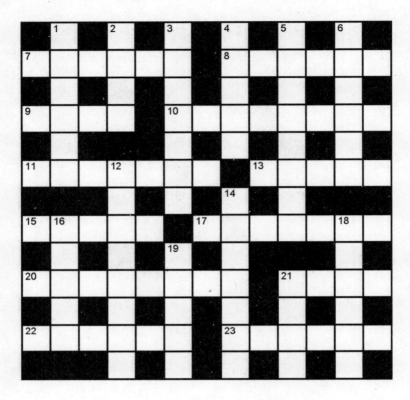

ACROSS

7 Timber fungus (3,3)
8 Person authorised to practice law; (6)
9 Small horse (4)
10 The skin of a lamb with the wool still on (8)
11 Padded cloth covering to keep a teapot warm (3-4)
13 Buckle under (5)
15 Bulbous plant, can make you cry! (5)
17 In less than perfect condition (7)
20 Small insectivorous bird (8)
21 Mentally or physically infirm with age (4)
22 Scream (6)
23 Projection used for strength, rim (6)

DOWN

1 Channel, rut (6)
2 Say a prayer (4)
3 Fashionable (7)
4 Chubby (5)
5 Emblem of the Nazi Party (8)
6 Amiable (6)
12 Chop suey served with fried noodles (4-4)
14 Take money from an illegal transaction (4-3)
16 The sound made by a horse (6)
18 Put into gear, employ (6)
19 Naturally having skin of a dark colour (5)
21 Agile ruminant (4)

ACROSS

7 Conventional (6)
8 Mistakes (6)
9 Single item, number under 10 (4)
10 Begged (8)
11 Taken into one's family (7)
13 Go along with (5)
15 Person on stage with lines (5)
17 Without much difficulty (7)
20 Brought back (8)
21 Nocturnal insect (4)
22 Improved (6)
23 Fixed with nails (6)

DOWN

1 Gave temporarily; let have for a limited time (6)
2 Leave out (4)
3 Rested on the surface of the water (7)
4 Assists (5)
5 Organised, like flowers? (8)
6 Drop below freezing! (6)
12 Commodities offered for sale (8)
14 Fixing (7)
16 Masticated (6)
18 Measures of liquids on the continent (6)
19 Cross (5)
21 Post (4)

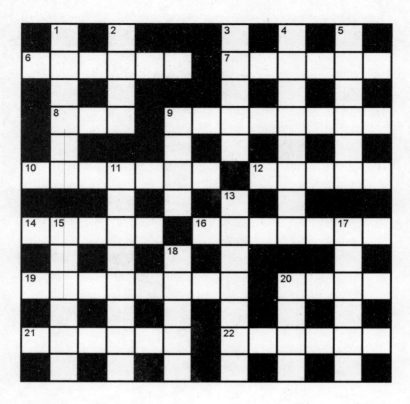

ACROSS

6 Place where recollections are stored (6)
7 Racket game (6)
8 Crazy (3)
9 The second lowest adult male singing voice (8)
10 The ultimate user, customer? (3,4)
12 Plastic flooring material (5)
14 A room used for reading (5)
16 A simulated battle (3-4)
19 Encounter (8)
20 Given colour that differs slightly from a primarycolourr (4)
21 A short sleep (usually not in bed) (6)
22 Confection from Montelimar in France (6)

DOWN

1 Informal terms for journalist (6)
2 Not warm (4)
3 Salt away, shop? (5)
4 An indefinite thing (8)
5 Internal organ or bean (6)
9 Meat from a cow (4)
11 One at a disadvantage and expected to lose (8)
13 The work of cleansing (7)
15 Swallowing - medication (6)
17 Humble task (6)
18 Fatigued (5)
20 And so it is...therefore (4)

ACROSS

7 A permissible difference, border (6)
8 In every case, without fail (6)
9 Follow instructions (4)
10 Decade (8)
11 Does not remember (7)
13 Move, period of work (5)
16 Sea (5)
18 At the front (7)
20 Systematic investigation (8)
21 Flying toy (4)
23 Make certain of (6)
24 Rhyming prose? (6)

DOWN

1 Plant stems used as garden sticks (6)
2 Unattractive (4)
3 Air-breathing arthropods (7)
4 Big (5)
5 Changed (8)
6 Me (6)
12 Elegant (8)
14 Pull at (3)
15 Possibly, maybe (7)
17 Removes dirt (6)
19 Command given by a superior officer (5)
21 Retain (4)
22 Conservative (4)

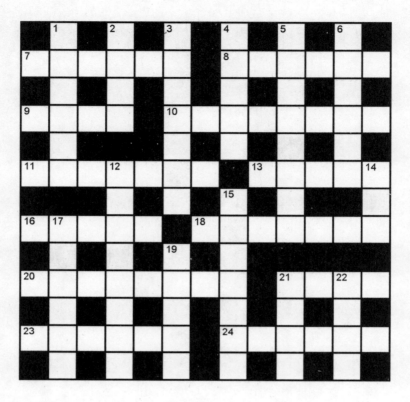

ACROSS

7 Crescent-shaped yellow fruit (6)
8 Sad (6)
9 Acquires (4)
10 Having lots of light (8)
11 Dangerous (7)
13 Held on to (5)
16 Turned fixing device (5)
18 Emerged from the egg (7)
20 Creative (8)
21 Created a picture (4)
23 Desire for food (6)
24 Reverberated (6)

DOWN

1 Television equipment (6)
2 Legal documents (4)
3 Place for ships to rest (7)
4 Characterised by dignity and propriety (5)
5 A member of a Catholic church (8)
6 Message carrying bird (6)
12 Formally arranged gatherings (8)
14 Any supernatural being who is worshipped (3)
15 Observed (7)
17 A travelling company of entertainers (6)
19 People who are dazzlingly skilled in their field (5)
21 Small highly nutritious seed - H Lad! (4)
22 Watched (4)

Colossal Book of Crosswords

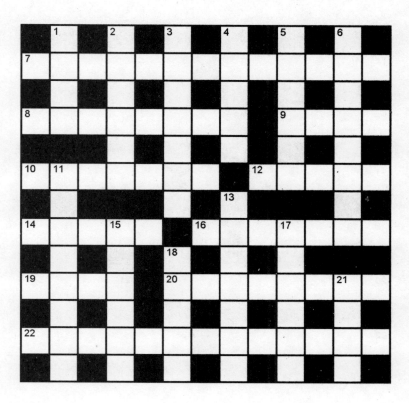

ACROSS

7 Industry that produces goods by making (13)
8 Diligence, hard work (8)
9 Ridge moving along sea (4)
10 A personal belief (7)
12 3rd (5)
14 Closes securely (5)
16 Conjectures, estimates based on little or no information (7)
19 Neckwear, fastens (4)
20 Non royal state (8)
22 Mechanically, without human intervention (13)

DOWN

1 Precipitation (4)
2 Season (6)
3 Carefulness (7)
4 Remains where placed (5)
5 Development, increase in size (6)
6 Everything that exists anywhere (8)
11 Former (8)
13 Large orange squash (7)
15 Punishment intended as a warning (6)
17 Underground railway (6)
18 Legal proceedings to find guilt or innocence (5)
21 Lazy (4)

ACROSS

7 Someone who travels about selling his wares (6)
8 Specified directions (6)
9 A mercantile establishment (4)
10 Enviousness (8)
11 Fresh fruits and vegetable grown to sell (7)
13 Web footed birds (5)
15 Comes apart through rubbing (5)
17 Emitting or radiating light (7)
20 Partition, split (8)
21 Possess (4)
22 A way of doing something (6)
23 With little effort or difficulty (6)

DOWN

1 Instead (6)
2 Bypass, leave out (4)
3 A planned undertaking (7)
4 Wide (5)
5 A native or inhabitant of Europe (8)
6 A period count of the population (6)
12 Time after sunrise and before sunset (8)
14 A relatively narrow body of water (7)
16 Lifts up (6)
18 Story books (6)
19 Breezy (5)
21 Person who invites guests to a social event (4)

Colossal Book of Crosswords

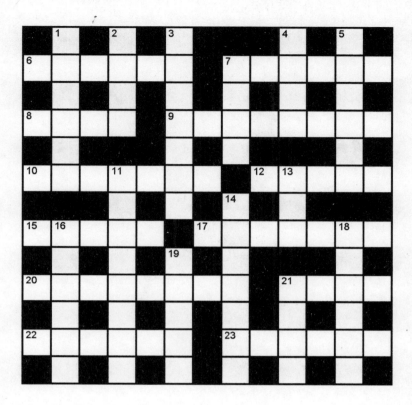

ACROSS

6 Be owned by; be in the possession of (6)
7 An angry stare (6)
8 Anti aircraft fire (4)
9 Engine outside a boat (8)
10 Wrap in swaddling clothes; of infants (7)
12 Isle in the English Channel (5)
15 One who is playfully mischievous (5)
17 An accumulation of jobs not done (7)
20 A worsening of business (8)
21 Fill to satisfaction (4)
22 A written version of a play (6)
23 Workplace for art or music (6)

DOWN

1 Shout very loudly (6)
2 People (4)
3 Completely lacking nobility - on bilge! (7)
4 Extinct bird (4)
5 Look for (6)
7 Giblets or courage (4)
11 Mental deterioration (8)
13 Writing fluid (3)
14 Decorate food (7)
16 Selection (6)
18 Get hold of (6)
19 Faction, power seeking clique (5)
21 A disparaging remark (4)

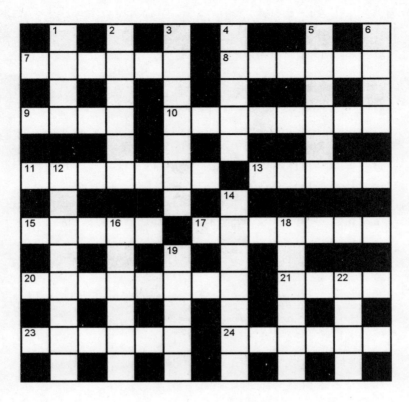

ACROSS

7 Inconsistent in quality (6)
8 Lower oneself with a double rope (6)
9 Pottery oven (4)
10 Disciplinarian (8)
11 For all time (7)
13 Rob from another (5)
15 A violent weather condition (5)
17 Item purchased at a good price (7)
20 Marked by or promising bad fortune (3-5)
21 A thin coat of paint (4)
23 An ancient writ (6)
24 A new embodiment of a familiar idea (6)

DOWN

1 (prefix) opposite or opposing (4)
2 Give expression to (6)
3 Numbered food additive prefixed by a letter (1-6)
4 Sprite (5)
5 A meeting of spiritualists (6)
6 Apartment (4)
12 Cause to appear in a lower class (8)
14 Cutting machine with looped toothed blade (7)
16 palm fibre used in hats and baskets (6)
18 Cheap showy jewelry or ornament - egg waw! (6)
19 Spread by scattering (5)
22 Thick piece of something (4)

Colossal Book of Crosswords

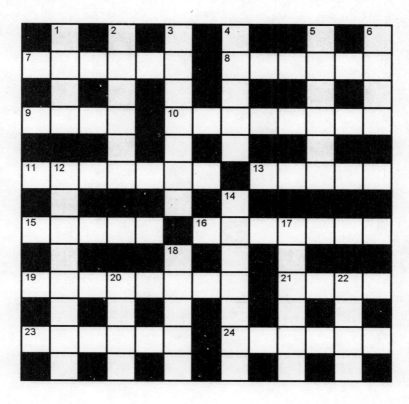

ACROSS

7 Make a hole in (6)
8 Rapid and indistinct speech (6)
9 Open pastry filled with fruit or custard (4)
10 An ambiguity in a law or ruling (8)
11 One who claims to have supernatural powers (7)
13 Fraudulent; having a misleading appearance (5)
15 Grasslike or rushlike plant (5)
16 Permanent transport system (7)
19 A member of a ship's crew (4-4)
21 Sit for a portrait (4)
23 The place where something comes from (6)
24 Photographic enlargement (4-2)

DOWN

1 The face of a timepiece (4)
2 Humorously sarcastic or mocking (6)
3 Recite in elocution (7)
4 Softly bright or radiant (5)
5 Shape (6)
6 Surrender, give up rights to (4)
12 Hard internal structure of humans (8)
14 A debt that is unlikely to be repaid (3,4)
17 Small dog (6)
18 Bread roll (5)
20 Edge of pavement (4)
22 Closed (4)

Colossal Book of Crosswords

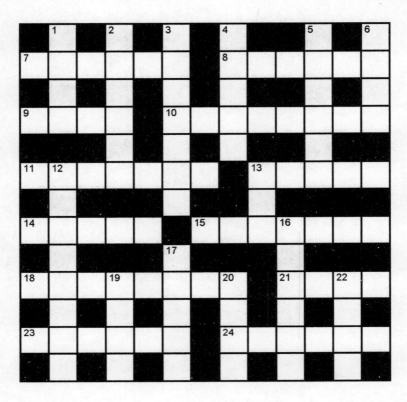

ACROSS

7 Enjoy the small or taste of (6)
8 One who moves from one country to another (6)
9 Closing section of a musical composition (4)
10 Enunciate (8)
11 Witty comeback (7)
13 Comfortable (5)
14 Bothersome, annoying (5)
15 Bon voyage (4-3)
18 Part of the face above the eyes (8)
21 A harp used by ancient Greeks (4)
23 Confederate, joined by treaty (6)
24 Home for horse (6)

DOWN

1 Kind of milky pudding (4)
2 Vegetable (6)
3 Force that holds us to the planet! (7)
4 From this time (5)
5 Self-interest (6)
6 Peter, only slightly smaller (4)
12 Water ice on a small wooden stick (3-5)
13 A swindle (3)
16 US currency unit (6)
17 Extremely exciting (5)
19 Depraved (4)
20 Run quickly over short distance (4)
22 Part played (4)

THE
SOLUTIONS

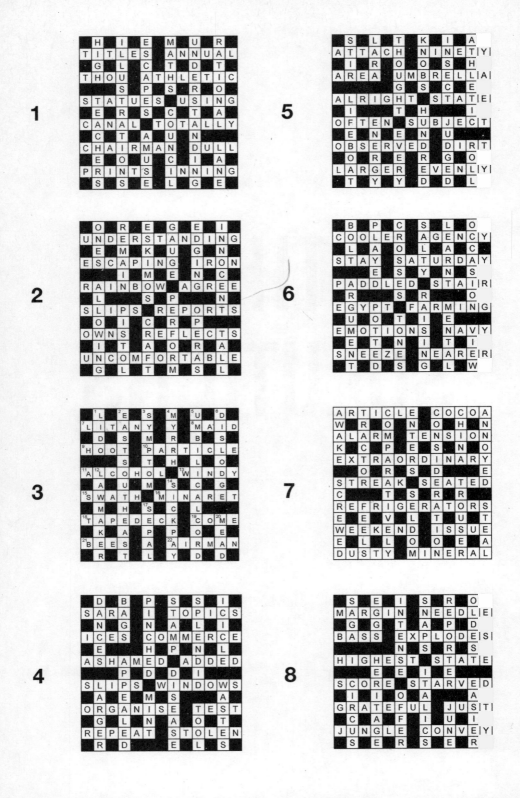

9

```
C O M P E T E   ·   S O L V E
R ·   N ·   S ·   T ·   ·   I ·   ·   ·   A
I N S T A N T L Y   ·   G A S ·
S ·   ·   B ·   A ·   L ·   H ·   ·   ·   T
P E D A L ·   B R E A T H E ·
·   ·   E ·   E ·   L ·   ·   N ·   ·   ·   R
I N V E S T I G A T I O N
N ·   E ·   S ·   V ·   N ·   ·   ·   ·   ·
S E L F I S H ·   E D G E S
E ·   O ·   D ·   M ·   R ·   ·   ·   U
C U P ·   E L E V A T I O N
T ·   E ·   A ·   N ·   G ·   C ·   N
S I D E S ·   T H E R E B Y
```

13

```
S L A P ·   P R O S P E C T
U ·   R ·   L ·   U ·   O ·   N ·   O
P R A Y E R S ·   C R A W L
P ·   B ·   S ·   H ·   K ·   B ·   D
L A S T S ·   E A S I L Y ·
I ·   E ·   D ·   D ·   ·   ·   E ·   R
E R R O R S ·   C R A D L E
D ·   E ·   ·   ·   E ·   A ·   F
·   W A S T E S ·   I S S U E
U ·   D ·   A ·   T ·   S ·   P ·   R
S W E L L ·   A V E R A G E
E ·   R ·   K ·   T ·   D ·   C ·   E
D I S A S T E R ·   J E T S
```

10

```
·   R ·   E ·   E ·   V ·   O ·   L
S U F F I X ·   A P P L E S
·   L ·   F ·   C ·   L ·   E ·   M
H E R O ·   I N V E N T O R
·   ·   ·   R ·   T ·   E ·   E ·   N
S P O T T E D ·   I D E A S
·   R ·   ·   S ·   R ·   ·   ·   D
H O B B Y ·   R O A S T E D
·   P ·   I ·   F ·   U ·   P
S E T T L I N G ·   R A N K
·   R ·   T ·   R ·   H ·   I ·   O
O T H E R S ·   L I N I N G
·   Y ·   N ·   T ·   Y ·   G ·   E
```

14

```
·   F ·   M ·   N ·   C ·   F ·   R
G A R A G E ·   A M A Z E D
·   V ·   N ·   I ·   K ·   R ·   V
N O T E ·   T H E A T R E
·   U ·   ·   H ·   S ·   H ·   A
C R A C K E D ·   W E L L S
·   H ·   R ·   R ·   S
A I M E D ·   D E N T I S T
·   M ·   R ·   G ·   V ·   T
C A R R I A G E ·   S E A T
·   G ·   I ·   Z ·   R ·   U ·   G
S E V E R E ·   S U N S E T
·   S ·   S ·   D ·   E ·   ·   ·   S
```

11

```
·   P ·   D ·   S ·   C ·   S ·   K
C H U R C H ·   H A W A I I
·   O ·   E ·   A ·   A ·   I ·   L
S N O W ·   R E S E M B L E
·   E ·   ·   P ·   E ·   M ·   E
A D M I R E D ·   D I A R Y
·   ·   N ·   R ·   L ·   N
A B O V E ·   S U R G E R Y
·   O ·   A ·   F ·   G ·   ·   E
B U R S T I N G ·   H E L D
·   N ·   I ·   R ·   A ·   A ·   A
E C H O E S ·   G U I L T Y
·   E ·   N ·   T ·   E ·   R ·   E
```

15

```
·   G ·   P ·   R ·   G ·   B ·   V
G A R A G E ·   A G R E E D
·   M ·   U ·   F ·   L ·   E ·   R
L E S S ·   E L E V E N T H
·   E ·   R ·   S ·   Z ·   I
C R A D L E S ·   T E A C H
·   E ·   ·   E ·   R ·   ·   ·   A
S A L E S ·   H E R S E L F
·   L ·   R ·   T ·   V ·   U
D I S A G R E E ·   B A R N
·   S ·   S ·   I ·   R ·   W ·   E
S E V E R E ·   S E A L E D
·   D ·   R ·   D ·   E ·   Y ·   D
```

12

```
·   C ·   S ·   C ·   S ·   S ·   F
S O F T E R ·   T R A V E L
·   R ·   U ·   E ·   I ·   M ·   E
R E E D ·   A B R U P T L Y
·   ·   I ·   T ·   S ·   L ·   I
O P P O S E D ·   F E R N S
·   E ·   ·   S ·   T ·   ·   ·   G
K N E L T ·   P R O T E S T
·   K ·   A ·   T ·   A ·   A
A N S W E R E D ·   L I P S
·   I ·   Y ·   U ·   I ·   K ·   I
O F F E R S ·   N E E D L E
·   E ·   R ·   T ·   G ·   R ·   E
```

16

```
·   P ·   I ·   B ·   C ·   I ·   R
M A N N E R ·   O U N C E S
·   C ·   T ·   U ·   N ·   V ·   S
P E T E ·   S K E L E T O N
·   ·   R ·   H ·   S ·   S ·   U
O R A N G E S ·   S T O R M
·   E ·   A ·   S ·   C ·   ·   ·   C
P A R T Y ·   T O N G U E S
·   L ·   I ·   H ·   N
V I G O R O U S ·   T O S S
·   S ·   N ·   P ·   I ·   R ·   U
R E L A T E ·   S P O O N S
·   D ·   L ·   S ·   T ·   T ·   K
```

17

```
F   I   A       S   C   R
PAINTS      PROPER
I   T   S   O   M   S
TREE    ULTIMATE
R   R   S   U   L
SPONGES     ENTER
L   A   D   P   I   S
SOUTH   PRECISE
U   I   M   O   A
IGNORANT    THEE
H   N   R   E   I   Y
REPAIR      SHOVEL
D   L   Y   T   N   D
```

18

```
B   E   P       S   E   M
RUNNER      TUNNEL
R   T   E   A   C   A
TYRE    CARRYING
R   I   S   C   T
PROTEST     CLAIM
E   A   E   P   O   M
SPLIT   SLIPPED
O   N   S   A   A
PROMPTLY    EASY
T   E   A   I   D   T
PEANUT      NOISES
D   T   E   G   A   P
```

19

```
C   U   H   O   B   S
RUSSIA      COUGHS
T   E   T   E   R   E
BEEF    CHANNELS
U   H   N   E   T
EARLIER     ADDED
M   D   S   S   R
BEGIN   SUGGEST
R   N   F   R   R
CIRCLING    OAKS
C   H   R   E   O   N
WATERS      REVIEW
N   S   T   Y   E   W
```

20

```
CHEW    IMPORTED
A   R   L   I   A   E   A
BARGAIN     SIXES
B   O   U   E   I   T   H
APRON   RUSSIA
G   C   S   L   D
EARTH   L   EVE
S   O   S   A   P
SCHOOL      ZEBRA
I   K   C   O   I   O   R
NOISE   PREDICT
T   N   A   E   R   L   E
ORGANISE    USED
```

21

```
CROW    HARMLESS
O   N   S   G   E   N   I
LEISURE     ADDED
U   O   F   N   S   L   E
MANUFACTURER
B   I   Y   R   S   E
INSECT      PERSON
A   I   I   H   M   C
EXPERIMENTAL
L   T   N   D   N   R   O
ALERT   DETAILS
V   E   L   E   S   A   E
ANNOYING    SLID
```

22

```
ACCOUNT     OPERA
U   O   S   H   D   N   N
NUCLEAR     DRAMA
T   O   I   I   L   B   L
SPADE   LOYALTY
S   L   E   S
PRAISE      RIDDLE
O   M   P   N
PLATEAU     STUNS
U   Z   I   R   T   N   I
LYING   PEELING
A   N   H   L   A   O   N
RIGHT   ENDINGS
```

23

```
F   P   A   M   D   W
JEWELS  O   ELAN
L   R   S   V   M   R
CLIP    UNICORNS
E   K   E   N   I
STUNNED     USING
E   D   D   C   T   G
INDIA   POOREST
D   C   C   N   A
REQUIRES    THIN
N   L   I   U   I   T
SCRAPE  LOOKED
Y   R   S   T   N   M
```

24

```
B   P   B   A   C   N
DEVICE      BRAZIL
L   S   A   O   N   L
SLIT    CHURCHES
O   H   T   E   T
SWOLLEN     CREEP
E   E   S   R   E
FADED   GERMANS
K   X   F   S
MERCHANT    SAIL
N   U   I   O   A   C
REASON      RENTED
D   T   E   E   S
```

25

```
C U S T O M S   C A B L E
O   H   P   U O R   L
C H E A P   M A N M A D E
O   L   O   M C K   C
A D V E R T I S E M E N T
    E   T   T   N   E
M U S E U M   S T U P I D
I   N   C   R   O
R E F R I G E R A T O R S
R   A   T   R T R   E
O U T S I D E   I D E A L
R   A   E   A O S   L
S A L E S   L E N G T H S
```

26

```
  N   D   R   B P P
P O L I C E   A N I M A L
  T   E   S   S C R
P I G S   T H E A T R E S
  C   I   S   U N
N E T T I N G   W R O T E
      R   G   B E
E N D E D   W I L D E S T
U   A   D   G   P
C R O S S I N G   S E A T
S   U   R   E L C
S E C R E T   S H O W E D
  D   E   Y   T W S
```

27

```
M U S T   S A T U R D A Y
O   E   P T   R O   E
U G L I E S T   G O U D A
N   L   R I   E B   R
T E S T S   C A S T L E
A   O   S   E   G
I S L A N D   S P I D E R
N   E   P   U   A
  G A R A G E   S E V E N
A   R   L N H I   D
C A N T O   C H E E S E S
T   E   N I S I O
S U D D E N L Y   T A N
```

28

```
  T S C   N O S
E A S I E R   A T R I U M
  P S A   M A N
S E N T   S W E E T E S T
    E H D   O H
S T A R T E D   T R A I N
H   D U   N
N O T E S   K N O C K E D
U   V A T   I
A S S E M B L Y   T E A S
A   O I R
I N S I T U   N E E D E D
D   T G S   A
```

29

```
  C P S P C   M
F A L L E N   A   L O O M
  M A A P O R   R
M E A N   P L E A S I N G
  E   P R E   I
C A S T L E S   B R I N G
  I   D F   G
A R E A S   L O U D E S T
  P P M R U
C O M P L E T E   R U B S
  R L A S I L
S T R E E T   T U N N E L
  S S S S G W
```

30

```
T Y P I C A L   C L I M B
H A A O A N   R
R A I N B O W   R A D I O
E N B E G I T
E X T R A   S T O M A C H
      G   T   N E
T A S T E D   C L O S E R
R C B   I
A M E R I C A   B I T E S
C N S R E A
T R E E S   A L A R M E D
O R U N R P L
R H Y M E   A N Y B O D Y
```

31

```
  P U W   S T A
C O R N E R   C R E E P S
  O D O   A L P
G L U E   N U M B E R E D
  R G P   P A
H E R S E L F   S H O R T
X T Y   C O E
S P E A K   L O W T I D E
  L N G L O
W O N D E R E D   L A D Y
  R I A E E E
T E N N I S   S U N D A Y
  S G S T S R
```

32

```
  B T P   S A M
C A M E R A   C I R C U S
  K N R   A T S
L E A N   T E R R I F I C
  I I E   S C
C R I S P E R   S T A I N
  H H S   C A
D Y I N G   B O A T I N G
  T A L   U A
S H U T T I N G   P U M P
  M I T   H P E
S I L V E R   E V E N L Y
  C E E D D T
```

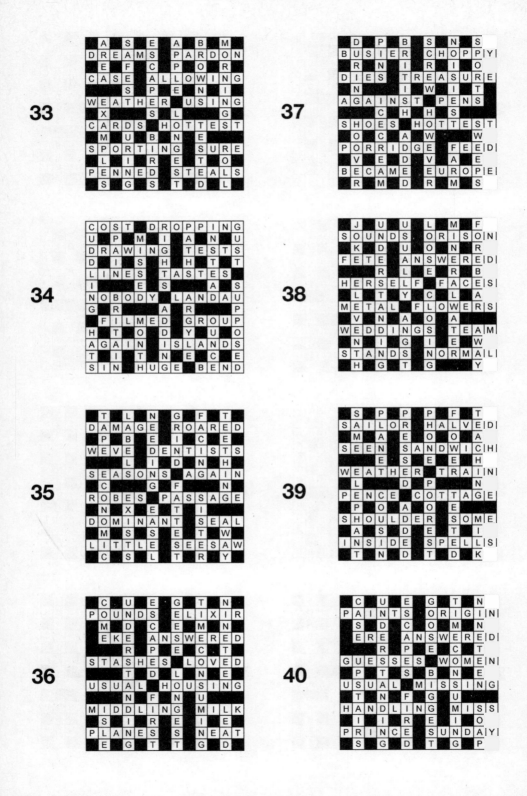

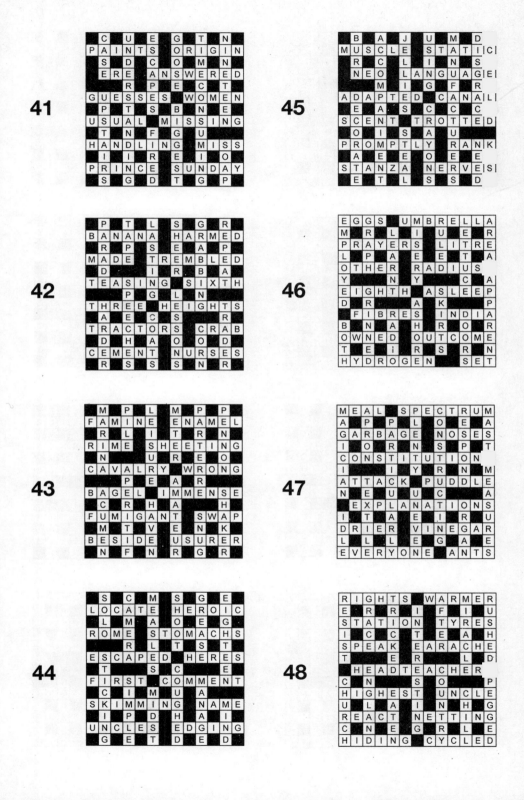

49

```
NOTICE CLOSES
E H H M O U W
AMERICA CARGO
R R C T K F R
BREAK HUSBAND
Y E E C S
 GRANDMOTHER
S U A E P
TONIGHT SUPER
O N R T E A
NOISE CHIMNEY
E N A S N C E
SIGHTS AGREED
```

50

```
DECIMAL FACED
E I O I O O R
CIRCUMFERENCE
A C S T C S
YOU TEENAGERS
 M A D P N E
INSECT WASTES
N T H R R R
STATEMENT ASH
T N M M T A
ENCYCLOPEDIAS
A E R T N O N
DUSTY EXTINCT
```

51

```
S C C S B F
POTATO HORROR
U M U E A L
TRAP SILENTLY
C I F C O
REMAINS SHOWS
N S S E
RAYS SMASHED
E W S A C
CATHOLIC ECHO
S E O K A O
SORROW EASIER
N E S D E S
```

52

```
FIST MILITARY
A O E N N L O
RELAXED TELLY
E V P I E O O
WHEELBARROW
E E A N S E S
LEGEND NEEDLE
L E A P C A
INSTRUCTIONS
A E I R I P O
CARGO PROTEIN
T A N L N R A
SPLASHED TAIL
```

53

```
T A T S E P
BAMBOO LUXURY
R B R A P E
STIR NONSENSE
E A T R E
PROVIDE DIDNT
E I O I M T
SPEAK IMMENSE
A T F A N
VISITING TOPS
R O R I I I
BEINGS NINETY
D S T E G S
```

54

```
W G E O A A
MELODY PIRACY
A L E A A R
BRAD WORKBOOK
E A T I S
WITNESS ACUTE
N J H A N I
DRUM FLOUNCE
E B A L M
SCRIBBLE EPIC
E L A R B
INTENT G AVID
T E E Y L S
```

55

```
R S D P C R
HOTTER UGLIER
D A E L O M
BEAN SPLASHES
D S S E M
GLASSES GRABS
A S L E
DUSTY WORKERS
G E S N I
THINKING LOTS
I N Z E L A
ENGINE SHELLS
G S D T R L
```

56

```
EXAMPLE CRISP
D T O N O R L
GULLS GENUINE
E A S A S A
DISTINGUISHED
E B E D E
FOSSIL HEATED
A L W R R
REFRIGERATORS
M L T A T U P
INITIAL ISSUE
N E E T O E
GASES HUNDRED
```

57

	W		O		T		B		D		P
S	E	A	R	C	H		U	N	E	V	E	N

Grid 57:
- SEARCH · UNEVEN
- IDEA · RESPONSE
- SHIRT · ESSAY
- CREAM · EARNED
- CITIZENS · TOYS
- SHINES · TROLLY
- Down letters: W O T B D P / E G I R M R / N S T N U / T S Y D T D / A T S N A / G O N I O / T E Y N K

58

Grid 58:
- ROCKETS · SACKS
- CIRCUMFERENCE
- PRETTIEST
- SYSTEM · LETTER
- APARTMENT · ARC
- ENCYCLOPEDIAS
- DUSTY · EXTENDS
- Down letters: O I Q U I O W / K C I F C E / Y U M M R R N E / E T N R A R / W N M M T A / E E R V N O E

59

Grid 59:
- BOXING · ORANGE
- USES · ORDERING
- SHOWING · GOOSE
- ENDED · BIGGEST
- SLEEPING · ZEAL
- UNREST · NOBODY
- Down letters: P J A P H A / P G R N I O / A U S D I / A D D T / D L L A / I V F I E D / G N S O S

60

Grid 60:
- FELLOW · OCLOCK
- LOOM · MECHANIC
- IGNORED · KINGS
- SCREW · LARGEST
- LOCATION · BABY
- WERENT · NORMAL
- Down letters: B P S T C A / L U I U E T / N M H N N / P R C N / O R D N U / K T R O A W / D S Y S K Y

61

Grid 61:
- STARVE · PLEASE
- GRAN · MACHINES
- PEANUTS · VERBS
- RIGID · MERRIER
- REPTILES · NETS
- ECHOES · TRAILS
- Down letters: S P H S M A / A O L A D S / U E E T M / V C S D R L / D A B N A / N I A I E A / E N T Y N K

62

Grid 62:
- DAMAGE · LUXURY
- TAIL · PADDLING
- PASTURE · CROSS
- STOOD · MUDDIER
- MEASURED · LIES
- SECRET · EQUALS
- Down letters: C C K G E T / N L E I P U / D E E O K / R S P E / H U T D V / M E U L O N / S S S H S D Y

63

Grid 63:
- ALSO · OBSERVER
- TOUCHED · EASEL
- OUTER · ESTATE
- GASPED · MIDDAY
- RUSSIA · CARGO
- IDEAL · GREATLY
- PRETENDS · DOGS
- Down letters: L T C A V I O / H N A G N I E / U G S E S / H Q R N N / L E O G H A N / M Z V E S I M

64

Grid 64:
- FAVOUR · ANIMAL
- CROP · NOTICING
- WEARING · AMONG
- STATE · WHITEST
- PROVINCE · NICE
- GALLOP · ENERGY
- Down letters: F C I N C W / I M O S R R / A I Y U I / X A G T S G / E I S I A / N E A V C A / L Y S S S E

65

```
      P E R   A   A
U N D E R S T A N D I N G
  N   C   I   D   Y
M O U N T A I N   I N T O
  E   P   Y   N   H
S T U D I E S   A G A I N
  E   S   C       N
M A Y B E   P A S S A G E
  C   U   G   B   T
S H O T   U M B R E L L A
  I   T   A   A   A   I
E N C O U R A G E M E N T
  G   N   D   E   E
```

69

```
D O C K   F I N I S H E S
E   H   P   D   N E   T
C L I M A T E   N E R V E
O   L   S   A   E     M
R O L L S   L A R G E R
A     E   S       L   G
T H I R D S   U S E F U L
E   N     O     T     A
  I T S E L F   A T T I C
C   E   G   F   T   E   I
A N N O Y   I M I T A T E
M   S   P   C   C   S   R
P R E T T I E R   R E D S
```

66

```
  A   F   A   M S   B
T R Y I N G   A P P L E S
  R   R   A   K   O   C
S I D E   I C E   R E A M
  V     N   S   T   M
W E T T E S T   B I K E S
      H   T   M   N
W A K E S   L O N G E S T
      A   U   M       C
D I S T A N C E   B U R N
  R   D   N   A   E
C H E E S E   T A S T E D
  S   R   S   E   N
```

67

```
  R   P   A   C M   N
T O W A R D   L O O K E D
  P   R   D   E   T   O
M E E T   R E A C H I N G
      E   E   N   E   A
H A R D E S T   T R U T H
  M   S   W       A
W E A R S   N I G H T L Y
  R   A   S   Z   I
Z I N C   O V A   D U S T
  C   I   U   R   I   E
C A N N O T   D I N N E R
  N   G   H   S   G   D
```

68

```
  T   U   T   O E   G
W I N N E R   N O R M A L
  R   D   A   I   O   U
H E R E   C R O S S I N G
      R   T   N   T
S C I S S O R   B E L L S
  O   T   R   S   X   E
C L E A N   R O Y A L T Y
  O   N   F   N   M
C U D D L I N G   I N T O
  R   N       N   A
P E N N E D   S H E L L S
  D   S       R   K
```

69 *(see 69 above)*

70

```
S O A K   P R E C E D E D
T   P   C   E   O E   U
A I R P O R T   N A V A L
N   I   M   U   S E   L
D E L I B E R A T E L Y
A   I   N   R   O   P
R E C E N T   J U M P E R
D   E   A   H   C   E
  I N S T R U C T I O N S
A   T   I   M   I   T   E
C A R G O   B R O T H E R
I   E   N   L   N   E   V
D I S A S T E R   T R U E
```

71

```
  F   C   E   S D   R
R E F O R M   P R I C E
  E   M   O   E   S   S
A T O M   T H E A T R E
  U   I   D   I   M
O P I N I O N   K N O B S
  R   I   N   B   G   L
P O R C H   S E C U R E D
  B   A   T   N   I
E A S T W A R D   S I G H
  B   I   R   I   H   R
A L M O S T   N E E D E D
  Y   N   S   G   D   Y
```

72

```
  U   T E   H   A V A
U N D E R S T A N D   N
  D   N   C   U   DAY
M O U N T A I N   I T
      I   P   T   N   H
D A I S I E S   A G A I N
  R       S   P       N
B R O W N   B A B B A G E
  I   I   S   R   U
O V E N   O V E R T I M E
  I   T   U   N   T   E
I N T E R N A T I O N A L
  G   R   D   S   N   N
```

73

```
  L   B   S     M   S   F
M O M E N T   A C T I O N
  N   D   A     R   A   R
A G E S   R E C O R D E D
  E   T   H     T   S
W R I T T E N   F I F T Y
      W   D     W   N
T O W E R   B I G G E S T
  R   N   B     L   W
M A T T E R E D   S E E D
  T   I   U     E   N
P O W E R S   S T A R T S
  R   S   H     T   P   S
```

74

```
  F   P   I     S   P   S
H A V I N G   A L L O W S
  I   C   N     N   U   I
G R A N   O R D E R I N G
  I   R   Y     A   G
S M A C K E D   C L A I M
  I   D   M         N
A D D E D   S A U S A G E
  D   X   C   T     T
E L E P H A N T   U S E D
  I   E   U   E     P   V
K N O C K S   R A I N E D
  G   T   E     S   D   N
```

75

```
M A P S   O P E R A T E D
U   R   A   O     E   H   U
S C I E N C E   Q U I C K
I   S   N   T     U   N   E
C O M P O S I T I O N S
I   U   C   R     E   R
A R M I N G   D E G R E E
N   I   C   T     M   A
  E X P E R I M E N T A L
L   T   M   S     N   A   I
A M U S E   S E T T L E S
M   R   N   U     S   K   E
B R E A T H E D   U S E D
```

76

```
  N   F   S     D   F   M
Z O D I A C   U N L O A D
  O   L   A   M   Y   G
A N T I   M A P   I R I S
  N   P   Y     N
R I N G L E T   E G R E T
  N   C   R     P   O   Y
U S U A L   D R A F T E E
  O   B   I   E   F
A M B I E N C E   I D E S
  N   N   E   M   C   A
G I V E U P   P L E A S E
  A   T   T     T   R   E
```

77

```
  O   C   S   K   A   L
O P P O R T U N I T I E S
  E   B   E   E   O   M
S N O W B A L L   M O O N
  E   M   T   I   N
S T A B L E S   O C E A N
  E   E   D   E       D
C A N A L   E X I S T E D
  S   U   U   T   I
S P I T   S T R U G G L E
  O   U   I   A   H   I
C O M M U N I C A T I O N
  N   N   G   T   S   N
```

78

```
  S   W   S   T   F   R
F I E R C E   R E A D E R
  D   I   A   I   S   M
F E E T   T W E N T I E S
  E   E   S   E   M
P A S S I N G   C R A B S
  M   O   M       E
H E A R S   D O C T O R S
  R   E   F   N   U
K I T C H E N S   N U T S
  C   O   E   T   N   O
P A I R E D   E L E V E N
  N   D   S   S   R   L   S
```

79

```
  T   C   P   E   T   C
S A I L O R   N O R W A Y
  X   O   E   D   A   R
D I G S   S P E N D I N G
      E   E   D   E   I
E V I D E N T   D R O V E
  A   T   B       A
A N G L E   H E   S E L F
  I   E   M   G   O
E S C A P I N G   L O O M
  H   R   N   I   E   W
P E N N E D   N A M I N G
  D   S   S   G   N   S
```

80

```
I N C H   S C H O L A R S
N   O   M   R   C   M   E
C O U R A G E   C H E S T
R   R   N   D   A   R   S
E N T H U S I A S T I C
A   F   T   I   C       C
S Q U E A K   T O M A T O
E   N   C   C   N       N
  D I C T I O N A R I E S
B   F   U   U   L   M   I
O D O U R   P I L L A R S
O   R   E   L   Y   G   T
M E M O R I E S   T E N S
```

81

```
  U   A L   C A S
E N A B L E   O C C U P Y
  D   S   T U T   E
Y O Y O   T E R R I B L E
  R   E   T   V   L
I C E B E R G   B E G I N
  O   O   S   C   N
F R O W N   P A S S A G E
  R   I   S   P   E
M I S T A K E S   W A L K
  D   H   I   U   I
S O C I A L   L I N I N G
  R   N   L   E G K
```

85

```
R O M E   S P E C T R U M
E   O   A H   A   E   I
W H I S P E R   B U M P S
A   S   R A L   O   T
R A T I O   S L E E V E
D   N   E     E     A
E X C U S E   S W E D E N
D   O   A   I     N
  C L I M B S   T E M P O
S   L   U S H   O   U
O B E Y S   U N I C O R N
F   G   I M   N   S   C
A G E N C I E S   M E R E
```

82

```
  G   C B   N E   R
L A B O U R   O U N C E S
  V   N U   S   T S
M E W S   S K E L E T O N
  I   H Y   R   U
S O L D I E R   S T O R Y
  U   E S M   A C
S T I R S   D E S I R E S
  L   A H   E   N
D I S T R I C T   M I S S
  N   I V   I E I
B E F O R E   N I N E T Y
  D   N S   G T
```

86

```
  J   C D   A T S
P O O R E R   S P O K E N
  K   I O   K W N
T E N S   P R E S E N T S
  P   P D   L   E
D A I S I E S   U S I N G
  M   D M   C
S E E M S   N O I S I E R
  R   E F   N   H
M I L L I O N S   A W A Y
  C   T R   T R G
P A R E N T   E L E V E N
  N   D Y   R S S
```

83

```
R O L E   E D U C A T E D
E   A N   U O H   U
S T U D E N T   N E E D S
E   G V   I T   A K
A C H I E V E M E N T S
R   R S   M M R   P
C O U N T S   A P P E A R
H   N N   H A O   O
  S U P E R M A R K E T S
A   S L   U A X   P
R O U T E   S U R V I V E
C   A S   E Y T   C
H I L L S D     I S N T
```

87

```
  T   B P   R P M
B R E A T H   O P E R A S
  E   M R   B R   G
V E R B   A M E R I C A N
  O   S S   O   Z
O P P O S E D   A D M I T
  R   S P   N
C O R A L   T R U S T E D
  M   N F   E   H
C I T I Z E N S   O W N S
  S   M W   E R A
B E H A V E   N A T I V E
  D   L R   T S Y
```

84

```
  H   I A   A C R
M A N N E R   C L O S E S
  T   T G   U M S
H E R E   U L T I M A T E
  R   I E   U   L
O P E N I N G   U N D E R
  L   A G   W I S
B O O T S   P R O C E S S
  U   I T   I A
I G N O R A N T   T O R E
  H   N X   T I A
D E B A T E   E X O T I C
  D   L S   N N
```

88

```
  F   M N   H F L
D A M A G E   I M A G E S
  V   T I   D R   G
P O L E   T R E N T   E
  U   H S   H   N
P R O C E E D   W E E D S
    R   R R   S
P A N E L   H O T T E S T
  M   A L   O     E
P A R T N E R S   S E N D
  Z   I A   T O S
R E I N E D   E R A S E R
  D   G S   R K S
```

89

```
H M F B U F
R E V O L U T I O N   R O
R   V   N   R   L   O
A S S I G N   D   I A N
    E   I   S   K   T
C R U S H E S   B E G I N
E   U   R   L   E
C A M P S   S I N G E R S
L   R   L   B   R
M I N E   A I R P O R T S
S   F   T   A   U   R
M E D I T E R R A N E A N
  D   X   R   Y   D   P
```

90

```
S   M   S   K   S   D
O P P O R T U N I T I E S
I   U   A   O   I   V
A T H L E T I C   T H O U
    D   E   K   C   T
M I S S I L E   C H O I R
N   Y   D   O
S T U D Y   H E A V E N S
E   E   R   S   I
S N A P   I N S I S T E D
D   A   D   E   I   A
R E F R I G E R A T O R S
  D   T   E   T   S   S
```

91

```
L   M   M   G   D   D
G A R A G E   A T O M I C
B   N   A   Z   M   V
B O R E   S P E C I F I C
U   L   D   N   N
C R I C K E T   V A S E S
    H   S   B   N
E A T E N   F A T T E S T
G   M   M   D   U
A R R I V I N G   S I N K
E   S   N   E   O   S
S E T T E E   R A N G E S
D   D   S   G   T
```

92

```
P   P   A   S   P   H
F L O O D S   P A R R O T
A   S   S   O   O   L
E Y E S   U N K I N D L Y
    I   R   E   U   O
B U B B L E S   S N O W Y
N   I   D   P   C   E
F I L L S   R E M I N D S
C   I   F   A   A
N O R T H E R N   T O U R
R   I   A   U   I   G
U N L E S S   T R O L L Y
  S   T   S   N   Y
```

93

```
T   E   A   D   S   C
C O N S I D E R   T O O T
O   C   V   U   R   N
P L E A S I N G   I T
  P   S   S   P   R
S N E E Z E   E S S A Y
U   D   G   S   S
F I L M S   D E N S I T Y
S   E   L   T   T
D A T A   O U T D O O R S
N   D   O   I   R   E
A C C O M P A N I M E N T
E   W   S   G   S   T
```

94

```
T H I R S T   R A V I N G
H   S   T   T   R   T   U
R E S E R V E   G R A I N
U   U   I   M   U   L   N
S L E E P   P R E C I S E
T   E   E   A   D
  M E A S U R E M E N T
B   A   A   I   L
A C R O B A T   S H A K E
R   L   A   U   T   L   G
K N I T S   R E A L I S E
E   E   I   E   K   E   N
D U R I N G   L E A N E D
```

95

```
C H A N C E S   E X T R A
H   L   O   T   N   O   S
E A T E N   E X C I T E S
A   E   V   A   Y   A   U
P E R P E N D I C U L A R
    E   R   Y   L   E
M O D E S T   W O R K E D
E   A   P   P   E
M E D I T E R R A N E A N
B   R   I   A   E   P   A
E C O N O M Y   D R I N K
R   V   N   E   I   N   E
S H E D S   D R A G G E D
```

96

```
A F R I C A   C L O U D S
L   O   O   P   E   N   E
L I C E N C E   M O U S E
O   K   N   R   O   S   I
W A S T E   S U N B U R N
S   C   O   A   G
  C O N T I N U A L L Y
A   R   A   C   S
D E C I M A L   H A T C H
Z   H   E   I   I   O   A
E X A C T   T R E A T E D
  R   R   Y   V   A   O
B A D G E S   Y E L L O W
```

97

```
C U S T O M S   C A B L E
O   L   A   U   O L L
C R E E P   M A N M A D E
O   E   M   C   Z   C
A D V E R T I S E   E A T
    E       T   N   E
M U S E U M   S T U P I D
A   R   R   R   R
R E F R I G E R A T O R S
K   L   V   T   J   I
E X A M I N E   I D E A L
T   M   T   A   O C   K
S E E M S   L E N G T H
```

98

```
C H A N C E S   E N T E R
R   L   O   P   N O   E
E A T E N   E X C I T E S
E   E   V   N   Y A   E
P A R   E N D   C O L O R
D   E   R   S   L   V
M O D E S T   C O U P L E
A   A   W   P   R
M E R I T   R A   E L F
M   I   I C E   S   A
A I R P O R T   D R E A M
L   E   N   E   I N   E
S I D E S   S T A R T
```

99

```
  P   C   A   S   R   P
M O T O R S   P O E T R Y
  O   N   S   L   V   O
S L O T   U N I F O R M S
  R   M   T   L   I
S P O I L E D   B U R S T
  O   B   D   L   T   E
A W F U L   E A S I E S T
  E   T   S   W   O
O R D I N A R Y   N E A T
  F   O   N   E   A   B
B U R N E D   R A R E L Y
  L   S   Y   S   Y   E
```

100

```
  B   W   T   W   M   C
D E C I D E   A N I M A L
  S   D   S   T   L   U
F I R E   T I C K L I S H
  D   I   H   I   E
M E E T I N G   L O A D S
      R   G   D   N
O W N E D   M O N S T E R
  O   A   M   C   L
N O I S I E S T   T R E E
  D   U   A   O   E   V
S E C R E T   R O L L E R
  N   E   S   L   N
```

101

```
  H   S   S   S   P   T
D A M P E N   P L U R A L   L
  W   I   E   R   L
Y A W N   F I E R C E L Y   Y
  I   F   D   H   E
T I C K L E D   P A I R
  I   D   S   S
I T A L Y   I N T E N S E
  A   O   E   O   E
B U N G A L O W   S A N G   I
  G   R   D   I   A   S
P H R A S E   N O D D E D   D
  T   M   R   G   S
```

102

```
  S   A   S   M   W   O
K I T T E N   A F R I C A   A
  S   O   A   R   I   L
I T E M   P O S I T I O N   N
  E   P   H   I   C
T R A I N E D   S N A K E
  M   D   C   G
S L I P S   C L A S S I C
  I   O   C   E   R
U M B R E L L A   P L O T   I
  I   T   I   R   O   N
I T S E L F   E L E V E N   N
  S   D   F   R   T   D
```

103

```
  Q   P   C   A   E   C
B U S I E R   F O L L O W
  E   N   A   T   E   R
B E D S   C R E E P I N G
  N   K   R   H   E
E S C A P E D   C A R R Y
  T   D   W   N
W H I T E   M E L T I N G
  O   A   G   T
Q U I C K E S T   B A T S
  R   K   E   E   E   T
A L I E N S   S H A K E S
  Y   D   E   T   R   D
```

104

```
  M   M   A   S   F   L
V A R I E D   A M A Z E D
  N   L   M   V   R   T
F A M E   I D E N T I T Y
  G   R   D   H   E
B E A C H E S   H E A R T
  R   D   M   S
F R I E S   N O   T E S T
  A   A   P   N   U
F R E T   I R S   S E N D
  E   I   N   T   W   S
G L A N C E   E R A S E R
  Y   G   S   R   N   T
```

105

```
  I   M   A   B   W   S
I D E A L S   U S E F U L
  E   T   S   L   A   N
D A T A   U N L I K E L Y
      R   S   E       I
O F F I C E S   D R U G S
  L   D   B           H
L O O P S   N A U G H T Y
  O   O   B   D   E
O R D E R I N G   N O O N
  I   T   T   E   T   U
U N L I K E   R U L E R S
  G   C   S   S   Y   S
```

106

```
      S   P   R   C   F
C A T T L E   O T H E R
  D   A   E   Y   A   A
P A I R   P L A N N I N G
      I   L   G       C
F I N D I N G   B I K E S
      O   G   C   N
G R O U P   D R A G O N
  E   B   G   I   I
S M A L L E S T   F I N E
  A   I   E   I   O   E
G I A N T S   C O U N T S
  N   G   E   S   R   Y
```

107

```
  A   I   A   S   J   S
E D I T O R   C H O I C E
  Z   E   T   R   U   R
S E A M   I C E C R E A M
  T       S   W   N   P
O B J E C T   R E F E R
  P   X   S   Y
S U P E R   G U E S S E S
  N   R   F   R   X
M I S C H I E F   T I P S
  Q   I   R   A   O   E
B U R S T S   C H A I R S
  E   E   T   E   D   T
```

108

```
  T   U   S   T   I   O
P I C N I C   R A D I U S
  L   A   R   U   E   T
C L U B   A C T U A L L Y
  L   T   H   L       I
S T R E T C H   U S I N G
  O   H   L       E
H U T C H   N E A R E S T
  R   H   G   G   E
D I S A G R E E   P A G E
  S   I   E   N   E   H
S T O R M Y   D R A W E R
  S           T       E
```

109

```
  S   M   A   Y   I   S
W I Z A R D   O   L O C K
  G   N   O   Y   L   R
T H R U   P R O D U C E R
  F   T   S   S   A
T R E A T E D   S T E M
  E   C   D   W   R   E
E M P T Y   L I Z A R D
  E   U   T       T
A M E R I C A N   I R O N
  B   E   O   E   O   I
N E A R E R   S I N G L E
  R   S   E   S   S
```

110

```
  W   U   E   C   I   D
P O I N T S   H A N D E D
  O   D   C   E   T   C
B L U E   A N S W E R E D
  R   P   S   R   M
D A I S I E S   K N O B
  P   T   D   H   A   E
S P E A K   W I N T E R
  E   N   F   G   T
S A N D W I C H   O P E N
  R   R   E   N   Y
T E N N I S   S T A Y E D
  D   B   T   T   L   D
```

111

```
  T   I   S   S   D   M
W A L N U T   T O I L E T
  L   T   A   I   S   A
E L S E   Y A C H T I N G
  R   I   K   I
O P E N I N G   S N A I L
  L   G   D   G   C
B O O T   R E D U C E D
  U   F   N       I
I G N O R A N T   S L I D
  H   R   C   I   H   N
D E B A T E   S E E I N G
  D   L   D   T   D
```

112

```
  S   S   P   O   F   M
T U N N E L   L E A V E S
  R   A   A   D   S   R
W E E K   C R E A T U R E
  E   I   R   E       I
M I S S I N G   T R I E S
  R   G   L           S
P E N C E   B A S K E T S
  O   B   R       I
C R O S S I N G   L I S T
  E   T   R   E   L   A
C A L L E D   S P E L L S
  R   Y   S   T   R   T
```

113

```
  B   W   V     S   E   F
P O T A T O     T R A G I C
  R   V   Y     A   S   D
E D G E     A L T I T U D E
E       G     E   W   L
G R U N T E D     N A M E D
    O     S     M     R
K N O W N     S E N D I N G
E     A   F   S         A
H A N D F U L S     F A T E
R     A   N     A   O   I
O B E Y E D     G R O O V E
Y     S   S     E   L   E
```

114

```
      T   T   S   H   T
H O R R O R     T H E I R S
  M   A   A     A   R   O
L A M P     C O R R I D O R
  T       T   S   T   P
H O R I Z O N     L A S S O
    N   R       H   G
S P A D E     C I N E M A
O   U   A     M     D
M E S S A G E S     C A V E
T   T   R   E     O   I
F I E R C E     L O W E S T
  C   Y   E     F     E
```

115

```
  L   P   M   A   C   B
P O T A T O     S H A D O W
  C   N   M   K   T   T
O A R S     E V E     E A T
  T       N   D   G   L
D E N S I T Y     H O M E
    Q   S   G     R
A B O U T     L A W Y E R
O   E   K     L     I
E X T E R N A L     E G G
I   Z   O     A   H
I N T E N T     P I R A T E
G   S   S         N
```

116

```
  V   E   M   T   D   D
G A R A G E     A T O M I C
  P   S   A   K   M   V
C O M E     S P E C I F I C
  U   L   N   N   D
C R A C K E D     M A R E
    H   S   C     N
D A R E D     S O F T E S T
M   M   M   N     I
C A P I T A L S     S O N G
Z   S   L   I   E   G
S E T T L E     S U N S E T
D       T   T     R
```

117

```
  R   S   D   S   C   S
B E E T L E     L O O K E D
  T   U   C   E   N   T
L A W N     I D E N T I T Y
  I   D   P   R   L
E N A B L E     W A T E R
  R   S   M   S
S A V E S     L E T T E R
  M   A   L   N   U
B A C K W A R D     B E S T
Z   I   N   I   E   H
R E I N E D     N E A R E R
D   G   S   G   R   S
```

118

```
D E C I M A L     F A C E D
E   I   O   I   U   O   R
C I R C U M F E R E N C E
A   C   S   T   C   S
Y O U     T E E N A G E R S
    M   A   D   P   N   E
I N S E C T     C A C T U S
N   T   H   R   R   R
S T A T E M E N T     A S H
T   N   M   M   T   A
E N C Y C L O P E D I A S
A   E   R   T   N   O   N
D U S T Y     E X T I N C T
```

119

```
  B   R   D   A   S   S
C A M E R A     R A N G E S
  R   C   I   A   E   N
H E R E     S U B J E C T S
    N   I   S   Z   E
S C A T T E R     M E A N T
  H       S   D     C
H E L P S     S E T T L E S
  M   O   B   N   U
S I L L I E S T     R O L E
  C   I   R   I   N   O
F A C T O R     S P E A R S
  L   E   Y   T   D   D
```

120

```
C A S K     N E U R O S I S
O   L   R   L   I   E   E
N I A G A R A     S C A L E
V   I   V   P   E   S   R
E O N     I     S T R A I N
R       R   N   E     D   C
S Y S T E M     E C Z E M A
E   E       D   O     R
  L A S S I E     S H A R E
L   L   I   S   T   R   L
A L I     N     I M A G I N E
S   O   U   R   R   S   S
S I N I S T E R     L E N S
```

121

```
T H I R S T   W A K I N G
H   S   T   T   R   M   U
R E S E R V E   G R A I N
U   U   I   M   U   G   N
S T E E P   P R E C I S E
T   E   E       N       D
  C O N S T R U C T E D
T   U   A   U           H
A T T E M P T   S H A M E
S   D   E   U   H   R   I
T R O U T   R A I S I N G
E   O   R   E   O   S   H
D A R T E D   I N V E N T
```

122

```
C H A N C E     E N T E R
R   L   O   L   N   O   E
E A T E N   E X C I T E S
E   E   V   E   Y   A   E
P E R P E N D I C U L A R
    E   R   S   L       V
M O D E S T   C O U P L E
A       A   W   P   R
M A D   T E R R A   E   V
M       I   I   E   D   O
A I R P O R T   D R I F T
L   E   N   E   I   C   E
S I D E S   S T A R T E D
```

123

```
T Y P I C A L   E X T R A
I   L   O   E   X   E   R
G R A I N   A T T E M P T
E   Y   S   N   R   P   I
R E F R I G E R A T O R S
  U   D   D   O       T
M E L T E D   T R I B E S
A       R       D   R
C O M P A R E   I C E   Y
H   O   T       N   A   A
I N I T I A L   A T T I C
N   S   O       O   R   H
E A T E N   P A Y M E N T
```

124

```
  P   D K   B E   A
S O L E M N   L U X U R Y
L   T   O   U   T   R
H E R E   C H E R R I E S
    R   K   S   A   S
S W I M M E R   M O N T H
A   I   D   C   R   E
T R E N D   C L A D   D
R   A   U   O   I
D I S T I N C T   N E E D
O   I   D   H   A   A
G R O O V E   E R R O R
S   N   R   S   Y   S
```

125

```
  D   A   E   S   C   C
S A N D A L   T R I B A L
  T   V   A   R   R   S
R A G E   S U I T C A S E
      R   T   P   U   E
C U R T A I N   E M P T Y
N   I   C   B   S   T
B R A S S   C L O T H E S
O   E   U   U   A
E L E M E N T S   N E A T
L   E   I   H   C   G
P E A N U T   E L E V E N
D   T   Y   S   S   D
```

126

```
  C   D   M   R   F   I
C A N A D A   A M O U N T
N   R   R   L   R   V
R A C E   B E L I E V E D
L       Y   C   N
E S C A P E S   C A R T S
    T   S   R   S
A D U L T   N E U T R A L
R   A   C   A   R
R A I N F A L L   G U M S
G   T   B   I   L   I
S O C I A L   S H A R E S
N   C   E   E   D   S
```

127

```
S I G N   V I A D U C T S
T   I   A   N   I   O   A
A D V I S E D   D E C A Y
N   E   H   E   N   O   S
D I S C O   E X T E N T
I   R   D   U   R
N I C K E L   B O T T L E
G   O   A   U       P
  C L O U D S   T R U S T
S   D   P   S   S   P   I
N E E D S   U N U S U A L
A   S   E   R   T   A   E
P O T A T O E S   P L U S
```

128

```
  M   M   I   W   T   A
W I Z A R D   R E H A S H
  C   N   E   A   E   P
T A X I   A C C U R S E D
  F   L   K   M   R
G A Z E L L E   R O B I N
L   S   Y   E   P   T
S P A T E   E V I L E Y E
H   A   H   E   A
H A W T H O R N   S P A Y
B   I   L   I   T   S
M E L O D Y   N E I G H
T   N       G   C
```

129

```
  H R O C S T
R I P O F F   A U T H O R
  F L F R   I   M
P I L L   B A R   L I M E
A   E   E Y   E Y
R E T R E A T   S T A G E
    S   T   N T   U
A L I K E   B O L O G N A
I   A   T   O   H
S P I T T O O N   E D G E
  I   W   D E   O
F I A N C E   A L L U R E
  N   G L Y S   E
```

133

```
  E S M F C R
U N L I K E   I R O N E D D
  T T S R N F
W I R E   S P E C T R U M M
  R I S A S
S E A S O N S   K I T E S S
    T G P N
B I K E S   R O O S T E R R
  M A G S A
B A L L O O N S   S O R T T
  G I O E N
T E N N I S   S H A P E S S
  S G E S T D
```

130

```
  S M E S A C
E T H I C S C   S T A R
  R T Q O T S
N I C E   U N W O R T H Y
  K I L A E
R E Q U I R E   B L O W
    N E F
S T O C K   J U R Y B O X
  R O E R C
P U T U P J O B   G L U E
  S P E I L
I T A L I C   S I G N A L
  Y E T H O R
```

134

```
  P R L A B R
P O L I T E   L E A N E D D
  L B S I L I
F I T S   S M E L L I N G G
  C O N E
M E   S I N G   B A R D
    P S P D
C A R E D   C O N S I S T T
  M C B S T
F A M I L I E S   S T A Y Y
  Z M T E C T
S E V E R E   S H A R E D D
  D N S R S
```

131

```
  S P B F F D
L I B I D O   A Z A L E A
  L K B T C F
P I P E   S P E C T R A L
  C L D I C
P A I S L E Y   B O N E
  O C D B U
T U B E R   A   S E E D
    N T P N
B R E A K O U T   S L A P
  E R W I N M
D E C I D E   S P A R E
  L O R E G L
```

135

```
  E W U S F F
E X T E N T   P U L L U P P
  T I I A N
V E E R   L I T I G A N T T
  N I E R E
A D V E R S E   C A U L K K
    L E V N
O L D E N   M A T T I N G
  E C N N I
B E E T R O O T   F E N D D
  W R N A O E
M A N I A C   G R O T T Y Y
  Y C E E T Y
```

132

```
  D H T A E M
D E C I D E   R O A R E D
  S T A M S S
T I P S   S W E E T E S T
  R I D D E
P E A S A N T   C A R D S
    T G C D
P O K E D   C O L D E S T
  U E F N H
E N O R M O U S   S N A P
  C I R I O D
P E A N U T   S T A R E D
  S G T P S
```

136

```
S O N G   C A R A V A N S
T Y E N R N I
R E L A X E D   R A C E D D
I O P A I E
C O N S E Q U E N C E S S
T R P G N C
L I P   I S S U E   T O O N
Y L M E M N
  N E V E R T H E L E S S S
E A N A I
V I S I T   A R T I S T S
E E A P S E T
R E S O L V E D   P L U S
```

137

```
R A C K   C R O S S C U T
E   H   G   E   T   O   R
S E A W E E D   R U P E E
I   P   N   A   I     E
D I S S E R T A T I O N
U     A   R   A   O   U   B
A S S   A   U   S   S E A
L     L   L   N   P     S
  H O U S E T O H O U S E
S   B   T   E   N       M
T A B O O   C O R N I C E
E   E   R   U   E   T   N
P E R M E A T E   P E N T
```

138

```
  M   M   P   R   N   N
P A T I N A   A M O R A L
R   S   Y   V   V   T
B I A S   S C E N A R I O
N     N       N       V
B A G S   E G   S A B E R
  W       B   D
E A S E D   B A N S H E E
I   E   V   P   N
P R O T R A C T   S L A M
M   P   L   I   I   M
R A C E   E   S O L D E R
N   A   T   M   K   L
```

139

```
  S   S   S   S   V   O
S T A T I C   C L I M B S
  A   A   A   R   A   E
O B E Y   T U E S D A Y
  L   T   W   U   E
P E O P L E   A C I D
    R   R   C   T
A T L A S   S E S S I O N
  R   I   F   N       C
N O I S I E S T   R I C E
  O   I   E   U   A   U
O P E N E D   R E C I P E
  S   G   S   Y   E   Y
```

140

```
S C R E W S   K I S S E S
T   I   I   D   N   H   T
R E V O L V E   D R A M A
I   A   D   S   I   M   N
P U L S E   T R A P P E D
S     S   R     O   S
  I N S T R U C T I O N
A   U   C   R       D
D A R K E S T   A M U S E
V   S   A   I   F   N   G
E V E N T   O F F I C E R
R   R   E   N   I   L   E
B E Y O N D   S C H E M E
```

141

```
I N S I D E   F L Y I N G
N   M   E   C   O   M   A
S   A M P   O   S   A N T
U   R   O   N   E   G   H
R A T E S   S E R V I C E
E     I   E     N     R
  E A R T H Q U A K E
P   N     U   U     P
L U G G A G E   S I X T H
U   R   R   N   T   R   O
S H I N E   C E R T A I N
    E   A   E   I   Y   E
S T R E S S   C A U S E D
```

142

```
B I C Y C L E   P I L O T
O   L   O   N   O   A   U
A G A I N   G E S T U R E
R   S   S   A   S   G   S
D I S T I N G U I S H E D
  E   D   E   B       A
S Y S T E M   S I M P L Y
W     R   W   L   L
E X T R A O R D I N A R Y
E   H   T   I   T   T   O
T O U R I S T   I D E A L
E   M   O   E   E   A   K
R O B I N   R E S C U E S
```

143

```
A F F A I R S   D I D N T
N   R   N   O   E   R   H
G I A N T   C O M P O S E
L   N   E   I   O   V   A
E N T E R T A I N M E N T
I   N   L   S       R
R A C I A L   S T R I K E
I   T   M   R   M     N
C O N   I K E   A I   E
H   O   O   L   T   T   E
E X T I N C T   I M A G E
S   E   A   E   O   T   D
T I D A L   D O N K E Y S
```

144

```
C U S T O M S   C H A I R
O   H   P   U   O   L   I
C H E A P   F I N D I N G
O   L   O   F   C   V   H
A D V E R T I S E M E N T
    E   T   X   N     L
R E S C U E   S T I C K Y
E     N   P   R   H
C O N S I D E R A T I O N
I   U   T   A   T   N   E
P O R T I O N   I T E M S
E   S   E   U   O   S   T
S H E D S   T U N N E L S
```

145

```
  B S S   L A S
MARKET   EARTHS
R I O M   T I
TRAP  PROVIDED
E   P N S   L
ENJOYED  STUDY
    C D   O I
TWICE  HUTCHES
E   U G T     D
TADPOLES  RAGS
L I I   O I
ATTEND  DEPEND
H D   E E E G
```

149

```
TROUSER  RISES
I W T E O K L
GENERALLY  ERA
H E A A L N
TRUST  TALLEST
  N C I T E
NEIGHBOURHOOD
O V N E N
USELESS  DISKS
G R M H U H
HIS  PRINCIPLE
T A T P E I D
SALTY  SADNESS
```

146

```
  A P V   A P H
GROOVE  TERROR
M O N   T E T
SOUR  THIRTIES
U U C T L
ORCHARD  FIRST
  E E S E
STILL  LEARNED
R P T S     A
BILLIONS  LORD
B E W I A N
PERSON  OXYGEN
S S S   N D
```

150

```
  S O I   S E L
COURTS  HANKIE
F G L O C K
DATA  APPROVED
N S S U W
REMINDS  BRAIN
X S S F A S
ATLAS  TONGUES
E T F R E
TRAINING  MAST
N O N E E A
WARNED  TANGLE
L S S S T T
```

147

```
  R A S D S C
BUNDLE  ECHOES
S D V B A N
USES  ESTIMATE
I N S P R
CARROTS  TOWER
  E H C O
INDIA  DAISIES
O N O U V
PRODUCES  BREN
W E E I E N
CAMERA  NEARLY
Y R N G M Y
```

151

```
  L R S O B M
TOMATO  COLOUR
O Y R E O S
USES  TRANSFER
E I N S U
ENGLAND  WORMS
A G D M
VAGUE  LEISURE
G N S S E
DESCRIBE  COWS
N H X R A A
ACCENT  VOTERS
Y S Y E S D
```

148

```
VOTE  CALORIES
I R A R V M I
SHARPER  EXIST
I C P I N T E
THEME  VISUAL
O A E T S
RIDERS  SEVERE
S R B X A
FIDDLE  TOADS
S V E E L O
CHINA  TENSION
A N L L D K A
REGISTER  REAL
```

152

```
  S E G S S V
COLDER  TOILET
A G O I L R
MATE  CARELESS
E S I E
CONVERT  SENSE
I Y J S
PILLS  VICTIMS
N L G E
ADVANCES  TIME
I G L A E B
CAMERA  WASHES
N S N S T R
```

153

```
    D O S   S P   S
W I G W A M   P I R A T E
N     L   A L   O   A
A N T S   S L I P P E R Y
E     H     T   O   V
D R I F T E D   A S H E S
      O   D   M     E
S C O R E   P U D D L E S
H   W   T   S       X
D I S A G R E E   H O P S
L   R   U   U   O   E
B L A D E S   M E M O R Y
Y   S   T   S   E   T
```

154

```
    A H   G V   C S
A F R I C A   A L A R M S
  F   K   R L   P   O
W E R E   D E V O T I O N
  C       E E   A   T
S T U D E N T   S I G H T
      R   S P   N
L E M O N   C L A S S E S
  R   P   B A       D
P R O P E R T Y   L O G S
  O   I   A E   A   I
T R U N K S   R E C E N T
  S   G   S S   K   G
```

155

```
    F L   M R   F T
S A V A G E   A M A Z E D
  V   T   A T   R   R
R O S E   S H E L T E R S
  U   H   S H   O
P R O C E E D   B E A R S
  E   M   S M   S
F R I E S   D E N T I S T
  E   M   G S       I
C A P I T A L S   S I N S
  D   S   M I   L   G
B E E T L E   N E A R E R
  R   S   S G   P   R
```

156

```
    D R   A D   A R
E R R A N D   A C C R U E
  Y   C   J I   I   L
T R O Y   O B S I D I A N
  O   U   Y     Y
S T I R F R Y   I S S U E
      O   N   B     I
B U R S T   R O I S T E R
  S   E   T W       M
S U R M O U N T   R U B Y
  R   A   B I   U   O
D E G R E E   E L D E S T
  R   Y   R S   E   S
```

157

```
    B S   P G   E C
A U T H O R   R E A S O N
  S   I   I E   S   W
L I M P   E G Y P T I A N
  E   S   S S   W   R
G R A N I T E   S A N D Y
      O   S S   R
S W I S S   B O R D E R S
  O   T   G L   A
S U R R O U N D   D U T Y
  N   I   E I   R   T
A D U L T S   E Q U A L S
  S   S   S R   M   E
```

158

```
O I L   A P P R O V E D
B A L A   A   A   A   O
S U S P E C T   T H R E W
E   S   S T   I   Y   N
R O O F S   E X O T I C
V   O   O D   N     I
E A T I N G   B A R G E S
D   I   G   B       O
  S P L A S H   R I V A L
E   P   G O   O   A   A
C H I N A   S C A R L E T
H   N   I T   D   V   E
O R G A N I S E   R E A D
```

159

```
D R O P   A C C U R A T E
A   P   L   A R   C   A
U S E L E S S   B I T E S
G   R   S   T A   I   T
H E A T S   L O N D O N
T   E   E       N   P
E N D I N G   R U S S I A
R   E   I   N       S
  E V E N T S   L E A S T
A   O   R   O   H   U
R A T I O   A M A T E U R
T   E   N   E D   A   E
S U D D E N L Y   A D D S
```

160

```
O I   A S   C D
S P E N D S   P O I S O N
E   V   H O   R   M
K N E E   A R T I C L E S
    S   M S   U   S
S C A T T E R   E M P T Y
L   I   D T   S   I
B A N G S   L E T T U C E
P   A   M N   A
U P S T A I R S   N O T E
I   I   D I   C   E
E N J O Y S   O P E N E D
G   N   T N   S   M
```

161

```
H I G H W A Y . C R A F T
A . A O . E . L R . U . .
U N U S U A L . U N T I E
N . G . L . D . M . I . S
T I E . D . O P P O S E D
. . . N . W . . T . . . A
D E B A T E . G R A S S Y
I . I . P . E . . . . . .
S T O R A G E . F A C T S
P . L . R . O . L . H . I
L O O S E . P E E L I N G
A . G . A . L . C . N . H
Y O Y O S . E X T R A C T
```

162

```
. D . S . P . S . R . G .
B O T H E R . U S E F U L
. R . O . O . G . C . E .
. S E T . J E A L O U S Y
. E . . E . R . V . T . .
I T A L I C S . S E N S E
. . . U . T . D . R . . .
T W I C E . B I C Y C L E
. E . K . F . G . . . E .
M A G I C I A N . R I S E
. P . E . R . A . S . . .
H O U S E S . T A I L O R
. N . T . T . Y . L . N .
```

163

```
C A L L . S T O M A C H S
U . E . F . I . O . O . T
S E A S O N S . R A T . O
H . V . S . S . A . T . P
I D E A S . U N L O A D .
O . . . I . E . . G . A .
N E A R L Y . A S L E E P
. L . . B . U . . . . P .
. F L O W E R . B R A K E
U . O . I . O W . S . A .
S E W E D . L E A T H E R
E . E . O . L . Y . E . E
S I D E W A Y S . U S E D
```

164

```
K I L L I N G . D R A F T
I . A . C . A . A . D . U
L O R R I E S . N . O D E
L . G . C . P . C . P . S
S P E L L . E L E C T E D
. . . E . D . . E . A . .
P O L I S H . W I L D L Y
A . O . . . H . N . . . .
D E C L A R E . I D E A L
D . A . N . L . T . X . O
L A T I N . P A I N T E R
E . E . O . E . A . R . D
D A D D Y . D O L L A R S
```

165

```
. A . E . P . P . H . G .
A F F A I R . R U I N E D
R . S . O . O . S . N . .
L I M E . M O U N T A I N
. C . I . D . O . U . . .
L A Z I E S T . G R A S P
. . . N . E . C . I . . .
S H O C K . T R I C K E D
A . L . I . A . V . . . .
A B R U P T L Y . F R E E
. I . D . E . O . O . N .
S T R E A M . N I N E T Y
. S . D . S . S . S . D .
```

166

```
O C C U P Y . A M U S E D
C . I . L . A . E . T . A
E N G L A N D . A P R O N
A . A . T . V . N . A . I
N U R S E . E X T E N D S
S . . . A . N . G . . . H
. I L L U S T R A T E D .
E . E . . . U . R . . . C
F L A V O U R . T O R C H
F . N . U . O . I . I . A
E X I S T . U N C O V E R
C . N . E . S . L . E . G
T I G E R S . D E G R E E
```

167

```
O U R S . U P S T A I R S
P . A . S . H . H . R . L
P O I N T E R . O P E R A
O . S . A . A . S . L . P
S H E E R . S E E S A W .
I . V . E . E . N . . . F
T I T L E S . P A D D L E
E . E . . . E . M . . . A
. V A L V E S . A D M I T
T . R . I . C . Z . E . H
R E I N S . A V E R A G E
U . N . I . P . D . L . R
E I G H T E E N . A S K S
```

168

```
. L . D . W . U . M . D .
C I N E M A . S T A T I C
. M . M . S . I . N . R .
L E G O . H O N O U R E D
. . . N . I . G . F . C .
L E S S O N S . T A S T E
. V . T . G . B . C . O .
F E A R S . H I S T O R Y
. N . A . T . C . U . . .
B I T T E R L Y . R O D S
. N . I . I . C . I . E .
I G N O R E . L O N G E D
. S . N . D . E . G . R .
```

169

```
 C  L  S     L  L     P
 V  A  N  I  S  H     I  C  I  C  L  E
 N     M     I  N     F     A
 S  A  M  E     P  R  E  V  E  N  T  S
 D        P     D     B     E
 M  A  T  C  H  E  D     G  O  O  S  E
       H     D     R     A
 B  A  S  E  D     D  E  N  T  I  S  T
 M     R     T     V     U
 C  A  R  R  I  A  G  E     T  E  N  T
 Z     I     K     R     D
 S  E  V  E  R  E     S  A  N  D  A  L
 D     S     N     E     E  Y
```

170

```
 C  A  S  H     C  H  U  C  K  L  E  D
 A     T     D  U     O     O     A
 N  E  A  R  E  S  T     N  A  N  N  Y
 A     F     L     S     G     I
 D  I  F  F  I  C  U  L  T  I  E  S
 I     B     S     !     S     G
 A  G  O     E  X  I  S  T     T  O  O
 N     U     R     N     U     O
 S  T  R  A  I  G  H  T  E  N  E  D
 B     D     T     I     A     N
 L  O  O  S  E     D  I  O  X  I  D  E
 O     O     L     E     N     L  S
 W  O  R  R  Y  I  N  G     U  S  E  S
```

171

```
    E     P        I        E     S
 P  U  B  L  I  C     S  E  N  S  E
    R     O     E     I     G     V
 G  O  A  T     B  O  N  F  I  R  E
    P        E     K     N     R
 C  E  L  L  A  R     H  E  R  E  S
       I     G     H     E
 K  N  I  F  E     L  O  R  R  I  E  S
    U     E     K     U        D
 W  R  I  T  I  N  G  S     S  L  I  M
    S     I     I     U        T
 H  E  L  M  E  T     N  A  R  R  O  W
    D     E        G        E     R
```

172

```
    T     C     T     A        P     A
 L  O  C  A  T  E     L  A  Y  I  N  G
    M     T     N     A     R     G
 C  A  B  S     S  U  R  F  A  C  E  S
    T        I     M     M     L
 H  O  R  I  Z  O  N     F  I  R  S  T
       N     N     R     D
 P  R  I  D  E     R  O  O  S  T  E  R
    O     I     T     A        I
 Q  U  A  R  R  E  L  S     C  A  S  E
    T     E     L     T     O     I
 P  E  N  C  I  L     E  N  A  B  L  E
    S     T     S     D     L     Y
```

173

```
    B     D     I     W     C     F
 V  A  C  U  U  M     A  B  O  A  R  D
    T     M     P  S     R     E
 S  T  O  P     R  E  T  U  R  N  E  D
    L        O     E     I     Z
 B  E  L  I  E  V  E     A  D  D  E  D
    N        E     H     O
 F  R  O  S  T     C  O  R  R  E  C  T
    E     T     T     L        O
 S  P  L  A  S  H  E  D     G  I  F  T
    O     N     E     I     O     F
 T  R  I  C  K  Y     N  E  A  R  E  R
    T        E     D     G  T     E
```

174

```
 A  C  C  E  P  T     P  R  I  S  O  N
 D     H     E     I     U     O     I
 D  I  A  G  R  A  M     L  E  M  O  N
 I     I     C     P     E     E     T
 N  E  R  V  E     A  I  R  P  O  R  T
 G     N     T     N           Y
    C  O  N  T  R  I  B  U  T  E  D
 H     R     E     P              C
 U  N  I  C  O  R  N     R  I  D  E  R
 M     G     B     T     I     R     E
 O  L  I  V  E     L  U  G  G  A  G  E
 U     N  Y     Y     Y  H     M     P
 R  E  S  I  S  T     S  T  E  A  L  S
```

175

```
 A  C  C  E  P  T     C  O  F  F  I  N
 R     A     A     C     F     O     E
 T  O  B  A  C  C  O     T  H  R  E  W
 I     L     I     N     E     M     E
 S  H  E  L  F     T  O  N  G  U  E  S
 T        I     R           L     T
    S  P  E  C  T  A  C  U  L  A  R
 S     R        S     P        P
 W  H  I  T  E  S  T     R  E  F  E  R
 A     M     A     I     I     A     A
 M  E  A  N  T     N  I  G  H  T  L  Y
 P     R     E     G     H     T     E
 S  A  Y  I  N  G     S  T  A  Y  E  D
```

176

```
 T  H  U  M  P  S     J  A  G  G  E  D
 W     P     R     M     F     R     E
 E  X  P  L  O  D  E     T  R  U  M  P
 N     E     T     A     E     N     T
 T  H  R  E  E     S  T  R  E  T  C  H
 Y        I     U        E        S
    C  O  U  N  T  R  Y  S  I  D  E
 O     R        E     H           B
 B  E  D  R  O  O  M     I  N  D  I  A
 T     E     U     E     F     R
 A  P  R  O  N     N  O  T  H  I  N  G
 I     E     C     T     E     L     E
 N  O  D  D  E  D     A  D  U  L  T  S
```

177

```
D A T I N G   S P R E A D
E   U   U   C   U   R   E
T O B A C C O   P O O L S
A   E   L   N   I   S   I
I S S U E   T E L L I N G
L     A   R       O     N
  A P P R O A C H I N G
B   O   S   I         S
A T T E M P T   G I A N T
T   T   A   I   H   R   R
T R E A T   N O W H E R E
E   R   C   G   A   N   A
R H Y T H M   S Y S T E M
```

178

```
D E S I G N   S H I V E R
E   A   R   C   E   E   E
B U F F A L O   A S H E S
A   E   N   R   R   I   I
T I R E D   N O T I C E S
E     M         L   T
  E M B A R R A S S E D
O   E       U         M
B U N D L E S   P L A T E
J   T   I   I   P   U   A
E X I S T   D R O W N E D
C   O   R   E   S   T   O
T U N N E L   S E E S A W
```

179

```
  T   U   I   C   E   F
W A L N U T   L U X U R Y
  X   D   A   A   P   E
S I D E   L I S T E N E R
  R   I   S   R   Z
U N U S U A L   L I M I T
  A   T   N   S   M   N
S T E A L   F O R E I G N
  I   N   N   M   N
R O A D S I D E   T I L E
  N   I   G   O   I   O
L A U N C H   N I N E T Y
  L   G   T   E   G   S
```

180

```
  A   I   M   U   N   F
B R O L L Y   N E E D E D
  C   L   S   I   I   S
T H O U   T H O U G H T S
  S   E   N   H   H   I
D O C T O R     A B O V E
  R   R   Y   O   O   A
I D E A S   P R O U D L Y
  I   T   O   D   R
I N F I N I T E   H A I L
A   O   L   R   O   C
O R A N G E   L O O S E N
Y   S   D   Y   D
```

181

```
  D   U   E   S   C   R
W I N N E R   H O O K E D
  V   F   O   O   N   S
  E G O   S K E T C H E S
  R     I   S   E   M
S E C T I O N   K N O B S
  C   U   N   S   T   L
T O W N S   S O U R C E S
  N   A   H   F   A
C O N T R A C T   T U N E
  M   E   I   E   I   E
K I L L E R   S H O R E S
  C   Y       T   N   D
```

182

```
  R   A   P   A   U   O
L U M B E R   C E N T R E
  D   B   U   C   N
D E E R   N A T I O N A L
  E   O   E   M   M
F L A V O U R   A F T E R
  A   I   N   R   O   N
S N E A K   R E W R I T E
  G   T   T   A   T
P U N I S H E D   A X L E
  A   O   E   B   O
A G E N C Y   R U L E R S
  E   S       S   E   D
```

183

```
  D   S   D   F   C
L E T T E R   E N O U G H
  N   A   I   W   L   I
S T I R   F R E Q U E N T
  A       T   R   M
S L A M M E D   O B E Y S
    U   D   S   I
S T A T E   S W E A T E R
  U   T   E   O     X
I N T E R V A L   P I C K
  I   R   E   L   A   U
U N S E E N   E X C E S S
  G   D   T   N   E   E
```

184

```
  C   I   B   S   P   L
R I D D L E   P A R T E D
  N   L   T   E   O   A
H E R E   W R A P P I N G
  M   E   R   E   E
C A N D L E S   T R A D E
    I   N   I   L
R I V A L   S T A Y I N G
  N   L   S   A     I
I N F O R M A L   A R C H
  I   G   E   I   L   K
A N N U A L   A N S W E R
  G   E   T   N   O   L
```

185

```
  S I M   O F F
S T U D I O   P O E T R Y
O   E   T   E E A
A R E A   H A N D L I N G
M   E   S   I   C
M Y S T E R Y   U N D E R
    H   S   T   G
A B O U T   O U T S I D E
E   R   A   E   O
S A U S A G E S   S I C K
U   D   I   I   T
S T R A I N   A C T I O N
Y   Y   G   Y S R
```

189

```
  C S O   A F S
W A I T E R   C H O R U S
R   E D   R R B   H
S E E M   E L E V E N T H
E   R   S C L   L
C R A S H E S   B A S E D
    P D L   S
C A V E S   F A S T E S T
C   C S W   T
O R D I N A R Y   L E A N
O F L E   I   R
S H I R T   R E N T E D
S C Y   K S
```

186

```
  B S C   S S P
B E F O R E   A C T U A L
C M N V   A P   P
B A S E   T W E N T I E S
M   R S   I   R
W E A T H E R   M O U S E
    R D L   N
S H O E S   M O N S T E R
A A S N   L
C R O S S I N G   S E E D
D U X E   E V
S E C R E T   S H A K E S
R E H   T L N
```

190

```
  F H T   G C B
S A V A G E   R E A D E R
V Z A E   P H   R
T O R E   C H E M I C A L
U   C H N   T V
T R I C K E D   L A C E S
A U R C   L
B R I E F   P O S S E S S
O   T N   E
M A T T E R E D   S A N D
R O I U   I S
D E G R E E   C A N O E S
D N S   T K S
```

187

```
  S T G   B F P
F A T H E R   A T O M I C
F I A D   R G   C
F E R N   B E L I E V E D
S   B Y   C O
S T O O P E D   B A R N S
P D F S   T
B A S E D   H O T T E S T
S R R R   T
P L E A S A N T   S E A T
E T F I   C T
D E F E A T   E R A S E R
P D S   S R S
```

191

```
  S I R   G A R
B E A T L E   R I P P E D
C E P O   P A   D
L O O M   L O W L A N D S
N   I L   R E
A D V I S E D   P E A R L
N S P N   L
A S I D E   A U S T R I A
U I S D   N
O P E R A T E D   D O T S
P E U I   O E
F E N C E D   N A M I N G
R T Y   G E D
```

188

```
  N L B   U C S
N O T I C E   N E A R L Y
R F T A D   P   E
O M I T   E A T   E
A I R   A P
P L A C I N G   M I D S T
  R G L   N
S H E E P   P A S S I N G
A A F R   I
A N Y T H I N G   S E E
D U R E   E D
B E A R D S   S H A K E S
D E T   T T D
```

192

```
  M V R   P C B
M A R I N E   H E L M E T
N E C O   I A   T
S N O W   O I N T M E N T
E   E R   E B
P R O V I D E   S E N S E
O S S R
S C A L E   H E R S E L F
A C R G   E
O R G A N I S M   G R A N
R N N E   D
B O R I N G   N E R V E S
T C S   T M R
```

193

```
  T   C   D   S   W       T
G A R A G E   C R A Y O N
I   M   N   A   R   I
S L A P   S P R I N K L E
O   I   E   I   E
G R A N I T E   U N I T Y
    O   Y   T   G
W R O N G   F R E S H L Y
E   S   S   A   O
S C R E A M E D   H E A P
K   N   E   I   E   D
F O S S I L   N E A R E R
N   E   L   G   D   D
```

194

```
  V   G   M   N O D   D
S A V A G E   A   O   I
P   L   A   M   M   V
R O S E   S P E C I F I C
U   L   S   N   N
C R U S H E D   M A K E S
  P   S   F   N
G A M E S   F A T T E S T
N   C   B   S   E
I N D I R E C T   S U N
U   M   A   E   A S
C A R E E R   S U N S E T
L   N   D   T   K   S
```

195

```
B O S S   S T R E S S E D
A   P   J   H   A   H   E
N O I S I E R   G R A I N
  N   G   U   L   M   T
D I S K S   S L E E P Y
E   A   T   O   B
A R R O W S   S C H O O L
F   E   P   E   A
  U G L I E R   R O M A N
D I D   O   E   O   K
A R O S E   F E A T U R E
T   N   A   I   L   T
A B S O L U T E   T H I S
```

196

```
R O W S   R E L A T I V E
E   C   Y   R   N   A
M I S T A K E   C A S T S
E   E   T   H   T   E
M A T H E M A T I C A L
B   R   G   T   N   H
E A T   P H A S E   T O O
R   E   I   I   C
  E X P L A N A T I O N S
A   T   L   U   T
C H I N A   F E R T I L E
I   L   R   U   E   R
D R E S S I N G   I N K S
```

197

```
C O T T A G E   S T E M S
O   E   U   N   O   X   A
C L A S S I C A L   C O T
O   T   O   A   E   L   F
A N G E R   U N R O L L S
  Y   I   R   L   F
C O M P A R A T I V E L Y
L   N   G   R   N
A N A L Y S E   O U T E R
S   S   E   M   N   U
S K I   A M E R I C A N S
I   U   R   N   N   N   T
C O M E S   T I G H T L Y
```

198

```
  D   B   H   S   A   P
B A N A N A   E F F O R T
  R   L   N   N   R   A
B E L L   D I S T I N C T
  E   L   E   C   T
E M P T I E S   H A B I T
I   D   T   C
B L A S T   C R E A T E D
I   P   A   A   D
S T R E S S E D   J E T S
A   N   I   E   U   H
T R A D E D   R U S H E S
Y   S   E   S   T   N
```

199

```
  S   M   V   C   F
B R E E Z E   A N I M A L
  A   V   A   G   N   R
T Y P E   S Q U E E Z E D
  R   L   E   M   W
P O W E R E D   C A S E S
  P   S   L   L
F E N C E   F E R T I L E
  R   A   S   I
W A R R I O R S   T A S K
  T   P   F   O   L   I
F O R E S T   N E E D L E
  R   T   Y   S   S   K
```

200

```
  W   D   D   S   C   G
N A T I V E   H O O V E S
  R   E   C   O   N   N
O M I T   I D E N T I T Y
  T   E   D   S   R   L
C H A M B E R   R A T E S
      E   D   M   C
A C U T E   L E A T H E R
  E   A   L   S   A
T R O L L E Y S   W A S H
  E   L   D   I   O   I
M A K I N G   N U R S E D
  L   C   E   G   D   R
```

201

```
S   A     C A G
SHOULD   RIBBON
O  T  D  O  B  V
HERO   REWARDED
   M    E  N  E R
BECAUSE   OVENS
Q  T  S  H  I  E
PUPIL   DEMANDS
A  C  F  I     T
STEAMING   IOTA
I  L  N  H  O  A
BOILED   TANGLE
N  Y        S  L
```

202

```
N  F  H  C  C  S
POTATO   LAUNCH
T  D  U  E  D  E
VINE   STANDING
C     I  N  L  E
REASON    FIRST
   O  G  P  N
THUMB   WEIGHTS
U  E  C  E     A
SNOWBALL   MULE
G  H  R  I  E  L
GREASE   NURSED
Y  T  D  G  E  R
```

203

```
B  U  D  A  C  R
SOONER   LOOSEN
R  F  E  I  N  S
ZERO   SKETCHES
   R  S  N  E  M
SCATTER   KNOBS
I  U  D  S  T  L
GRAND   SOURCES
C  A  S  F     A
SUBTRACT   TIME
L  E  N  E  I  E
JAILED   SHOULD
R  Y  Y  T  N  T
```

204

```
   G  A  S  O  P
PLAGUE   PUBLIC
I  E  C  E  S  G
ADDS   RELIEVED
E     E  T  R  O
PRIVATE   EVENT
   I  S  M     E
SCALE   BARRIER
H  L  C  T     N
METALLIC   LATE
R  G  O  H  I  I
URGENT   EFFORT
Y  R  H  S  E  E
```

205

```
SETS   INSISTED
T  U  C  E  N  R  U
AIRPORT   TOADS
N  N  M  T  E  I  T
DISAPPEARING
A     E  D  S  E  P
ROBOTS   LEADER
D  U  I  P  C     E
INSTRUCTIONS
S  D  I  R  I  M  E
HELLO   PROVEN
E  E  N  L  N  N  T
DISASTER   ASKS
```

206

```
D  P  S  U  R  S
AIR  C   SHOOTS
T  E  A  U  C  R
HALF   THANKFUL
   E  T  L  E  G
DIARIES   STAGE
N     N  R  R  L
ASKED   REPLIED
T  N  F     S  O
HISTORIC   CUP
N  E  E  U  A  O
SCARES   ESTATE
T  S  H  D  E  S
```

207

```
POINT  R   LIFTS
O  C  R  E  O  R  P
SPECIALLY   AGO
T     U  A  A  M  T
STEAM   TALLEST
V  P  I     W  E
NEIGHBOURHOOD
I  D     N  I  R
BREATHS   NAKED
B  N  H  H  G     R
LET   ELIMINATE
E  L  M  P  N  F  A
STYLE   SIGHTED
```

208

```
S  H  E  S  F  S
REVEAL   TRIPOD
C  E  E  A  G  U
GULL   MATCHING
R     E  E  T  D
GERMANY   MIDST
   I  T  T  N
OPEN   ROUGHLY
U  E  S  T     U
UMBRELLA   HUMS
P  A  I  L  O  B
PEELED   LOUDER
D  S  E  Y  R  R
```

209

```
  H U E     P P R
T E N N I S   H O R S E
  R   F   C O   O S
S O L O   A T T E N D E D
  R   P   O   U   M
S C A T T E R   S N O B
  I   U     D C     L
C R A N E   L I M I T E D
  C   A   G   S     A
S U I T C A S E   T A P E
  L   E   I   A   I E
G A L L O N   S P O O N
  R   Y       E   N S
```

210

```
  S O L   S P U
B A M B O O   P I L I N G
  L   E   E     A   T
N A V Y   A N A L Y S I S
  D   T   R   T   E
A S S U R E D   K I N D
    N   D   F   M
M I L K Y   S L E E V E S
  R   I   F   I     X
S O U N D I N G   C A P E
  N D   N   H   O     E
S E A L E D   T O W A R D
  D Y       S   S T
```

211

```
  S S P   A   T P
C U C K O O   T O W E R S
  B I   S   O   I I
S W I M   T U M B L I N G
  A     I S   I   C
C Y C L I N G   A G R E E
    A   G S H
S T O U T   P L A T E A U
  A   N S   A     M
S P E C I M E N   L I O N
  P   H E   T   I U
R E V E A L   E N D I N G
  D S L   D   S T
```

212

```
  C R W   E   F F
M A R I N E   V A R I E S
  N   P   A E   E N
A C R E   T E N D E N C Y
  E     H   T Z   E
G R E A T E R   M I D S T
    C   R M   N
S T A T E   W E I G H E D
  H   I   W A   Y
P R E V I O U S   S T E W
  E   I   A L   O L
D A R T E D   E R A S E R
  D Y       S   K T
```

213

```
  D M B   T S P
R E V O L U T I O N A R Y
  A U T   T E   E
C R I T I C A L   E A S E
  H H E   Z   S
R O O S T E R   J E S U S
  P     R W     R
L E A P S   H A T C H E D
  R I   E R H
B A R E   N O N S E N S E
  T C   I   S H
D E T E R M I N A T I O N
  D D Y   G S W
```

214

```
  W   S R   T F
A T T A C H   A F R A I D
  R R   O Z   E E
S E A M   P R O B A B L E
  S   P   R S D
A S S U M E D   N U R S E
    N   D L   R
W E E K S   C O V E R E D
  R I   V N   A
H A U N T I N G   M A S S
  S D   E I   O I
F E L L O W   N E A R L Y
  R Y     G N Y
```

215

```
  B I S   T P
S A D D L E   R A R E L Y
  M L   G U   O E
A B L E   M U S C U L A R
  O   E T   B S
R O B B I N G   C L U E S
  E   T C E
A S I D E   T O S S I N G
  A   R C N   E
S Y N O N Y M S   C L A M
  I   O C U   A R
A N I M A L   L A B E L S
  G S E   T S Y
```

216

```
  P D B   S P I
C O L O U R   P I R A T E
  O N O   E E S
T R U E   T W E N T I E S
  H D E   L
W R I T T E N   K N I F E
  H R F   D
A G A I N   H O U S I N G
  H R E L     E
F O O T B A L L   B I T E
  S I R   O E T
S T R E E T   W A S H E S
  S S H   S T D
```

217

```
O  S     U     T  A     I
UNDERSTANDING
C     C  U  K     D  S
DECORATE     INTO
   N     L     N     A
READILY     AGING
X        Y  S        C
APPLE     SHIFTED
L     A     I     O
FOUR     LANGUAGE
R     G     I  I  R     R
DETERMINATION
R     R  B     G  H     W
```

218

```
F  L  A     S  A     S
AUTUMN     COWBOY
T     N  Y     R  A  O
HUNG     BREAKING
R     O     W  E     E
DEPENDS     ANGRY
X     Y     N     E
WHEAT     SADDLED
O     M  F     U     R
TRAILING     FLAP
R     N  F     H  E     S
FOREST     TALKER
R     D  H     Y  T     R
```

219

```
P     A     E  F  A     R
DISTINGUISHED
L  T     T  N     H     P
REPAIRED     OATH
C     I  S     R     I
COOKIES     MEALS
R     S     C        E
ADULT     POSSESS
E     O  S     L     I
GRIN     THOUGHTS
I  D     A  U     N     O
UNCOMFORTABLE
G     N  F     S  L     D
```

220

```
CLEANS     STREAM
O  X     U  R     E  X     A
ARTICLE     ACTOR
S  R     L  S     R  R     I
TEASE     EASTERN
S        S  A     R     M  E
   ABBREVIATED
T     A     A     T        R
ACROBAT     HASTE
R  R     A     I  L     T  C
GRIND     OPERATE
E  E     G  N     T  G     S
THREE     LEVELS
```

221

```
L     R  R     P  I     D
SAVAGE     RANGES
B  K     L  I     T     P
ROPE     ANSWERED
U     X     M  R     N
TRICKED     HERDS
R     D  H     S
FREED     FATTEST
O     A  W     R     U
BATTERED     SANK
R     I  I     E  U     S
TENNIS     SINGER
D     G  T     T  S     T
```

222

```
FURNACE     VOTED
I  U     N  S  O     H  I
FANTASTIC     ELF
T        L  A     R     F
HEAVY     BELIEVE
   M  S     L     F     R
ABBREVIATIONS
S  U     S     R     R
SELFISH     ALERT
U  A     T  M  C        U
MAN     ELECTRONS
E  C     M  N  O     R  K
DRESS     TURKEYS
```

223

```
CHOP     UNICORNS
H  T     S  A     O  E     A
EXHAUST     NOSEY
A  E     R  U     S  P     S
PERSPIRATION
E        R  E     I  N     B
STATIC     STUDIO
T  N     S  B  U           U
   AGRICULTURAL
F  R     N     T  I     O  D
LYING     TROUBLE
E  E     L  O     N  I     R
WORRYING     ENDS
```

224

```
Z     S  A     S  S     F
CIRCUMSTANCES
N     R  A  U     A     A
ACCEPTED     KITE
   E     E  Y     E     H
URANIUM     ASKED
E        R  H        R
USUAL     DEEPEST
T     P  S     R  R
SOAP     EMOTIONS
R     L  E     I  N     O
DETERMINATION
D     S  S     E  S     N
```

225

```
E O A N D M
ANIMAL  UNIQUE
 G I R  V S
VAST  INSPIRED
 G G E  S U
LENGTHS  FILMS
 O T  B O
WAGON  BURNING
 L D K R  E
HAUNTING  BEAK
 R E N L U R
AMUSED  ANSWER
 S S S R Y R
```

226

```
RECESS  STATIC
E O H C  O O H
COMPARE  WORSE
I M M N  E N E
TRAMP  THREATS
E O I  D E
 INFORMATION
L O E  I C
ATTRACT  CIVIL
W I F R K O O
YACHT  ENEMIES
E E E S T C E
RESORT  ASPECT
```

227

```
S C F F C R
THRONE  UNITED
 O M E R R P
SWAM  DIRECTLY
 U I Y U A
LEANING  SMACK
 N I G K F E
STUCK  DISEASE
 E A K S R
PRETENDS  EARN
 I I E I N O
UNROLL  NECTAR
 G N T G E R
```

228

```
N U W F A P
WINNER  RIBBON
N C I O B I
HERO  TOWERING
 M E N E T
BONFIRE  AVOID
 P O S W I N
APART  ARRANGE
 O T M O T
INVASION  ITEM
 E B D G O Y
UNCLES  LONGED
 T E T Y S D
```

229

```
T E W C S D
PAUNCH  ORIGIN
 M C E V T S
NERO  EXERCISE
 U L R O O
STARVED  SMILE
 R A D T V
COUGH  COVERED
 P E K S V
DIAMONDS  ELSE
 C E O I E
WALNUT  NICKEL
 L T S G D
```

230

```
P S A A D F
POUNDS  SPEAR
 O E P K C I
BLUE  EVENINGS
 Z C D D H
BENEATH  TENTS
 X S P E
DARES  NETTING
 M R R R O
APPROACH  SURE
 L O F A S A
REGRET  PREFIX
 S S S S D L
```

231

```
T A B P W P
NUMBER  OTHERS
 N S U E O I
ZERO  SIMPLEST
 R H S L O
ENABLED  TYING
 U S A E
GIFT  AFFAIR
 S I S F S
CASSETTE  KNEE
 N S A C I X
OCCUPY  TENNIS
 E E S S G T
```

232

```
S P B T U T
MARINA  RENTAL
 L K N E C T
FIRE  SANCTITY
 V H D U L
RATCHET  FOXED
 L E L U
RAVEL  DESSERT
 N M B F A
INHALANT  SUNG
 E T G I T G
MALICE  SHARES
 L S L T R R
```

233

```
T   U   D   I   C   R
D I N N E R   N A I L E D
  D   F   I   D   R   P
H E R O   F I E R C E L Y
  R   T   X   U   A
S E T T L E S   S M A C K
  G   U   D   M   F   E
D Y I N G   R E L E A S E
  P   A   F   A   R
S T A T I O N S   E N D S
  I   E   L   U   N   E
H A U L E D   R E C E N T
  N   Y   S   E   E   Y
```

234

```
Z   H   J   O   E   A
D E C O   U   I G N O R E
  R   N   P   L   G   R
S O M E T I M E   I T E M
      S   T   D   N   S
F E A T H E R   H E A T S
  L   R   K   E
H E R E   S E C O N D
  V   V   P   T   R
R A K E   L U C K I E S T
  T   N   A   H   G   I
C O N T R I B U T I O N
  R   S   N   P   N
```

235

```
U   D   L   S   D   B
I N S I D E   P O E T R Y
  T   S   A   I   T   A
C O A T   T E N D E N C Y
  I   H   E   R   E
S T U N N E D   S M A L L
  R   G   R   C   I   E
V A L U E   G R A N I T E
  I   I   M   A   A
P L A S T I C S   T E L L
  H   D   H   I   O
A N G E L S   E N O U G H
  G   D   T   D   N   S
```

236

```
V   H   C   G   C   S
P A L A C E   R O A R E D
  R   V   N   I   R   V
W I P E   T H E O R I E S
  E   R   F   I   R
A D M I R E D   R A C E S
  D   D   L   G
C L U E S   R E V E R S E
  E   N   O   I   U
P A S T U R E S   S A N D
  V   I   D   U   I   S
K E T T L E   R U N N E R
  S   Y   R   E   G   T
```

237

```
T   D   T   R   L   C
V A N I S H   A N I M A L
  L   E   I   C   F   T
P L U S   E L E V E N T H
  E   V   S   B   L
T R I C K E D   W O M E N
  O   S   L   A
S T U N S   H E A T I N G
  E   F   H   T   O
A R G U M E N T   S L I M
  R   S   A   E   S
M O D E S T   R O A R E D
  R   D   S   S   T   S
```

238

```
S   O   T   B   E   S
J U M P E R   A R M I E S
  B   E   A   N   O   A
S T U N   F I G H T E R S
  L   F   S   I   C
M E R M A I D   M O T H S
  O   C   F   N
S P A D E   G R A S S E S
  E   I   W   E
B O N F I R E S   T I D Y
  P   I   I   H   A
A L I E N S   L I K I N G
  E   D   T   Y   E   G
```

239

```
L   R   P   N   F   D
S A L I V A   A Z A L E A
  D   S   R   K   S   L
H I D E   S W E E T P E A
  D   L   D   F   T
H A M S T E R   M O D E L
  P   Y   F   O
W A T E R   S A W D U S T
  B   C   L   R   U
D R A I N A G E   S P R Y
  O   F   T   A   E   R
C A N I N E   S H A R E S
  D   C   X   T   R   Y
```

240

```
C U S P   D O W N H I L L
A   P   R   R   O   L   O
P E R T A I N   N Y L O N
  E   T   A   E   N
I N E P T   T E S T E R
S   L   E   S   D
L I S T E N   L E S S E E
E   E   F   N   M
  G A L E N A   A N O D E
C   S   R   T   M   P   N
O N A I R   C O E X I S T
M   L   O   A   L   N   E
E N T I R E T Y   T E N D
```

241

```
P . S P . A . S . A
CUCKOO . STORMS
M . E . S . K . C . B
SPOT . SPECIFIC
. C . E . D . A . T
RICHEST . PLAIN
N . S . A . . O
OCCUR . SMOKING
L . N . B . U . I
VISITORS . SPIN
N . T . X . I . S . T
SEVERE . NEEDED
. D . D . R . G . M
```

242

```
T . S . D . A . C . S
CATTLE . SLOWED
L . O . R . K . N . T
CLAP . IDENTITY
E . . V . D . R . E
CRACKED . RACES
. H . D . H . C
BOXER . FEATURE
R . R . P . R . E
WARRIORS . SLIP
N . I . N . E . L . N
AGREED . LOOKED
E . S . S . F . T . D
```

243

```
F . U . E . C . I . N
POINTS . AUNTIE
U . D . C . U . V . N
FREE . ANSWERED
R . P . E . S . T
GUESSES . OTHER
P . T . D . L . I . E
USUAL . HANGING
T . N . T . R . A
HANDLING . TEST
I . I . R . E . I . E
PRINCE . SCORES
S . G . D . T . N . N
```

244

```
B . S . C . C . D . F
REPAIR . ABOARD
H . V . A . G . M . E
BAKE . SPECIMEN
V . . H . S . N . Z
PERCHED . PAGES
O . D . F . N
NEWLY . FATTEST
R . L . B . S . U
BASEMENT . SUNS
S . G . A . E . A . S
LEGEND . SENSES
R . S . S . T . K . T
```

245

```
M . S . P . O . U . D
LAMINA . LINDEN
R . Z . R . D . C . N
DIME . SHEETING
N . . L . N . U . I
BANSHEE . HORSE
. W . Y . . U . E
EAGER . USURY
N . E . R . Y . E
INITIATE . SANE
. E . P . V . A . P . D
GAME . E . SHAKER
. L . A . L . T . R . R
```

246

```
A . A . R . S . H . S
ENABLE . TRACKS
N . L . L . A . M . A
SURE . ATTEMPTS
A . . A . X . E . E . E
PLASTER . PRESS
. E . D . S . E
APART . FINDING
A . V . W . L . O
CREATIVE . LADY
E . N . N . N . I . D
UNITED . COFFEE
T . S . Y . E . T . D
```

247

```
WORTHY . SUFFER
I . E . A . T . N . O . U
DEFENCE . TARTS
E . E . D . M . I . M . H
SCRUB . POLLUTE
T . . A . E . . L . D
. GINGERBREAD
S . N . A . A . . S
WHITEST . TIDAL
I . T . V . U . T . R . E
NOISE . RELEASE
G . A . N . E . E . M . P
SPLITS . IDEALS
```

248

```
F . M . R . C . B . N
PARADE . LEAVES
V . L . F . U . S . C
ROLE . ELEMENTS
U . . R . S . M . A
TRICKED . PEARS
. R . E . H . N
BLUES . FASTEST
E . A . U . R . U
BATTERED . SINK
. P . U . G . E . O . S
DEGREE . SENSES
. D . E . D . T . G . T
```

249

```
S   P . C   A   B   F
ENOUGH  SLOWLY
A   M   O   K   T   O
SKIP    OVERHEAD
E   S   D   E   T
ASSUMED GRASS
    N   S   F   E
APRIL   PADDLES
O   V   A   S   F
STRENGTH    LIFE
T   R   I   I   A   O
LESSON  OCCURS
D   E   G   N   K   T
```

253

```
T   D   B   G   A   M
CAREER  ROBBER
L   T   U   E   B   A
WEVE    STEERING
R   H   K   E   T
TRUMPET AVOID
E   I   D   P   I   M
BLUNT   LOCATED
I   A   R   S   T
SECTIONS    INTO
V   I   P   E   O   H
REMOTE  SANDAL
D   N   D   S   S   T
```

250

```
C   M   H   A   L   M
BANANA  POISON
N   T   T   P   F   D
BAKE    COLLEGES
D   H   Y   B   R
MARSHES POINT
P   D   H   A
PAVED   WESTERN
F   C   K   I   I
TRAINING    SOCK
A   F   N   H   O   H
HIDING  TARGET
D   C   S   S   T   R
```

254

```
P   T   A   C   O   D
VARIED  AGREED
L   R   O   K   N   F
LAME    PREPARED
C   T   S   M   N
RESCUES LENDS
H   D   P   N
SHEET   CONTEST
E   M   D   S   C
FAMILIES    SCAR
T   S   V   E   U   L
BEETLE  SERVED
D   S   R   S   F   S
```

251

```
U   S   S   W   R   A
GROWTH  HOURLY
G   A   O   E   S   L
VEIN    REACTION
N   T   T   L   W
ATLASES MIDST
F   N   D   N
SWIFT   RINGING
A   E   M   F   O
MISCHIEF    LOUD
T   T   N   E   A   G
LEGEND  RHYTHM
R   D   S   S   T
```

255

```
WATERY  FLUFFY
O   I   E   P   E   O   E
REGULAR MORAL
T   E   I   O   O   E   L
HORSE   BONFIRE
Y   E   V   A   G   D
REMEMBERING
C   A   I   E   C
HARMFUL STAIR
A   N   E   I   C   P   E
PIECE   THUMPED
E   S   L   Y   E   L   I
LATEST  ASPECT
```

252

```
R   P   B   R   E   A
HUMOUR  INSECT
I   S   I   V   T   C
ONES    DRAMATIC
I   G   L   B   D
TUMBLED OLDER
N   I   S   I   N
TITLE   DENSITY
V   I   R   H
FEATHERS    MENS
R   I   S   E   E
ASPECT  LONGED
E   S   S   F   T   D
```

256

```
O   F   O   T   S   S
ABSORB  ESTATE
T   O   S   M   R   A
HALT    EXPLAINS
I   R   O   P   Z
INVOLVE SPEAK
B   E   S   E
BURST   LOADING
N   E   C   M   E
DECREASE    MEET
A   V   M   O   E   D
ASLEEP  NEATLY
Y   D   S   E   N   E
```

257

```
  D P C A C S
H O R R O R . S P O R T S
  N O U K R A
F E R N . S T E E R I N G
  U H D E D
P R I N T E D . U S U A L
  E C D L P R
L A T I N . R E C O R D S
  L A R T N
D I R T I E S T . D I S H
  S I A U I P
S E C O N D . C A N V A S
  D N Y E G N
```

258

```
  V O C S E C
M A N U F A C T U R E R
  I T P A A E
S N I F F I N G . S E A T
  I T E T
C E N T R A L . D R A I N
  C L P V
D O M E . C R E A T E S
  N S S O R
H O S T . H U N D R E D
  M A I O E O
D I S T I N G U I S H E D
  C E E N T
```

259

```
  H P G M U L
P O O R E R . O I N K E D
  S O A L D M
V E I N . S K E L E T O N
  U S S R N
O R A N G E S . E S S A Y
  E C S L T D
M A G I C . R E L A X E D
  L A L T N
D I S T R I C T . D I S K
  S I N U I E
R E M O V E . C A N C A N
  D N S E G T
```

260

```
  D B A C P D
V A R I E D . H E A D E D
  M T A E V P
B A K E . P R E C E D E D
  G T R M N
R E A C H E S . H E R D S
  H D C N
A S K E D . S O F T E S T
  H M S N P
C A P I T A L S . S E A S
  D S V I E D
K E T T L E . S T A T E S
  S S D T L S
```

261

```
  T O A C T S
S A C R E D . H E A D E D D
  P D M E S T Y
H E R E . I D E N T I T Y
  R R R E L
D R E S S E D . A D M I T
  E E D R N
S L A N T . M E S S A G E
  I E T L I
S E P A R A T E . L A W S
  V R X A V I
S E V E R E . S E E I N G
  D R S E R G
```

262

```
  S R I C C M
G O V E R N . H O O V E S
  L L I A N A
Y O G A . T H R I V I N G
  T I T E I
H O L I D A Y . D R I N K
  B O L T S G
S T I N G . B E C A U S E
  A S T N T
F I G H T E R S . I T E M
  N I A I O A
D E E P E R . O W N E R S
  D S S N N
```

263

```
  S M I E C M
C O V E R S . A N I M A L
  F D L R R J
T A X I . A R T I C L E S
  T N H U S
A L R E A D Y . E M P T Y
  O R S C S I
S W O R D . C O N T A C T
  L A W O A
R A I N F A L L . N E A R
  N E I I C G
I D E A L S . N E E D E D
  S N T G S S
```

264

```
  T I S S C R
M A G N E T . C L O S E D
  X T U A N S
T I R E . D E L I C A T E
  R E E L
O P E N I N G . U N D E R
  L A T C T S
S O U T H . P O O R E S T
  U I H N A
I G N O R A N T . T U N E
  H N T A I E
D E C A D E . C O O K E D
  D L S T N D
```

265

```
 L I D   L I R
MANNER OUNCE
 V T E V V S
GATE SKELETON
 R S D S U
PRINCE  START
E A D C I C
TASTY GOGGLES
L I T N A
VIGOROUS TEST
S N W I O
RELATE SPOON
D L R T N G
```

269

```
 C O H O C G
BAMBOO COUPLE
 M E U E D A
RELY STANDING
 R I N L D
HANGING FIRST
 U G P N
CLOAK LUGGAGE
E R S R I
HARDSHIP WRAP
G I E O E N
FUNNEL SWEETS
E G L E P S
```

266

```
 T C A T N I
VARIED OCEANS
 X R V A I T
ZINC ASSIGNED
 U N T H R
STOMACH ABOVE
H S E C O A
COSTS TROUBLE
R A H A R
DOWNWARD HOME
U C N L O U
AGREED ENOUGH
H S Y S D S
```

270

```
 T S D I U T
PHRASE MANNED
 O L F P I S
PUNT IDENTITY
 A C L E T
PFENNIG ODOUR
L D T S N B
NYMPH CABARET
B E C N T
SLIPSHOD IDLE
O P A A O A
OWNERS LENGTH
N R E S S E
```

267

```
 A C D S S U
EXPERIMENTING
 L L S N I K
REPLACES TRIM
 A U E C N
ADDRESS SHEDS
E S R L
AVOID GOODBYE
O M S B I
STOP TOBOGGAN
I A O E I T
CONCENTRATION
N T Y S S M
```

271

```
 T O G E I U
HORROR ADDING
 M A A G E C
NAIL SILENTLY
 T T S E T E
WORRIED FIRST
E S A F
SWIMS CRAYONS
I O K C U
ELEVENTH LORD
D I O E O S
PLANET READER
Y G S S N S
```

268

```
 V B P L C S
MANAGE AMAZED
 R S A B R V
NINE CHERRIES
 E H L I R
ADVISED RACES
 D S D G
BIKES RELEASE
S N D S U
PROTEINS SENT
A I V E O S
SETTEE RENTED
L Y S T S T
```

272

```
 H R C S E I
MANUFACTURING
 L N B A A V
STINGING SOAP
 E N E D
BOARDED FRIES
P T B R
TIRES DENTIST
N L M N A
MINE OPENINGS
O V U A L L
UNSEEN TROJAN
S N T H R D
```

273

```
  R D C I T     T
DATA  I   TERROR
T W   R E A   W
CHIN  COMBINED
E     U S   L R
BRITAIN   FIRST
    I T     N
FLOCK  PROGRAM
A   K A E     B
TWILIGHT  ROOF
Y   I E   A A
LESSON  INSURE
R   H T   N T D
```

277

```
  Z E E   S C F
PIANOS  PROFIT
N C   C O N   I
ECHO  ALTITUDE
  U P S   R   I
AWARDED  PIANO
  H A D L B   G
WEIGH  REQUEST
R E W   I T
MERMAIDS  IRON
  V E N U O   P
LEANED  RANGE
  R T Y   E S N
```

274

```
  R A S F M   L
BUNDLE  IMAGES
  S D G N R   A
USES  MEDICINE
  I E S H E
GAINING  GIDDY
    I T C N
USING  DRAGGED
  T E T I   A
FARTHEST  SURE
  R I S   O T
RECENT  COUGHS
  D S S   S P
```

278

```
PACIFIC  DEBTS
I A E O   O C
CONTAINED  ONE
K R   C O M N
STAFF  EXTREME
  D U N   R R
REVOLUTIONARY
E E   R P N
FORMULA  EIGHT
U T N T R   E
SKI  IMITATION
E S T O T L D
DRESS  NEEDLES
```

275

```
  S L A B F   R
VARIED  I AGES
  V V A T R V
CASE  PRETTIER
  G T S H A
REACHES  HELLO
  H D R S
BAKES  E TASK
  M R G L   E
CARRIAGE  SANG
  Z I T A I S
SEVERE  SINGER
  D S S E K S
```

279

```
  G H G A S   T
CAREER  GATHER
  L R O A U N
ELSE  CLIMBING
  O E N B I
SPIDER  GOOSE
  I Y P R
OCEAN  RAINING
  O G S R A
OPPONENT  COME
  I N V I O I
BEHAVE  ADDING
  S L N L E G
```

276

```
  C W P O D   N
THRONE  PRISON
A R O E N   R
PRAM  PERFORMS
G L A S A
DECADES  SAILS
  F P U
CRAFT  HEARING
E E M R   E
MISCHIEF  RACK
N T D U U T
JEWELS  MIDDAY
  D D T E   R
```

280

```
  T C B N I   D
VAPOUR  OUNCES
K N U T T V
NETS  SKELETON
  I H S R T
TEDDIES  UNTIL
N E S C A O
STORE  SORTING
I A N N I
STATIONS  OATH
L I V I N H
REMOVE  SHAKEN
  D N L T L M
```

281

```
  P R C S I I
M A N U F A C T U R I N G
  R N B A   I V
S T U N N I N G   S L A P
    E   N   E       D
C A R R I E D   C R I E D
  W       T   H     R
F A C E S   D E N T I S T
  K   A   T   L   H
B E A R   H A P P I E S T
  N   N   U   I   R   H
D E T E R M I N A T I O N
  D   D   P   G   Y   T
```

282

```
D E C I M A L   F A C E D
E   I   O   I   A   O R
C I R C U M F E R E N C E
A   C   S   T     C   S
Y O U   T E E N A G E R S
    M   A   D   P   N E
I N S E C T   P A T T E D
N   T   H   R   R   O
S T A T E M E N T   A L L
T   N   M   M   M   T
E N C Y C L O P E D I A S
A   E   R   T   N   O E
D U S T Y   E X T E N D S
```

283

```
    L   I C   A   E R
M A N N E R   D A N G E R
  V   T   A   D   T   S
F A R E   S T E V E   O U
    R   H   R   R   U
P R I N T E R   S T O R Y
  E   A   S   N   A   C
W A S T E   D E S I R E D
  L   I   L   A   N
D I N O S A U R   M O S S
  S   N   Y   E   E   N
F E M A L E   S A N D A L
  D   L   R   T   T   P
```

284

```
  T   C T   S   A U
M O T H E R   O W N I N G
  M   I   A   L   G   L
V A I N   G O V E R N E D
  T   E   E   I   S
T O R N A D O   L E A S T
    O   Y   E   S
M O U T H   P L A T E A U
  T   I   S   A   C
C H I C K E N S   C O T S
  E   N   T   A   I
D R I N K S   I N V E N T
  S   G   E   C   E   G
```

285

```
S O U L   F E B R U A R Y
T   N   S   N   A   U   O
R E D U C E D   P U S S Y
I   E   H   U   I   T   O
C A R G O   R I D E R S
T       O   E       I   D
L I K E L Y   B A N A N A
Y   I   F   S       U
  A N Y O N E   S W I N G
O   G   C   N   U   M   H
R I D G E   C O M P A C T
A   O   A   E   E   G
L E M O N A D E   R E A R
```

286

```
  S   K K   M P   C
N O T I C E   I S R A E L
  D   D E   N   A   M
F I T S   P R O M I S E
U       I   R   S   N
A M U S I N G   W I D T H
    Q   G G   N
A B O U T   B A D G E R
  O   E K   L       E
E X T E R N A L   B O M B
  I   Z O   O   I   A
I N T E N T   P E R M I T
  G       S   D   N
```

287

```
  P   U F F   R S
B O U N C E   A G E N C Y
  L   C R   R   F   O
S O L O   T O M O R R O W
      M   I S   I   T
S W I F T L Y   A G R E E
  A   O E   A   E   R
E N T R Y   A D D R E S S
  D   T V   V   A
N E G A T I V E   T A I L
  R   B E   R   O   B
F E L L O W   B A R K E D
  D   E S   S       X
```

288

```
  L   U S   S R   L
C A N N O N   C R E D I T
  V   S E   A   D   K
L A C E   E N L A R G E D
  E   E Z   E   A   W
S P O N G E S   A G A I N
  L   D N   S
N O R T H   D E G R E E S
  U   H D   U   E
I G N O R A N T   T O R N
  H   R R   R   U   U
B E C A M E   A P R O N S
  D   X S   L   N   G
```

289

```
  V   V   K   W   F   R
P A R A D E   A M A Z E D
  P   S   T   G   R   V
D O M E   T H E A T R E
  U   L   S   H   A
C R I C K E T   R E P L Y
      H       C     S
F I R E D   C O N T E S T
  S   M   F   N   U
C A P I T A L S   S I N K
  B   S   D   I   A   S
S E T T L E   S I N G E R
  L       T       E   T
```

293

```
F I G H T E R   W O V E N
L   A   R   E   I   I   O
L I N S T A L L E D   B E T
E   F   A   E   R       I
S H E L F   T O R N A D O
  S   I   C       T     N
E E C C   O   E X I T S
X   A   N   X   O
P A L A C E S   A U N T S
A   A   H   H   M       P
N E T   E L I M I N A T E
D   O   A   P   N   C   A
S T R I P   S W E A T E R
```

290

```
I N S E C T   S H O C K S
N   T   A   C   E   O   T
S H A M P O O   L E A V E
I   R   A   N   L   S   A
S C R U B   T R O T T E D
T   L   R       A   Y
  I M M E D I A T E L Y
O   E       B   H       C
P L A T E A U   R E F E R
E   N   G   T   E   A   E
N O I S Y   E N A B L E D
E   N   P   D   T   S   I
D I G I T S   A S P E C T
```

294

```
  D   A   D   B   I   R
M A N N E R   O   N O E L L
  T   D   E   W   V   S
R A G E   S K E L E T O N
  A   S   D   S   U
P R I N T E D   S T O R M
  E   S   P   I   C
F A C T S   G O G G L E S
  L   H   V   S   A
V I G O R O U S   T O S S
  S   M   T   E   I   A
B E H A V E   S P O O N S
  D   S   S   S   N   K
```

291

```
  P   Z   W   T   D   P
C O L O U R   A N I M A L
  W   O   I   K   R   P
P E T S   T W E N T I E S
  R       T   N   I   R
E S C A P E S   D E N S E
      N   N   L   S
G E E S E   H O T T E S T
  U   W   D   N       E
C R E E P I N G   S H E D
  O   R   A   E   E   M
A P P E A R   S C A R E D
  E   D   Y   T   T   D
```

295

```
  H   S   S       P   M
D I S O W N   F L O R I D
  F   P   I   L   S   N
W I S H   C O U R T E S Y
      I   K   E   O   T
M O B S T E R   O P A R T
  N   T   R   B   E   E
M E R I T   B E D R O L L
  S   C   S   R   A
L I G A T U R E   T A C K
  D   T   I   A   I   A
C E M E N T   V I V I F Y
  D   D   E   E   E   E
```

292

```
  D   E   P   D   E   T
F R A N C E   O W N E R S
  A   C   A   O   C   A
U G L Y   C A R R Y I N G
  C   H   S   C   S
S C O L D E D   F L U F F
  O   O   S   B   O   E
S L E P T   A I R P O R T
  L   A   W   C   E
C E R E M O N Y   D E E R
  G   D   R   C   I   V
M E D I U M   L E A P E D
  S   A   S   E   S   N
```

296

```
  T   A   R   S   F   A
M A R B L E   C H O R U S
  I   L   A   E   R   N
C L U E   C O N N E C T S
  O   H   T   C   I
T R U S T E D   C A K E S
      P   S   B   S
D A R E S   C R I T I C S
  R   C   T   I       O
D O M I N A N T   S A N G
  U   F   W   I   T   V
I N D I A N   S T A T E D
  D   C   Y   H   R   Y
```

297

```
 S C R   P O N
CHOOSE EMPLOY
 O N M   E P T
SETS AMPHORAE
 I I S   R T
STUDENT STRIP
 H E S D U O
BOARD LEANING
 R A G N   I
CONTAINS TIDE
 U I V   I I I
IGNORE TWELVE
 H N N Y S E
```

298

```
 S A B   S B S
STUDIO TROOPS
 U V T A L E
KNEE TOGETHER
 E R O E   C
RHYTHMS RIGHT
 O I S H   E
AMUSE REQUEST
 E E F   I N
SWIMMING IDLE
 O E R H O I
DRINKS TENDED
 K T T S   S
```

299

```
 D E A C A D
PINNED HANKIE
 S C A A N R
ECHO PULSE  E
 U T K   C
STARVED ANITA
 O A D W O O
OMEGA SISTERS
 O E F L   I
TREMBLED OPEN
 R E E E N A
MOUNTS STAIRS
 W T H T L N
```

300

```
 P E B H B T
SLEUTA AMOURS
 A R R W   O
UNDO RESEMBLE
 I H A L
CHEAPER INDEX
 E M R G   Y
TRAIN SUCCESS
 O C S A   O
DISASTER TOUR
 N B U D T R
SEALED ENOUGH
 S E Y D N E
```

301

```
 F U R A C R
BRONZE COILED
 E F A T R V
ZERO SPEECHES
 R O D U A
BEATING SMELT
 G U S M F E
TYING DEPENDS
 P A C A R
STATIONS EAST
 I E R U N O
SAILED RECENT
 N N Y S E E S
```

302

```
DATING NOTICE
 E A U I P T I
AFRICAN EXACT
 T T L G R L H
HASTE REALISE
 A E   A R
INTRODUCING
 D O   I O S
IMITATE UPSET
 S S W N L P R
CHINA TADPOLE
 O E R S   I S
SERVES STALKS
```

303

```
 T B D M C R
FAVOUR IRONED
 K S E L R I
SETS STEERING
 S S E D
HANDLED ASHES
 C U S C P E
BEARS COLOURS
 A P N   N
OINTMENT DISH
 V I A A I O
FAVOUR CANVAS
 N N L T G K
```

304

```
 S U C T S R
SOONER RIPPED
 F S A A R F
SALE SUPPOSED
 E H S U R
PRINTED STARE
 E D P   E
PARTS TORNADO
 L H B S U
VIGOROUS TASK
 S M X E M A
BECAME SEEING
 D S R S G K
```

305

```
. A S . D . S P . S . .
U N L I K E . P R O P E L
. T . L . P . I . L . R
K I E V . R E T R I E V E
. . E . E . C . A . . .
O P P R E S S . T E E N Y
. L . T . S . V . O . T
C A R O L . S E L F I S H
. T . N . D . R . F . .
E Y E G L A S S . I D O L
. P . U . T . I . C . .
B U R E A U . F R E S C O
. S . D . M . Y . R . E
```

306

```
. B . M . P . C . F . G
F A R I N A . A L E V E L
. N . N . S . T . A . N
C E D E . S W E E T P E A
. D . K . R . H . T . .
D R Y E Y E D . F E T I D
. O . T . Y . C . R . C
B E T E L . S A W D U S T
. . C . C . R . U . .
R H E T O R I C . S O S O
. E . O . I . A . T . O
D E C R E E . S E E S A W
. L . S . R . S . R . R
```

307

```
. H . I . E . N . C . I
L I T M U S . E T H I C S
. F . P . T . E . A . E
B I E R . U N D E R . R I
. E . A . S . G . I . .
E Y E S O R E . F E I N T
. E . S . Y . T . K . .
B A S I L . T O P M A S T
. R . O . W . L . U . .
B L I N K E R S . M E L T
. I . I . E . T . M . A
U N U S E D . O V E R D O
. G . M . Y . Y . R . Y
```

308

```
. M . M . G . T . S . .
M A R I N A . R E H A S H
. G . S . S . O . O . A
R I S C . M O T J U S T E
. E . A . H . L . I . .
C E L L I S T . A D O R N
. G . L . K . E . E . I
F O R A Y . M A U R I C E
. T . N . F . R . B . .
T R E E F E R N . L E S T
. I . O . V . E . A . O
S P R U C E . S A D D L E
. S . S . R . T . E . O
```

309

```
. P . P . B . W . B . R
P A N A M A . A P E M E N
. L . T . N . F . R . M
F E T E . S C E P T R E S
. N . . H . R . I . D .
C A N T E E N . E E R I E
. L . L . E . F . E . .
R I V E R . H A R D E S T
. . A . F . N . I . . .
P R O T R A C T . S A S H
. A . H . T . A . N . P
D I V E S T . S T E F A N
. N . R . Y . Y . Y . R
```

310

```
. F . G . C . C . K . T
C A R E E R . A D E L E
. K . R . O . B . T . L
G E R M . S P L U T T E R
. A . I . E . L . V . .
A S U N D E R . B E G I N
. E . M . R . B . S . .
F A C E T . M A R I N E R
. P . A . W . P . N . .
G L A S N O S T . T U F T
. A . L . R . I . E . R
U N R E S T . S A N D A L
. E . S . H . M . T . Y
```

311

```
. L . U . G . B . A . S
D I N N E R . E N D I N G
. K . D . O . G . V . E
C E D E . W E A K E N E D
. . R . I . N . R . Z .
R E A S O N S . A T T I C
. X . T . G . L . I . N
S P R A Y . M E S S A G E
. L . N . W . I . E . .
S O L D I E R S . M U M S
. D . I . E . U . E . O
L E A N E D . R A N D O M
. S . G . S . E . T . D
```

312

```
. C . C . P . C . F . G
P A G O D A . A . E D E N
. F . R . R . G . A . N
P E T E . S W E E T P E A
. . S . L . Y . H . T .
S C U P P E R . D E V I L
. I . O . Y . H . R . C
I N A N E . S A W D U S T
. N . D . C . P . U . .
B A S E B A L L . S A S H
. B . N . T . E . T . I
B A T T L E . S C E N T
. R . S . R . S . R . E
```

313

```
. L . T . G . C . C . B
G A Z E B O . O M E L E T
. V . N . D . U . N . N
L A N D . S P L A T T E R
. E . E . D . . . D
G S T R I N G . H E L I X
. H . H . D . W . V . C
E I D E R . S A T I A T E
. P . A . S . R . C
A L A R M I S T . T O P S
. O . T . X . I . I . U
P A R E N T . M A N T L E
. D . D . Y . E . G . P
```

314

```
. S . C . B . S . I . R
L A B O U R . W I N K E D
. F . G . U . E . D . F
J E W S . S U P P O S E D
. . . H . T . O . R
S A D D L E D . F R I E S
. M . O . D . C . . . E
W E A R Y . L O N G E S T
. R . O . M . N . . . E
D I S T R I C T . M A S K
. C . H . D . A . I . T
S A T Y R S . C A N V A S
. S . . . T . T . I . Y
```

315

```
. T . T . H . T . B . D
M A L I C E . H O O D O O
. X . M . A . I . D . T
D I M E . D O G G Y B A G
. S . M . H . S . G
A D M I R A L . O T T E R
. O . G . N . V . . . O
A G O N Y . S I N C E R E
. F . A . A . T . . . K
F I S T U L A R . I N T O
. G . U . K . I . N . A
S H I R T Y . O U G H T
. T . E . D . L . S . A
```

316

```
. P . B . L . W . T . R
S A L I V A . A C U T E
. T . L . S . V . R . M
M E T E . S C E P T R E
. . . I . R . L . D
C A L I B E R . T E P I D
. I . G . S . B . . . E
D R I N K . P A N D A S
. L . I . V . P . . . U
D I S T R A C T . S A S H
. N . E . L . I . T . P
D E C R E E . S H E E R
. R . . . T . E . R . Y
```

317

```
O V E R A C T . R E C A P
L . E . P . I . O . H . L
I L L G O T T E N . E R A
V . . . S . T . D . V . U
E . S I T . L E O P A R D
. . T . L . E . . . L . I
P E R F E C T I O N I S T
O . U . . . A . R . E
F A N B E L T . P O R C H
A . G . P . T . H . . . E
C O O . O I L T A N K E R
E . U . C . E . N . I . O
D I T C H . D U S T P A N
```

318

```
. B . U . O . U . E . F
R E I N C A R N A T I O N
. L . I . R . I . H . O
C L O S E S E T . N U T S
. O . M . E . . . I . S
S C A N D A L . A C U T E
. E . N . T . . . E
A S I D E . F O R C E P S
. S . O . S . R . A
E P I C . P . S U P P L Y
. O . I . I . . . E
R O L L O N R O L L O F F
. L . E . E . N . . . T
```

319

```
. A . A . H . J . P
R U N W A Y . U N L O C K
. F . R . D . I . E . O
E A S Y . R E C O U R S E
. I . A . Y . R . T
I T E R A T E . F I R S T
. . . E . E . P . S
C R Y P T . H O L Y S E E
. E . H . G . I . . . N
A V E R S I O N . F A D E
. E . A . S . T . E . E
B A L S A M . E N T R A P
. L . E . O . D . E . R
```

320

```
. P . V . S . S . O . H
D A M A S K . C O U P O N
. R . L . Y . O . T . T
M A G I . W I L D F O W L
. S . A . D . I . A
U N L E A R N . S T A T E
. O . D . D . . . E
A G I L E . M E R C U R Y
. O . I . P . V . O
W A T E R S K I . H E R E
. R . I . A . A . E . U
K E N N E L . T H R I F T
. A . . . M . E . E . F
```

321

```
S O M E . C H O P S U E Y
E . A . N . I . R . G . .
T O M B O L A . I N L A Y
A . M . A . T . C . I . .
S W A S H B U C K L E R .
I . . . S . . . S . E . .
D I S B A R . B A N T A M
E . M . . B . F . . I . .
. T A H I T I . E L L I S
I . S . D . G . A . O . S
O C H R E . C O R O L L A
T . U . A . A . D . L . R
A P P O S I T E . E S P Y
```

322

```
H I M S E L F . H Y E N A
A . A . L . A . A . N . .
V E R V E . T I T A N I C
O . Q . C . I . E . U . H
C O U R T . M A R T I A L
. . E . R . A . . . O . .
T R E M O R . I O N O R E
E . . M . L . N . V . . .
Q U O T A T I O I . A R K
U . F . G . B . O . T . E
I N F A N C Y . N P I N E
L . A . E . A . . O . E .
A L L O T . N . S I N U S
```

323

```
. C . S . S . A . P . P
L A T E N T . B L I G H T
. R . L . U . A . N . A
L E A F . D O C K H A N D
. I . E . K . O . T . T
A D A M A N T . B L E A R
. E . P . T . Q . E . S
M E L O N . S U C C U M B
. D . R . N . A . A
S P I T T O O N . M A S K
. O . A . T . T . E . E
P L U N G E . U . R E E F
. L . T . D . M . A . R
```

324

```
. K . P . D . A . P . R
C E L E R Y . L A R D E R
E . N . N . I . O . M
S P I N . A M B I T I O N
. Y . M . I . E . T
F O R F E I T . O C T E T
U . A . C . P . T . S
S T O R K . S O C I E T Y
M . T . C . L . O
T O P H E A V Y . N O R M
. D . I . B . M . I . I
F E N N E L . E N S I L E
. D . G . E . R . T . L
```

325

```
. C T . M . T . D . A
B O L E R O . A B O A R D
. M . L . N . P . W . T
S A N E . O L E A N D E R
. P . C . R . I . R
K E Y H O L E . O N A I R
. L . O . E . P . G . A
P L A T E . F I R S T L Y
. I . O . G . P . T
A P P L A U S E . R A J A
. T . E . L . T . E . U
P I C N I C . T H E O R Y
. C . S . H . E . T . Y
```

326

```
. S . B . C . R . V . H
W A T E R Y . O C E L O T
. G . N . A . U . S . N
J A Z Z . N O T A T I O N
A . E . I . E . A . L
B E D S I D E . A L O U D
. O . E . U . V . L
S C O P E . E N V I O U S
A . R . S . L . R
M E A N T . E N G I N E
P . N . I . A . I . O
C U T O F F . R E N O W N
S . . S . F . N . S . T
```

327

```
. . B . A . D . H . C
S C R A W L . O X Y G E N
. O . B . U . T . D . M
C O S Y . M . T A R G E T
. . . I . Y . O . T
A M B I E N T . L E V E L
. A . C . A . O . L . R
A L T E R . A P T E R Y X
. T . P . P . C
G R A N U L A R . T Y P E
E . E . U . E . R . I
H A N S O M . S H I R T Y
T . S . E . S . C . Y
```

328

```
. E . M . E . E . F . S
A S S E N T . B R O G U E
. P . R . O . O . R . B
S Y N C . N O N S E N S E
. . H . I . Y . I . O
C I C A D A S . A G E N T
. M . N . N . N . N . I
S P A T E . R E J O I C E
. U . B . U . E . F
U N E A R N E D . F I V E
. I . N . A . F . I . E
S T O K E R . U R C H I N
. Y . S . M . L . E . N
```

329

```
M . S T . L I . K . .
C A N A P E . I N N I N G
U . L . L . M . T . I
F L E A . L I B R E T T O
. D . I . O . R . W .
A B I D I N G . O L D E N
O . R . G . H . O . A
J U L E P . M A S C A R A
I . S . B . C . U . .
L A S E R . K . T I C K
L . I . I . S . O . U
B O S N I A . A C R O S S
N . G . R . W . Y . P
```

330

```
. A C . B . H . W . I
E N T O M A . E X H A L E
T . N . C . A . O . L
D I S C . C . D R O I T
. E . H . Y . P . I .
O N E R O U S . P I G M Y
E . T . S . D . N . E
B O U G H . B R I G A D E
P . R . S . Y . C . .
T H I A M I N E . O D D
Y . N . B . Y . U . E
S T O D G Y . E A G L E T
E . . . L . D . H . R
```

331

```
. W . I . I . I . B . I
M A N N E R . S O L E M N
D . D . I . S . O . P
F I L E . D O U B T F U L
. T . I . E . T . D .
I G N E O U S . L I K E N
R . R . M . B . N . N
M A M M A . N A U G H T Y
V . I . A . R . P . .
C I N N A B A R . A R C H
T . A . B . O . P . O
T A T T O O . O C E L O T
S . E . T . M . R . P
```

332

```
. E . C . I . T . P
E T H I C S . B A O B A B
N . V . T . O . R . R
M A X I . H O M I C I D E
. L . M . B . . . O .
C L O S E U P . S P A N K
A . E . S . N . I . E
A D O R N . L E I S U R E
L . V . S . E . T . .
D E T A C H E D . E A R L
F . N . A . F . . U .
G U T T E R . U N C O I L
L . S . K . L . . N
```

333

```
. C . A . A . B . P O
S H O U L D . R A R E F Y
O . T . E . A . E . F
B U S H . N E W S C A S T
O . O . L . I . H . .
O U V R A I S . D O N O R
P . I . D . V . U . O
Z L O T Y . V A R S I T Y
I . A . A . N . M . .
A F F R I G H T . E D I T
T . I . I . A . T . R
B E F A L L . G R A T I S
D . N . E . E . L . S
```

334

```
. I . S . P U C . B
A D H E R E . S T U D I O
L . L . A . U . R . E
B E E F . S T R I D E N T
. I . A . Y . . . N .
P A Y M E N T . M I M I C
I . P . T . C . . A .
C R O O N . C O R A C L E
L . R . C . M . S . .
L . I N T E R I M . T U B A
N . A . A . A . U . R
P E N N O N . N I T W I T
R . T . E . D . E . O
```

335

```
. F . U . S R . H . E
D A I N T Y . A M O U N T
I . C . M . L . B . V
U R G E . P I L A S T E R
R . T . Y . O . L . .
F I R E D O G . E N V O I
L . M . M . W . S . P
E L B O W . T H I C K E T
U . N . S . I . H . .
S N I P P E T . O M E N
O . O . E . I . D . .
T R A U M A . S . C O G S
Y . S . R . H . E . E
```

336

```
. C . S . O . A . F
H I C C U P . C R I S P S
T . A . I . T . S . U
W E A N . N . O T H E R S
. D . I . R . I . L .
C R E A T O R . E N V O Y
E . L . N . C . G . I
S H A M E . B O A T I N G
E . O . U . N . A . .
E A R N I N G S . C U B E
R . G . I . U . K . U
A S P E C T . M A L I C E
E . R . E . E . E . K
```

337

```
. A N . P . U E . B .
S C R O L L . D E S I R E
. N . R A D . P . U . .
R E A M . U N E R R I N G
. A . D . R . I . E . .
P F E N N I G . A T T I C
. R . . T . P . D . . .
H E N C E . A R S E N I C
. S . O . G . C . . . .
R H E T O R I C . O P U S
. M . T . I . E . R . P
G A L O R E . D E P U T E
. N . N . F . E . S . O
```

338

```
. A . O . U S . D . S .
S L A L O M . T H W A C K
. T . D . P A . E . O .
N O V A . T E M P L A T E
. . G . E . P . L . F .
B R U E G E L . D I A R Y
. O . P . N . J . N . E
E S T E R . J U G G L E R
. E . N . W . S . H . .
P H A S E O U T . O K R A
. I . R . I . U . U . .
U P R O A R . C O S T L Y
. S . N . Y . E . E . E
```

339

```
. H . F . C S . C . H .
P E S E T A . C H O R A L
. R . A . P . R . R . M
F O O T . T A I L P I P E
. H . A . P . U . E . .
A S C E T I C . U S U R P
. U . R . N . K . C . .
A B I D E . W I T H E R S
. H . U . S . N . R . .
P U L S A T E S . I F F Y
. M . T . R . M . S . R
G A M E T E . A N T H E M
. N . R . W . N . I . T
```

340

```
. E . E . B A . N . T .
E L I X I R . C L I P O N
. B . H . I . O . G . D
S A K I . M A R C H E D .
. B . F . N . T . L . .
O M N I B U S . O W L E T
. A . T . L . G . A . R
O R B I T . L E F T I S T
. J . O . C . E . C . .
H O U N D I N G . H A Z Y
. R . I . G . E . M . E
N A U S E A . E L A P S E
. M . M . R . S . N . T
```

341

```
. S . V . N U . A . M .
S P H E R E . D A M S O N
. U . N . A D . M . L .
K N E E . T E E T O T A L
. . T . E . R . . . S .
E C L I P S E . G H O S T
. H . A . T . B . E . E
B O U N D . F A I R E S T
. W . B . P . B . A . .
I C E L O L L Y . L O D E
. H . I . A . S . D . I
B O N N E T . I R I S E S
. W . D . E . T . C . T
```

342

```
. B . T . C E . O . R .
G A Z E B O . G I N G E R
. D . N . R R . U . S .
B E N D . D E E R S K I N
. . E . O . T . . . D .
A S C R I B E . L A G E R
. T . H . A . J . M . N
B A G E L . P U B E R T Y
. R . A . M . S . R . .
A L A R M I S T . I R I S
. I . T . S . I . C . D
A N N E X E . C R A Y O N
. G . D . R . E . N . L
```

343

```
. C . D . B A . I . B .
J E K Y L L . G E N I U S
. L . S . O E . C . N .
C L E F . S E N D O F F .
. . U . S . T . N . I .
A B A N D O N . S I G N .
. O . C . M . A . I . H
U N I T E . L U D D I T E
. E . I . G . R . E . .
A M M O N I T E . R O D E
. E . N . V . O . A . E
K A R A T E . L A T E N T
. L . L . N . E . E . Y
```

344

```
. M . S . M B . R . B .
B I K I N I . L I A B L E
. L . T . S A . B . I .
F E A T . N E C K B A N D
. . I . A . K . I . K .
E C O N O M Y . O T H E R
. E . G . E . M . W . R
B R U T E . R E L A P S E
. E . E . S . M . R . .
O B A N . T W O . R U I N
. R . A . I . E . B . .
T U R N O N . B A N N E R
. M . T . K . A . S . X
```

345

```
  C G   O   A A   R
T H R O A T   B I G T O P
  E   A   T   B R   L
D E F T   O P E R A B L E
  S   M   Y   R   O
V E T E R A N   T I N N Y
  G   N   S   A
A F O O T   D E A N E R Y
  R   T   B S   A
V I T R E O U S   S O S O
  A   I   W   I   H
T R I P L E   O U T S E T
  Y   R   N   E   R
```

346

```
  E H   S   N D   V
A M P E R E   E L E V E N
  E   L   A X   B N
A R I D   F O U R T E E N
  G   O   S   E
G E A R B O X   Q U I R E
  E   D   L
S P E L L   P U P P I E S
  R   I   L M   N
L E G A T O   B   S O M E
  P   N R   A I   E
L A N C E R   G A L O S H
  Y   E   Y O   K H
```

347

```
  A S   L   P B   Q
E S T A T E   S H U T U P
  S   I   A A L   A
B A W L   F O L K L O R E
  I   L   M E T
B L O A T E R   S T O O P
  C   T   R I
P L E A T   B A R N O W L
  I   N S   N   H
V E T   H S   S P I T
  I   H E   A L   M
U N F U R L   C H O O S Y
  G   S F   K G   Y
```

348

```
  B W   O   C F   F
L A Y O U T   Z E A L O T
  R R   T E L   E
P I C K   O S C U L A T E
  U   M   H I   U
A M A L G A M   O B E S E
  I   N G   L
W A T C H   C A D E N Z A
  R   E   I T
E M I N E N C E   R E N T
  O S E   W A   I
T U N E U P   A E R A T E
  R   E T   Y E   H
```

349

```
  D T   P   C T   S
B E T R A Y   A B R U P T
  T O   J R O   R
D E E D   A C A N T H U S
  C   M   T T   C
S T E L L A R   B E R E T
  I   S   W R
A C U T E   F A L S I F Y
  L   E   F R   A
F O U R L E A F   M I C E
  V A   I A U   I
S E X T O N   R I T U A L
  R   I T   E T   L
```

350

```
  M G   I   C A   A
H A Z A R D   H O S T E L
  R L   E O S   R
S L O E   A P P R O V A L
  I   L   S R   T
A N O M A L Y   O T H E R
  A   Y   W E
T W I S T   E A R D R U M
  E   S T   L   P
R E M E D I A L   J I B E
  K U   T A E   E
P L A S M A   B U R E A U
  Y   E N   Y K   T
```

351

```
  F F   P   E R   U
S A L A M I   S E E I N G
  B L   G S Q   I
O R A L   G R A T U I T Y
  I   Y   I E
A C T I O N S   T R A D E
  C   G T   E
A F T E R   C O U S I N S
  A C   B B   E
U M B R E L L A   P A C E
  O E   A C A   T
H U M A N S   C E R E A L
  S   M T   O T   R
```

352

```
  T B   G   P C   W
C I N E M A   O T H E R S
  C A   R R A   I
S K I M   A C C U R A T E
  E   G   H M   E
S T A R T E D   F I R S T
  E   S S   N
I M A G E   S U R G I N G
  E A   C B   A
E M E R A L D S   A I M S
  B D   O I U   I
S E L E C T   D I N I N G
  R   D H   Y T   G
```

353

```
  F  H  I  T  V  F
C O B A L T  U R A N U S
  E     R  E  T  S  R
I T E M  R O O T C R O P
  U     A  R  U  R
  S H I R T     B L E E D
  N     E  M  A
S T A T E  W A R R I O R
  U     E  E  R  R
E M E R I T U S  F A I L
  U  N  H  H  A  S
P L E A S E  A U T H O R
  T  L  R  L  E  N
```

354

```
  S  F  F  C  S  G
M O R O S E  O R P H A N
  I  A  S  M  L  T
B R I M  T W I L I G H T
  E  O  C  T  E
A E R O S O L  S P O R T
     V  N  I  E
A B B E Y  U N C A N N Y
  L  R  T  C  C
T O L L F R E E  B A C K
  W  E  U  N  A  E
D E P A R T  S O N A T A
  R  P  H  E  K  Y
```

355

```
  S  V  F  A     B
S Q U A R E  B I L L O W
  U  L  R  A  I  N
F E T E  V I T A L I S E
  A  O  E  A  A
S K Y B L U E  S C R I M
     R  R  I  A
C O C O A  S M A S H U P
  U  W  V  A  P
S T U N N I N G  R U B Y
  L  I  P  I  A  E
G A M E T E  N O R M A L
  Y  S  R  E  E  T
```

356

```
  S  B  P  P  U  R
P A T I N A  R E N D E R
  L  L  I  E  C  T
B I K E  S P E C T R A L
  V  L  N  U  K
B A N S H E E  M O N E Y
     P  Y  F  U
E A V E S  M A E S T R O
  B  C  L  R  A
I R R I G A T E  S U N G
  O  F  Y  A  H  G
N A T I V E  S T A R E D
  D  C  R  T  M  R
```

357

```
  Z  R  P  U     C
L I B I D O  L E G I O N
  R  D  R  T  L  L
A C N E  T O R T I L L A
  O     E  A  T  I
O N G O I N G  S T E E D
     V  D  A  E
O C T E T  O S T R I C H
  L  R  A  E  O
L I  H U B  X  G I F T
  P  A  U  U  E  F
D O I N G S  A R M P I T
  N  G  E  L  S  N
```

358

```
  J  M  B  U  N  S
C O Y O T E  S P O T T Y
  Y  R  T  A  N  A
D O S E  R E G I M E N T
  U  O  E  E  C
I S O L A T E  S T E E L
     O  H  B  A
R E A D Y  T A B L E A U
  M  E  C  L  U
K E Y S T O N E  Y O R E
  T  T  C  F  A  U
M I K A D O  W E P T
  C  R  A  L  S  T
```

359

```
  B  S  A  A  Q  M
O R P H A N  B R U T A L
  I  I  N  Y  O  G
W O O F  U N S T R I N G
  T  I  S  U  E
A S H Y  S M I T H
  U  Y  D  I
C I R C A  A R T D E C O
  T  O  P  A  E
C A T H O L I C  C A G E
  B  E  A  H  E  L
C L A R E T  M E N T O R
  E  E  E  A  T  W
```

360

```
  W  O  S  E  B  P
L A P T O P  T R U A N T
  V  I  E  H  R  E
H E R O  C H E E R F U L
  S  I  R  E
F I R E M A N  S M E A R
  N     L  C
I N L A Y  C O M P O T E
  U  U  A  T  O
C E L L U L A R  V I A L
  N  A  T  O  L  Q
A D V I S E  D R O G U E
  O  T  R  E  V  A
```

361

```
W . O . S . E . B . P .
L A P T O P . T R U A N T
V . I . E . H . R . E .
H E R O . C H E E R F U L
. S . I . R . . . E .
F I R E M A N . S M E A R
N . L . C . . . . .
I N L A Y . C O M P O T E
U . U . A . R . . A .
C E L L U L A R . V I A L
N . A . T . O . L . Q .
A D V I S E . D R O G U E
O . T . R . E . V . A .
```

362

```
V . R . W . E . E . G .
P A R A D E . L I C H E N
L . T . A . O . L . N .
D E N T . T A P W A T E R
A . H . E . I . . R .
W R I N G E R . A R S O N
E . . R . B . . . U .
V A L E T . L E F T I S T
D . I . L . R . H . .
E Y E G L A S S . R O B E
M . H . Y . E . U . E .
T I T T L E . R A S H E R
X . Y . R . K . T . R .
```

363

```
P . G . B . O . B . U .
G A T E A U . P U R P L E
R . N . M . E . O . T .
M A G I . P A R A K E E T
U . K . A . E . R . .
O I L S K I N . S N A I L
N . . N . W . . O . .
R I V A L . B A N G E R S
M . W . T . S . I . .
S I G N P O S T . G O W N
C . I . O . A . G . A .
W A L N U T . G A L O R E
L . G . H . E . E . D .
```

364

```
. C . R . A . O . A . F
H O N E S T . V I S I O N
M . D . F . O . S . O .
A B L E . I N I T I A T E
E . R . D . Z . . F .
I T E M I S E . C E D A R
O . . T . M . . L . .
S M A S H . N E T B A L L
M . . G . L . . U . .
H Y S T E R I A . T A L E
G . R . N . T . U . .
C U R A T E . G R O U S E
N . M . L . E . N . T
```

365

```
K . T . G . L . S . C .
M O T H E R . L I K E L Y
S . I . E . A . E . O .
T H U S . N A M E L E S S
E . . A . A . E . E .
P R E C E D E . . T A T E
. A . E . I . O . .
A C O R N . U N S N A R L
R . D . H . F . . E .
B E R I B E R I . D O F F
C . G . L . D . A . U .
T H R A L L . E N M I T Y
E . N . O . L . E . E .
```

366

```
H . H . O . O . P . R .
B A K E . U . F R A C A S
L . C . T . F . G . I .
C O O T . S E A G O I N G
I . I . L . D . . D .
A V O C A D O . H A I R Y
I . . E . A . . O . .
C L O T H . S T R O P P Y
L . I . T . R . R . .
B A L L Y H O O . C H O P
I . L . R . P . H . D .
S N E E Z E . H A I R D O
Y . R . E . Y . D . S .
```

367

```
. B . A . N . T . E . I
N U N C I O . H U M A N E
S . Q . I . E . B . T .
T H O U . S U M T O T A L
I . . O . E . D . G .
E P I T O M E . C Y C L E
O . . E . C . . I . .
C R A F T . L A M P O O N
K . I . N . R . I . .
O C C A S I O N . A F A R
H . N . A . Z . L . .
M O D C O N . G A Z U M P
P . E . Y . E . A . S
```

368

```
R E P L A C E . M I S E R
E . R . N . D . O . E . O
B R O W N . G R O U N D S
U . J . O . E . . I . .
S U E . Y E S . I R O N Y
. C . A . . N . R . A .
R O T U N D . I C E C A P
I . I . C . B . R . I .
P R O C E D U R E . T A M
O . N . F . M . I . A .
F R I D G E F R E E Z E R
F . S . I . E . N . E . E
S A T I N . T E T A N U S
```

369

```
  U F   I T   P   W
O R I E N T   S L O G A N
  G   D   E   A   R   G
L E G O   M O R E O V E R
  R       I   U       R
I M P A S S E   A S T I R
  U       E   E       N
S L A T E   S T R A N G E
  B   U H C   B
R E P R O A C H   S O H O
  R   B S   I   O   E
T R Y O U T   N O R M A L
  Y   T   E   G   B   L
```

370

```
  M B   S S   U   T
S I E R R A   P E N U R Y
  R   A T U   S   E
L O U T   C I R C U L A R
      H   N B   S
S N O R K E L   I S S U E
  O   E L   D T   R
A N I T A   B E L A T E D
  M   O M   N   N
P E T U L A N T   T A P S
  T   C D   I I   A
B A C H   A   S T A R V E
  L       M T   L E
```

371

```
  V F   R   T O   B
G I G O L O   H O C K E Y
  A   D   S E   U   H
G L A D   T R I L L I O N
  E       R R   A   L
S T I R R U P   C R U D E
  Y     M   W   E
S P E C K   B A L C O N Y
  E   R D   R   O
A C C I D E N T   P L A Y
  A   S A   I   I   L
A S S I S T   M I N N O W
  T   S H   E   G   E
```

372

```
  T T   B P   S   F
D E S I R E   A L K A L I
  D   N A D   I   A
R I O T   R E D C R O S S
  U     H   Y M   H
O M I N O U S   V I N Y L
      O   G L   S
C A B B Y   P E R H A P S
  U   I B   I   I
O F F L O A D S   R O C K
  A   I B   U   E   K
L I T T L E   R U D D E R
  T   Y L   E   O   T
```

373

```
  U J   S U   F   O
I N S U L T   S C R I B E
  C   M I A   E   T
L I S P   L I G N E   U S
  A     T   E R   S
F L A T T E N   J E W E L
      R   D P   I
U S U A L   T R I N K E T
  K   C S   O   M
G I F T S H O P   L O B E
  M   I R   A   A   A
O P P O S E   N O D U L E
  Y   N W   E   Y   M
```

374

```
  U J   S U   F   O
I N S U L T   S C R I B E
  C   M I A   E   T
L I S P   L I G N E   U S
  A     T   E R   S
F L A T T E N   J E W E L
      R   D P   I
U S U A L   T R I N K E T
  K   C S   O   M
G I F T S H O P   L O B E
  M   I R   A   A   A
O P P O S E   N O D U L E
  Y   N W   E   Y   M
```

375

```
  C W   W A   R
P H R A S E   M E S S U P
  U   R   E I   B
S K I M   P A T C H   B B
  K       I Y   E   E
T A T T I N G   C R O R E
  R     G G   O
B E G I N   H O B N A I L
  M   U O   A   N
M I S M A T C H   B U F F
  G   V T   E   R   A
U R S I N E   A B O U N D
  E   R R   D   W   T
```

376

```
  S T   B B   J
S T E R E O   L I N E A R
  O   I O   U   R
A L T O   K A R M A   G O
  E     I T   S   O
U N L E A S H   S T U N K
  N     H L   E
S I G N   L E P R O S Y
  H   A A   U
O   G E E U P   T I F F
  G   I M   D   I   F
T U R N I P   A U L A I T
  N   G O   Y   E   X
```

377

```
  M   S   T     S S K
G A T H E R   C U P T I E
  R   U   I   A   A   T
B O R N   V E L O C I T Y
  O   I   P   E       E
E N T H R A L   E M E N D
  I   L   D       A
A B I D E   W I T N E S S
  E   E   D   A       U
S A M A R I U M   A W R Y
  C   W   T   O   Q   V
G O K A R T   N E U T E R
  N   Y   O   D   A   Y
```

381

```
  C   L   O     P H R
L A Y O U T   S K E W E R
  N   S   T   A   A   M
C Y S T   O B L I V I O N
  O       O   M   M   V
U N M O R A L   O S I E R
      N   N   M   E
P I N C H   D I S T U R B
  C   O   O   D       A
W H O M E V E R   C U T E
  O   I   O   I   A   I
B R U N E I   F A R R O W
  G       D   F   T   N
```

378

```
  O   A   A   U   A S
S V E L T E   N E B U L A
  E   M   R   C   S   E
I R I S   O I L F I R E D
  L       B   E   N   P
P Y R A M I D   E T H Y L
      P   C   T   H
C R Y P T   G E N E R I C
  A   E   S   N       R
T S U N A M I S   F L I T
  C   D   O   I   A   S
S A D I S T   L O C K E R
  L   X   E       E   S
```

382

```
  S   D   S     S T W
P L O U G H   T A U G H T
  E   C   I   A   N   I
L A C K   E N G A G I N G
  Z       L   E   S   G
C Y A N I D E   O T H E R
      E   S   B   E
P R O X Y   P I N N A C E
  A   T   P   L       A
A B U D H A B I   P I N T
  B   O   I   O   A   C
D I S O W N   U N R E A L
  T   R   T       S A N
```

379

```
  E   S   S   A   M A
A R C T I C   S W I T C H
  I   Y   R   I   C   C
A C R E   U N D E R C U T
          M   E   O   S
I S O T O P E   F O R T H
  K   O   Y   I   R   O
B I S O N   E N D G A M E
  V       M   G   A
O V E R S I Z E   N O S Y
  I   I   D   N   I   I
B E Y O N D   U N S U N G
  S   T   Y   E   M   K
```

383

```
  S   E   E   O   R K
G O K A R T   C H O P I N
  L   S   E   E   O   S
R E L Y   R E A L T I M E
  M       N   N   C   E
A N K A R A   F R O T H
      M   L   W   O
N I M B Y   B A G P I P E
  N   R   G   R       A
A S T O N I S H   P A L M
  O   S   D   E   O   T
A L L I E D   A D M I R E
  E   A   Y   D   P   Y
```

380

```
      D   C   Y   S
A L L U D E   U P W I N D
  U   C   L   M   A   A
S P A T   L E M O N A D E
  I       Y   S   I
I N T E N S E   S O R R Y
      X   T   W   N
S T E T   G I N G H A M
  O   E   E   T       B
A P P R O A C H   R A J A
  H   I   R   E   U   E
C A V O R T   R E D U C E
  T   R   H   S   E   T
```

384

```
  O   V   G     E G
P H O B I A   R E A S O N
  A   O   N   E   R   S
C U R E   U R B A N I S E
  L       A   E   I   I
E M U L A T E   I N E P T
  I       U   L   G
G A F F E   P A R S N I P
  N   E   B   Y       M
A N Y W H E R E   C O P Y
  A   O   R   T   R   U
C L A R E T   T H E I R S
  S   K   H   E   W   E
```

385

```
  S O M   S S   F
B I O P S Y   C A M P U S
  G   U S   R A   R
O N U S   T R I L L I O N
  A   E   M   L   R
F L O W E R Y   O F T E N
  I   Y   O   R
  S U L K   J U R Y B O X
  W   D D   T   C
H A L F W I T S   C U L L
  T   O A   I O   O
S H O W E R   D E D U C T
  E   L Y   E A   K
```

386

```
  N A   T E   U   B
L O O F A H   N O T I F Y
  V   R   T M R   R
M A G I   O N E H O R S E
    C U   R   S   U
E M B A R G O   S T A R T
  U   H   U   F
S L O O P   A N A L Y S T
  B   B   I K
P E N T A G O N   E C H O
  R   U L   O   T O
F R E S C O   W A N G L E
  Y   E O   N   A E
```

387

```
  F N   E   P S   A
S I T U P S   O C C U L T
  G D   C   L R   P
M U T E   A T Y P I C A L
  R   P   P   B   C
W E L L S E T   U B O A T
    U E   B L
B A R M Y   D I N E T T E
  B   I K   G   A
M O U N T I N G   M I K E
  A   A T   E   A E
D R Y R O T   S P I R I T
  D Y   Y Y   T M   N
```

388

```
  O R   R M F   N
A L L U R E   O B E Y E D
  D M   M M   M G
V A M P   N A U T I C A L
  G   A   P   N T
R E C L I N E   B I Z E T
    O   T   R   N
F U N N Y   R E V E N U E
  N   E W   E       N
T E A S P O O N   F A W N
  V   U   U T   I
V E R M I N   R E F I N E
  N   E D   Y E   D
```

389

```
O H   A P T   F
A F F A I R   R H O D E S
  F Z   T I   M R   Y
R I T E   L A V A T O R Y
  N   E Y   H   I
A G A I N S T   Y U C C A
    N S   B M
B L U S H   B A R B E L L
  A U R B   O
A D U L T E R Y   S M O G
  E A A   S I   F
U N I T E D   I N R O A D
  E Y   T E   H
```

390

```
  C A   A A V   S
C H O C K S   S P E E C H
  O H   C C R Y
F R E E   E N O R M I T Y
  A   T T   O   H
I L L I C I T   J U L E P
    N C T   T
P A R S E   N O T H I N G
  N T S B   O
I N F A N T R Y   T Y R E
  E N A   J U   M
W A R C R Y   U P B E A T
  L E S   G G   E L
```

391

```
O W V   S S   V
S T R O V E   I N K C A P
  I R S   N E   S
F O R E   P E E R L E S S
  S   E W   A
F E A T U R E   S T I L L
  R S   R O
P L E A D   L E O N I N E
  O I W   S   A
H O R N P I P E   A B U T
  S   V R   U   S
D E F A C E   V O R T E X
  N D S   E A   A
```

392

```
H P W F   V   E
S A L A M I   E N I G M A
  H P   D V R   P
S A K I   O P E R A B L E
    S W   R G   O
S C A T T E R   T O K Y O
  A   R   W   E
I M A G E   P H I L T R E
  P R F   E A
C A V A L I E R   B U T T
  I V   R E   O S
E G R E S S   B R U T A L
  N L   T Y   R R
```

393

```
A R G O   S N I F F I E R
C L C   A R M   E
C H E K H O V   E X P E L
I A E   A N R   Y
D O N K E Y J A C K E T
E S   O   H S   I
N I C K E L   O P U S E S
T R B   S O   I
  V A C U U M F L A S K S
P Z R   O I   M
L Y I N G   C A S S A V A
U E E K   H L M
M I S T R E S S   F L A Y
```

394

```
L B L   L H C
F E L I N E   A M A Z O N
A E O   R S Q
O V E R   N A V Y B L U E
E A A E E
E S T U A R Y   B E R T H
N D L N
A G I L E   H E R S E L F
R I F T I
J A C K B O O T   E N V Y
I E R U D E
E N B L O C   C U D D L E
Y Y E E Y Y
```

395

```
T W J   M A
R E M O T E   T R O U G H
L R A U T R
C L A M   L A T C H K E Y
E O U B E
U R A N I U M   R A I S E
O S S L
A G A T E   W O O L L E N
E I S M N
L E M O N A D E   F L A T
G N T D E M
L E G A C Y   A M U L E T
E L R Y D L
```

396

```
C V A   I Q
P H L E G M   D U G O U T
O N A A N A
S P I T   L A P   O K R A
P G T R T
P Y J A M A S   B A I Z E
R M S N
P R O B E   F E R T I L E
U O E N A
U M B R E L L A   O D D S
P E D D R
P L E A S E   O R C H I D
E L R R E E
```

397

```
L H D C S T
R E B U K E   O X C A R T
G L S B A I
L I R A   P A R A V I O N
O O A E N
K N O W I N G   E N R O L
I D M G
Q U A F F   S I L E N C E
N E A N A
P R O L O G U E   U N T O
E E O R C
D A M S O N   A L I G H T
D S Y L T Y
```

398

```
F T E G F B
R E C A L L   R E A M E R
T T L O T D
M E L T   I N V E I G L E
O P E M I
U N H O R S E   M A N N A
U E H E
S T R A P   T A N G E N T
R I Y O
V I L L A G E R   P U F F
E A L I H L
I N D I G O   C L E R I C
T R O K R P
```

399

```
M S O S A G
W A R M U P   P R I M A L
M O T E R R
S M U G   I L L U S O R Y
O M L T E
A N G L I A N   P R A T E
I L A I
J I F F Y   A D E P T L Y
N E S I I
S K U L L C A P   S A V E
J I U O A E
F E N N E L   S I C K L E
T E L L K Y
```

400

```
R I T E   P A T H E T I C
E A E V A H O
H O S A N N A   B L E A R
E T I T I A R
A H E A D   A S T U T E
R R R L
S Q U I R T   G E N E V A
E N U X M
  E N L I S T   C R U M B
I E M M I B S
S H R U B   O U T L O O K
L V U S E A
E L E V E N T H   S T U N
```

401

```
  T   L   T   A M   S
L A B O U R   W E E D E D
  K   A   I   F   C   D
M I F F   T R U T H F U L
  N   I   L   A   C
I G N E O U S   U N D E R
      E   M   V   I
B U N C H   D I E C A S T
  N   S   R   T
S W I M M I N G   A H O Y
  R   A   D   U   M   L
M A N U A L   L I M P E T
  P   L   E   O   N
```

402

```
  D   A   B   T   A   H
T O R P O R   E M B L E M
  L   S   E   M   I   L
R O S E   A P P E N D I X
  U   K   O   I   U
B R O O D E R   S T U M P
      U   R   S   I
A B A T E   S C H O L A R
  A   M   M   R   N
M O N O X I D E   H E I R
  B   D   N   E   A   M
G A Z E B O   C I R R U S
  B   D   R   H   M   S
```

403

```
  V   L   D   S   G   B
K I M O N O   H O O K U P
  L   R   C   E   O   R
D I C E   K N E E D E E P
  F   A   T   W   A
S Y R I N G E   M I X U P
      N   E   C   L
S T I F F   T A B L O I D
  E   A   O   L   N
I N I M I C A L   F A T E
  D   O   T   O   L   A
V O L U M E   F L I N C H
  N   S   T   F   T   T
```

404

```
  O   B   C   B   L   S
I G U A N A   A B A C U S
  R   K   P   S   T   L
C E D E   S H A K E U P
  R   U   L   N   H
B I C Y C L E   A T L A S
  D   E   G   T
H O A R D   T R A I L E R
  L   A   Q   A   N
B A N K R U P T   G E A R
  T   I   O   I   E   M
J E T S E T   F O S S I L
  R   H   H   Y   T   D
```

405

```
  S   A   F   U   A   M
S H U F T I   S Y S T E M
  E   F   N   H   T   S
I D E A   A M E T H Y S T
  D   I   N   R   M   M
O V E R A C T   F A T A L
  I   E   B   T
P L U M B   T R I P L E X
  L   O   O   O   A
P A T H E T I C   Y E L L
  G   A   H   A   O   I
D E V I C E   D E F A M E
  R   R   R   E   F   E
```

406

```
C O M E   C H A I N S A W
A   O   M   O   R   C   A
P E R V E R T   R O O S T
    E   N   R   E   U   T
P O S T A L O R D E R S
O   G   D   E   G   F
D R O V E R   H E R E T O
S   C   A   P   M   R
N E W T E S T A M E N T
A   A   R   Y   B   G   I
B A N J O   C A L O R I E
U   I   H   E   E   T
T R A N S F E R   E T C H
```

407

```
  P   G   O   M   A   C
T H R E A D   A S L E E P
  L   R   D   M   L   N
R E A M   M E M O R I S E
  G   E   A   O   O
I M P L A N T   Q U E R Y
  I   T   F   N
T W I S T   E A R D R U M
  E   T   P   R   N
B A L L Y H O O   P I L L
  K   E   O   F   O   E
L E S S O N   F A M I S H
  N   S   E   P   S
```

408

```
  T   F   B   A   M   M
B O D I C E   G L U T E N
  G   L   E   L   L   T
S A R I   S H O U L D E R
  N   W   W   O
O W N G O A L   S K I R T
  E   X   P   I
A L I G N   D I S S E C T
  L   O   B   C   I
D R O P K I C K   Z E A L
  E   H   R   U   Z   C
P A T E N T   P A L T R Y
  D   R   H   S   E
```

409

```
. L . C . E . P W . O .
B Y P A S S . S W I T C H
. C . L . T . A C . U .
S E E M . U N L I K E L Y
. U . . A . M . . . A .
I M P L O R E . D A I R Y
. . . U . Y . M . . W .
S P E C K . S I R L O I N
. L . K . A . N . . N .
D U T Y F R E E . M E R E
. N . . D . O . R . A U .
E G O I S M . A C C E S S
. E . P . A . L . E . H
```

413

```
. L . S . C . C O . S .
M I G H T Y . R E P A I R
. Q . A . P . Y . T . L
D U N G . R E P R I S A L
. I . . E . T . C . G .
I D O L I S E . W I D E N
. . . O . S . H . A . .
P I T O N . C O I N A G E
. S . K . D . L . . R .
A L L E Y W A Y . G L A D
. A . R . E . S . R . T
U N C O I L . E X O T I C
. D . N . L . E . T . S
```

410

```
. B . E . D . A H . F .
B R A N D Y . S L O G A N
. E . I . N . S . O . N
S W I G . A N E C D O T E
. M . M . T . . O . A .
M A T A D O R . N O I S Y
. L . . . R . . . I . .
F L O O R . H I G H W A Y
. . . U . C . P . . A .
V I R T U O S O . I S L E
. V . S . M . S . R . A
H A R E E M . T E D I U M
. N . T . A . E . O . D
```

411

```
. T . I . S . R S . M .
N O O D L E . O U T W I T
. W . O . A . A . R . R
Y A W L . W I S E A C R E
. R . . E . T . T . O .
O D Y S S E Y . T I A R A
. . . O . D . B . F . .
S C U B A . N E W Y O R K
. O . . E . D . . A . .
P U T U P J O B . N O T E
. P . T . E . U . E . I
M O S A I C . G R E E N S
. N . H . T . S . D . G
```

412

```
. B . F . O . O D . S .
C A V O R T . F L E S H Y
. Z . U . T . F . M . R
L A I R . O R A T O R I O
. A . . M . L . L . N .
O R D I N A L . L I N K S
. . . G . N . E . S . .
A M E N D . U N C H A I N
. E . O . M . D . . N .
C A R R I A G E . W A V E
. G . A . T . M . I . E
B R U N C H . I M P I S H
. E . T . S . C . E . T
```

413 see above

414

```
. D . I . F . T W . S .
F I S C A L . A T R I U M
. S . E . A . U . E . B
S C U M . P A N A T E L A
. A . . P . T . C . U .
L A U N D E R . P H O N E
. I . . R . P . . A . .
E R E C T . C A R P O R T
. S . O . M . G . A . .
P T O M A I N E . R I F E
. R . E . D . B . T . A
G I F T E D . O . L U C K
. P . . Y . Y . Y . T
```

415

```
. W . L . T . E C . N .
W R A I T H . N A R R O W
. E . N . Y . E . I . V
T A C T . R E M E M B E R
. T . . O . Y . I . N .
C H R O N I C . S N E A K
. . . L . D . D . A . .
I M P E L . N E O L O G Y
. A . A . U . M . . A .
A M E N A B L E . P R I G
. M . D . O . S . O . E
C A M E R A . N I C E T Y
. L . R . T . E . K . Y
```

416

```
. T . C . D . Y . . J .
B O R R O W . U P B E A T
. I . O . I . M . C . C
S L E W . N A M E S A K E
. E . . D . Y . T . E .
S T I P P L E . L I S T S
. . . I . E . L . N . .
A D U L T . V I R G U L E
. R . C . A . S . . E .
S Y P H I L I S . N U T S
. R . A . O . O . E . T
F O U R T H . M I C K E Y
. T . D . A . E . K . R
```

417

```
  B P C E S B
W E A L T H   V O O D O O
H   E   O   E   N   U
S O F A   C O N V I N C E
L   I   T   N   L
E D I F I C E   O L D E N
    R   E   H   A
G R O U P   C A T W A L K
E   I   T       E
S T A T U A R Y   P I N T
U   F   S   A A   T
A R M L E T   R E G A I N
N   Y   Y   D E   L
```

418

```
  B H I A I B
S E C O N D   L A D D I E
H   O   O   O   E   R
K I N D   L E F T O V E R
N       I   T   L   M
A D V E R S E   R O V E R
    M   E   B   G
O W L E T   B A B Y L O N
H   R   S   R
R A D I A T O R   K I C K
L   T   U   A   N   E
R E F U N D   C L I E N T
R   S   Y   K . T   T
```

419

```
  G L D C S F
B E G O N E   L A T H E R
I   V   A   O   E   L
I S L E   F O U N T A I N
H   A   T       N
D A U P H I N   B A G E L
    O   D   B   M
A G G R O   L A W Y E R S
R   K   D   N       U
L U N C H E O N   R I N G
M   H   R   O   I   N
A P L O M B   C O N V E Y
Y   P   Y   K   K   L
```

420

```
  B F O A M H
B U L L E T   B E A M E D
R   E   T   O   T   A
A R E A   O L D G U A R D
O   O   M   E   R   T
O W N G O A L   C A C H E
    O   N   C   T
U N C L E   B A L E F U L
E   D   S   D   P
G U I D A N C E   M U S H
R   U   A   N   O   H
B O N S A I   Z E A L O T
N   T   L   A   N   T
```

421

```
  C R K S C T
S A L O O N   W A L N U T
P   S   O   A   A   S
S T A Y   C O M P R I S E
O   O   K   P   I   L
G R A B B E D   I N S E T
    O   R   J   E
A S C O T   C A N T A T A
I   K   D   V       A
I N S E C U R E   T A L C
B   N   V   L   E   E
C A D D I E   I N N I N G
D   S   T   N   T
```

422

```
  O E E S B
P L E X U S   W A I V E R
D   I   Q   A   G   D
C H I T   U N T A N G L E
A   K   I   H   E   A
S T I R F R Y   C O M M A
    E   E   K   U
B U R S T   D I S S E N T
N   O   H   N   U
T R O U S E R S   C E D E
E   R   N   H   A   I
B E A C O N   I N F U S E
L   E   A   P   E   M
```

423

```
  D M Y A W D
P A Y O F F   M E A G R E
M   O   R   B   S   E
P A I N   O V E R H A N G
G       N   R   C
K E Y N O T E   P O O H
    E   S   B   I
D O U S E   B O W L I N G
R   T   L       O
H I L L S I D E   S I R E
G   I   A   T   O   M
W I N N E R   U N L O A D
N   G   A   S   O   L
```

424

```
  P P M B S H
C H E R R Y   A R T F U L
A   I   S   N   R   M
G R O G   T A J M A H A L
O   I   O   G       N
E S S E N C E   A G R E E
    L   L
A B B E Y   A B R E A S T
L   C   P   O   Q
R O O T B E E R   F O U R
W   I   T   E   L   A
E S C O R T   D R O W S E
Y   N   Y   W   H
```

425

- FAVOUR — OBEYED
- BOOT — LIMABEAN
- MYSTIC — LATHE
- CROAK — VETERAN
- AGRARIAN — WITH
- DEFAME — REPINE

426

- FOREST — MUSEUM
- DIRK — IDENTITY
- PYJAMAS — BRAND
- MAGIC — FANCIER
- SIGNPOST — TATA
- GROTTY — APRON

427

- RELATE — WEAPON
- FIZZ — KITEMARK
- OFFLOAD — LAPEL
- SCANT — GELDING
- EMPHATIC — LASH
- PLENTY — REALLY

428

- AMOUNT — BEHEAD
- TOSS — MEMBRANE
- STUTTER — MIRTH
- ASSAY — BRIGAND
- DAIQUIRI — LIME
- MUTINY — ATRIUM

429

- SLALOM — MEAGRE
- AVOW — NIGHTOWL
- PRORATA — SIGHT
- GRUNT — ARSENIC
- OLDFLAME — HUSH
- MODERN — LOCUST

430

- SHALOM — RUNOUT
- NOOK — OBLATION
- SERRIED — WORRY
- APPAL — PISTIL
- PRESSMAN — LIKE
- RUSSIA — ROTTER

431

- EMERGE — EXODUS
- MAID — DISLOYAL
- SKILIFT — DINER
- STINK — TOMTOM
- MISHMASH — CURT
- TEDIUM — EGGNOG

432

- VOUCH — ICECAP
- ALOE — REUNITED
- DECENCY — QUIRE
- RUGBY — TENDRIL
- KAMIKAZE — NONE
- ELDEST — SHERRY

433

```
  M   T   E   A   P   F
C I T R O N     L O R D L Y
  N   I   T   A   A   O
L U N G     H A R D C O P Y
  E   R   M   T   P
E T E R N A L     S I B Y L
      A   L   F   C
G O U G E     P A G E A N T
  Y   W   R   O
A S S E M B L E     C O V E
  T   E   O   A   A   I
S E L D O M     S O L A C E
  R   B   T   L   E
```

437

```
  G   I   D   A   C   D
T R A N C E     L O O K I N
  O   C   A   I   L   M
R U S H     N O V E L I S T
  S   E   E   I   U
V E S P E R S     S E A M Y
      E   Y   F   R
A C R I D     P O L Y M E R
  O   G   A   R   S
T R A N S M I T     G A T E
  R   O   B   I   R   A
M A L I C E     F E A L T Y
  L   R   R   Y   N   E
```

434

```
  P   S   S       W   R
P E A N U T     F R A C A S
  R   U   I   O   T   G
N U M B     R O U L E T T E
  S   R   L   R   A
Z E A L O U S     U S A G E
      A   P   V   K
W O O D Y     P I G I R O N
  B   Y   G   R   E
F L A S H I N G     E D D Y
  A   H   V   U   D   E
S T R I K E     L E G U M E
  E   P   N   E   E   A
```

435

```
  A   L   I   G   S   E
E T H I C S     A T T E S T
  H   N   O   N   E   C
F O L K     T A J M A H A L
  M   O   A   L   P
M E S S U P     S T E E R
      H   E   B   H
S C O O P     L I L Y P A D
  H   R   P   P   F
M I S T R I A L     L O G O
  N   A   A   A   U   H
P O P G U N     N E C T A R
  S   E   O   E   K   N
```

436

```
  S   A   A   S       A
F L E X E S     L U X U R Y
  E   I   S   E   T
P A S S     I D E N T I F Y
  Z   S   T   O   U
H Y D R A T E     O P A L
  E   S   R   I
S E N S E     P E N C I L
  X   I   B   M   I
P O O D L E   O   P A N G
  T   E   R   V   U   E
K I D N E Y     A R M O U R
  C   T   L   L   P
```

438

```
  L   W   S   S   H   R
B I G A M Y     A B A C U S
  B   N   M   V   L   N
L I E D     P O O R L A W S
  D   T   Y   M   A
H O R I Z O N     S A T Y R
      N   M   B   R
A G A T E     B U S K I N G
  L   E   U   L   E
C O R R I D O R     N A P E
  B   N   D   U   O   H
M A D A M E     S A U C E R
  L   L   R   H   N   W
```

439

```
  A   T   O   B   A   S
B L O W U P     R A G O U T
  L   E   P   A   N   R
L U R E     R A T I O N E D
  R   E   S   S   T
R E L A P S E     S T A Y
  I   S   O   I
U S U R P     C U P C A K E
  C   L   G   T   I
D E S I R O U S     F U S E
  N   N   O   I   L   M
B I G E N D     D R O V E R
  C   S   Y   E   P   T
```

440

```
  A   C   S   S   A   R
S P I R I T     T I L L E R
  P   E   O   U   T   S
F L A W     M A N D O L I N
  E   A   G   G
E S S E N C E     E B O N Y
  L   H   B   E
S N O O P     C A V E M A N
  A   N   N   L   S
K I N G S I Z E     R I S E
  L   A   N   F   A   I
S E X T O N     U N J U S T
  D   E   Y   L   A   T
```

441

```
 .  P  .  H  .  P  .  W  .  U  .  .
 M  A  R  I  N  A  .  A  N  N  E  A  L
 .  T  .  V  .  I  .  D  .  C  .  D  .
 R  I  L  E  .  S  W  E  E  T  P  E  A
 .  N  .  .  .  L  .  R  .  U  .  L  .
 H  A  M  S  T  E  R  .  M  O  P  E  D
 .  .  .  C  .  Y  .  B  .  U  .  .  .
 R  A  V  E  N  .  C  A  P  S  U  L  E
 .  I  .  N  .  H  .  P  .  .  .  A  .
 B  R  E  A  K  O  U  T  .  S  E  R  F
 .  M  .  .  .  R  .  N  .  I  .  W  .
 F  A  C  I  L  E  .  S  T  A  M  E  N
 .  N  .  O  .  Y  .  .  .  E  .  Y  .
```

442

```
 .  R  .  J  .  V  .  B  .  T  .  R  .
 R  E  T  I  N  A  .  A  Z  A  L  E  A
 .  P  .  V  .  M  .  B  .  P  .  T  .
 P  I  N  E  .  P  L  E  B  E  I  A  N
 .  N  .  .  .  I  .  L  .  R  .  K  .
 L  E  I  S  U  R  E  .  L  I  N  E  N
 .  .  .  A  .  E  .  V  .  N  .  .  .
 U  M  B  R  A  .  N  A  U  G  H  T  Y
 .  E  .  D  .  L  .  N  .  .  .  U  .
 A  R  R  O  G  A  N  T  .  S  A  N  S
 .  M  .  .  .  P  .  A  .  E  .  N  .
 N  A  T  I  V  E  .  G  O  A  T  E  E
 .  N  .  C  .  L  .  .  .  T  .  L  .
```

443

```
 .  B  .  O  .  C  .  S  .  C  .  B  .
 T  R  I  L  B  Y  .  W  O  O  E  R  S
 .  I  .  G  .  G  .  I  .  N  .  U  .
 R  O  T  A  .  N  O  N  E  V  E  N  T
 .  N  .  .  .  E  .  G  .  E  .  E  .
 D  Y  N  A  S  T  Y  .  S  N  A  I  L
 .  .  .  D  .  S  .  N  .  E  .  .  .
 B  E  A  R  S  .  H  O  O  D  L  U  M
 .  I  .  .  .  T  .  .  .  N  .  .  .
 W  H  E  A  T  E  A  R  .  A  L  S  O
 .  U  .  T  .  N  .  U  .  N  .  U  .
 U  N  T  I  E  S  .  B  A  K  E  R  Y
 .  T  .  C  .  E  .  Y  .  H  .  E  .
```

444

```
 .  A  .  N  .  D  .  V  .  S  .  P  .
 I  N  S  A  N  E  .  O  N  E  W  A  Y
 .  V  .  .  .  B  .  R  .  R  .  R  .
 T  U  N  E  .  R  E  L  I  G  I  O  N
 .  A  .  .  .  I  .  E  .  E  .  L  .
 S  L  I  T  H  E  R  .  C  A  R  E  T
 .  .  .  R  .  F  .  L  .  N  .  .  .
 S  C  R  A  P  .  L  E  E  T  I  D  E
 .  R  .  N  .  B  .  A  .  .  .  E  .
 W  O  R  S  E  O  F  F  .  C  A  R  P
 .  C  .  M  .  X  .  L  .  H  .  A  .
 F  U  T  I  L  E  .  E  L  I  X  I  R
 .  S  .  T  .  R  .  T  .  T  .  L  .
```

445

```
 .  B  .  S  .  A  .  S  .  S  .  S  .
 B  E  L  I  E  F  .  M  I  N  U  T  E
 .  C  .  G  .  F  .  E  .  O  .  A  .
 T  O  W  N  .  A  L  L  O  W  I  N  G
 .  M  .  .  .  I  .  L  .  B  .  Z  .
 L  E  A  D  E  R  S  .  C  A  N  A  L
 .  .  .  E  .  S  .  B  .  L  .  .  .
 T  A  R  T  S  .  D  R  I  L  L  E  D
 .  G  .  .  .  A  .  O  .  U  .  X  .
 B  E  L  I  E  V  E  S  .  B  O  T  H
 .  N  .  L  .  E  .  H  .  I  .  E  .
 S  C  R  E  E  N  .  E  A  T  I  N  G
 .  Y  .  D  .  S  .  S  .  E  .  D  .
```

446

```
 .  C  .  K  .  S  .  T  .  G  .  S  .
 S  L  E  I  G  H  .  R  O  U  B  L  E
 .  I  .  N  .  O  .  O  .  N  .  A  .
 W  E  N  D  .  W  O  O  D  P  U  L  P
 .  N  .  .  .  M  .  P  .  O  .  O  .
 E  T  E  R  N  A  L  .  F  I  L  M  S
 .  .  .  N  .  R  .  N  .  .  .  .  .
 A  C  U  T  E  .  G  E  N  T  I  A  N
 .  A  .  H  .  S  .  L  .  M  .  .  .
 A  N  N  O  U  N  C  E  .  A  G  E  D
 .  N  .  R  .  E  .  A  .  B  .  N  .
 B  O  S  N  I  A  .  S  T  U  R  D  Y
 .  N  .  .  .  K  .  E  .  T  .  S  .
```

447

```
 .  F  .  E  .  P  .  C  .  S  .  A  .
 T  R  E  A  T  Y  .  R  E  P  A  S  T
 .  I  .  S  .  R  .  O  .  L  .  Y  .
 E  N  V  Y  .  A  D  O  R  A  B  L  E
 .  G  .  .  .  M  .  N  .  T  .  U  .
 M  E  R  M  A  I  D  .  S  T  U  M  P
 .  .  .  E  .  D  .  P  .  E  .  .  .
 T  S  A  R  .  .  B  A  H  R  A  I  N
 .  H  .  I  .  B  .  C  .  .  .  M  .
 F  E  E  D  B  A  C  K  .  D  U  P  E
 .  A  .  .  .  I  .  W  .  I  .  R  .
 A  F  R  A  I  D  .  C  L  A  U  S  E
 .  N  .  .  .  Y  .  Y  .  E  .  W  .  H
```

448

```
 .  T  .  B  .  A  .  W  .  A  .  M  .
 S  H  O  U  L  D  .  H  A  L  T  E  R
 .  R  .  Z  .  R  .  I  .  T  .  D  .
 F  U  Z  Z  .  E  N  F  E  E  B  L  E
 .  S  .  .  .  N  .  F  .  R  .  E  .
 O  H  M  S  L  A  W  .  B  E  R  Y  L
 .  A  .  .  .  L  .  C  .  G  .  .  .
 A  V  E  R  T  .  C  O  R  O  N  E  R
 .  .  .  E  .  M  .  N  .  .  .  N  .
 F  A  L  S  T  A  F  F  .  B  I  T  E
 .  P  .  .  .  O  .  R  .  U  .  E  .  R
 T  E  R  R  O  R  .  S  T  E  R  E  O
 .  D  .  T  .  Y  .  .  .  E  .  F  .  E
```

449

```
  M   B   E   V   B   A
W A L R U S   E M I G R E
  N   A   T   R   N   M
L I E N   U N S T A B L E
  A   A   O   U   E
I C E B E R G   B R O T H
  I   Y   M   A
S C U R F   N U C L E A R
  O   D   P   L   L
E G G S H E L L   R A C K
  N   E   T   I   O
L A T E N T   O C T A V O
  C   D   Y   N   E   E
```

450

```
  M   S   P   D   I   P
B A N A N A   U N C L A D
  L   L   L   M   E   T
F L E A   E M P H A S I S
  M   T   S   G   E
T S H I R T   T E E N Y
  E   E   B   C
G A B B Y   W A V E L E T
  F   O   R   R   N
D A Y B R E A K   T O M B
  R   C   A   I   I
H E R A L D   C A R A F E
  R   T   Y   E   F
```

451

```
  R   B   T   E   S   H
R E S U M E   A C U M E N
  S   L   D   V   I   C
L I C K   I D E N T I T Y
  S   O   S   A   I
S T A N D U P   A B A C K
  E   S   O   L
S H A W L   N U M E R A L
  A   T   W   T   B
D I N O S A U R   A L L Y
  R   W   I   A   B   O
A D O N I S   N E L S O N
  O   S   T   K   E   M
```

452

```
  M   S   W   S   L   P
K I P P E R   P L A Y U P
  K   I   E   U   T
D A W N   T H E O R I S E
  D   I   D   E   C
N O T H I N G   C A C H E
  A   G   H   T
A T O L L   B O R E D O M
  E   L   B   L   R
U N L O V E L Y   B O A R
  D   W   S   S   A   T
S E V E R E   E N B L O C
  R   D   T   E   E   R
```

453

```
  J   L   I   L   S
H A R A S S   S K I M P Y Y
  L   C   E   S   T   O
C O K E   C A U T I O U S S
  P   U   E   G   S
E Y E S O R E   E A G E R R
  U   E   S   T
B E A N O   N U M E R A L
  G   D   D   F   S
F O U R L E A F   A P S E E
  I   I   L   U   B   I
A S C E N T   S L E D G E E
  M   D   A   E   D   N
```

454

```
  A   N   R   C   A   T
I M P E D E   A S S I S T T
  B   R   E   J   S   E
A U T O   N A U S E A T E E
  S   T   N   M   S
W H I S P E R   A B B E Y Y
      R   E   L
A G A I N   S C R E E C H
  A   N   M   O   L
W I N D F A L L   F R E E E
  E   O   N   O   E   V
S T R O B E   G O L D E N N
  Y   R   Y   L   R
```

455

```
  P   B   O   B   H   U
B E H E A D   O R I E N T T
  D   A   D   N   D   V
D A R N   M A C K E R E L L
  N   E   E   I
E T C H I N G   J E L L Y Y
  A   T   P   L
W O R T H   D R A F T E E
  C   C   V   O   N
M E C H A N I C   C O C K
  L   W   E   T   O   O
M O S A I C   O N W A R D
  T   Y   K   R   L   E
```

456

```
  N   P   B   U   C   C
C I N E M A   L O O S E N N
  T   E   H   T   R   L
S W A P   A I R E D A L E E
  I   M   A   U   A
E T E R N A L   F R E R E E
  I   S   P   O
A D A G E   B O G Y M E N
  R   H   H   S   E
C E N T R I S T   L I C E
  A   F   V   A   A   O
T R I U N E   G A Z U M P
  Y   L   S   E   E   A
```

457

```
  B A O   A E C
H U N G E R   G A M M O N
  S O G   R I   H
W I N G   A V E R S I O N
  L   N E   S   R
T Y P H O I D   E A R T H
  E   C   N   R
C H A R M   H A L Y A R D
  E A   A M   A
D I A L O G U E   R I V E
  G D   A D   A I
T H I R S T   A N G I N A
  T Y E   Y E E
```

458

```
  K H O   S G B
P A R E N T   W O O D E D
  R E   T I A   F
S A I L   O B S I D I A N
  T   M H   L
S E V E R A L   N E W L Y
    S   N R   G
A D O P T   L A C O N I C
  A E   I M   N
T R I C Y C L E   H I D E
  N I   I K A   U
D E T A I N   I N T A C T
  L L   G N E E
```

459

```
  M A P   C   B
S U R V E Y   I N S U R E
  S E   J V   A
S E E R   A V I A T R I X
  U   M L A S
I M M O R A L   B R E E D
    U S L
Z L O T Y   S A R C A S M
  U M   S T   P
I M M O D E S T   P L A N
  B D D   I E R
G E N E R A   C H A I S E
  R D N   E R E
```

460

```
  G C D   D T F
P A N A M A   I T A L I C
  Z S S R   P E
G U S H   H A T   W A R D
  M   I Y   A C
S P A R I N G   O T T E R
    E G C   E
F U D G E   B L A R N E Y
  U   R I   M
S T A L L I O N   C U B E
  O A V   K O L
S W A T H E   E X C E E D
  S E R   R A M
```

461

```
  C B   R P E
S H E A T H   A M O U N T
  I N U Z   N C
F L O G   S N O W D R O P
  L   S R   R
T Y P I C A L   B E R E T
  N R L   D
F L U F F   T I M O T H Y
  I O S   G   E
U N B R O K E N   B E E R
  E M A   I E H
P A T E N T   T R E P A N
  R D E   E T W
```

462

```
  V N A   A S J
R I B A L D   L O T I O N
  S I J I R   G
S A I L   O X B R I D G E
  G   U I D   L
D E C L A R E   B E S E T
  I N P   N
G R U F F   C H A T T E R
  O E C Y   M
G U M B O O T S   N O I R
  B E M   I O G
S L A L O M   C A N A R Y
  E T A S E E
```

463

```
  P G W   G O S
P O M A D E   I N V I T E
  L P I Z   E A
N O D E   G E M   N A T I O
  N   H O U
H Y D R A T E   R I S E R
  E Y C   A
H A N D Y   I R I D I U M
  G F B   I   N
D E C A D E N T   H E I R
  N C T T O S
S C H E M E   E N B L O C
  Y D L R O N
```

464

```
  L F A   A G C
L I K I N G   G R A T I S
  V S A A R   C
N I G H   I N T E R N A L
  N   N E I D
E G O T I S M   U S U A L
    E T O O
F L O S S   A M O N G S T
  A T C I   E
B R E T H R E N   J E E R
  Y U E O U M
E N A B L E   U N R U L Y
  X E L S Y Y
```

465

```
  B P P   S S H
C E L L A R   T I N H A T
D   A   O   A   O   T
A E O N   F I R E W O R K
C   F   E   F   E
S K I P P E R   T A R D Y
    R   R   S   L
S A T I N   U T I L I S E
N   N   T   R   T
S C O T F R E E   O M I T
H   I   I   T   K   G
P O U N C E   C H R O M E
R   G   D   H   A
```

469

```
  T F O   R V F
A R D E N T   E L I C I T
  O   T   A   O   L
  P U P A   O S C U L A T E
  G   M   H   E   E
C H A T E A U   S N O R T
    R   N   H   C
A G R E E   P I E E Y E D
  R   S   D   D   A
H O T P L A T E   E L S E
  C   A   U   O   E
S E A S O N   U P H O L D
  R   S   T   T   O
```

466

```
  S L S   P F C
T A L E N T   A G E O L D
  E   Y   R   C   I
H A N K   P A R A K E E T
  R   T   Y   L   N
D Y N A M I C   P E T T Y
    S   C   H   S
M O O S E   L I N S E E D
  C   A   O   D   S
F E A S I B L E   S A C K
  L   S   O   O   A
B O V I N E   U N R I P E
  T   N   S   T   E
```

467

```
  M G G   J P S
G Y R A T E   E A R T H Y
  R   S   O   A   E
W I S P   L A N D L O R D
  A   O   S   I   P
D O T A G E   O F F A L
  A   Y   S   I
U S U R P   R E D C O A T
  T   N   V   B
M A N D R A K E   P E R K
  R   O   V   R   O
S V E L T E   A N N U A L
  E   L   L   L   D
```

470

```
  F G O   C S O
R U B R I C   L I K I N G
  H   U   C   O   U
D R A B   L O C A L I S E
  E   U   K   L   V
G R E N A D E   S C O N E
    E   E   B   A
W A G O N   D I S P L A Y
  D   N   B   L   B
M A C A R O N I   I T A L C
  G   T   R   O   E
P I R A N A   U P S H O T
  O   L   X   S   T   M
```

471

```
  S A T   P S F
T A U R U S   O P A Q U E
  L   C   A   S   N
M O T H   R O U G H   R A
  O   I   P   C   U
K N O W I N G   W O U N D
    H   A   B   R
A C R I D   B O N D A G E
  R   P   J   W   O
T A I L C O A T   E A S T
  D   A   E   I   D   S
F L A S H Y   E L I C I T
  E   H   T   P
```

468

```
  B S I   O H T
G O B L I N   T I E D Y E
  U   A   T   H   A   C
S N U B   E L E C T R O N
  C   G   R   W   O
B E L A T E D   P A I N T
    B   R   P   V
D O U S E   W I N E B A R
  R   I   C   L   C
B I A N N U A L   K I T E
  G   T   R   A   I
D I T H E R   G R O U N D
  N   E   Y   E   W   G
```

472

```
  C M U   F I G
C A R E E N   O X C A R T
  S   E   S   L   E   O
S U N K   C O L I S E U M
  A   R   A   Y   K   N
B L U S H E D   G A U D Y
    E   W   O   T
B L E A K   N U M E R A L
  E   S   S   T   N
N A R C O T I C   P O K E
  D   A   E   A   L
P E O P L E   S A U C E R
  N   E   P   T   M   T
```

473

```
  L G B   U F S
BYGONE PROMPT
  C L A S L   I
FEED THEOLOGY
  U   L T O O
UMPTEEN   SWAT
  A S W   U
ADEPT PITPROP
  O E T T   P
BLUDGEON TUTU
  L E N E Y I
GAUCHO SIPHON
  R K N S E N
```

477

```
  D S U G E A
PRIEST LIVELY
  Y L I O E L
SILL LAVENDER
  C   I E T G
HEROISM RIVER
  A E O D
CROFT ELDERLY
  A   F D A
NIOBIUM ACNE
  D A L A V D
GOATEE ICECAP
  M H R D R U
```

474

```
  M B G   A C
DILUTE FOLLOW
  C Z L L   Q
CHEZ ANALOGUE
  E   T K C E
GLOTTIS CATTY
    I N D T
AMITY CADENCE
  U U S Y   A
ATHLETIC BUMF
  U A O   A E
WARREN REVERE
  L   E E Y A
```

478

```
  F E O A I C
ELIXIR BANDIT
  E H A B C T
MAGI TEETOTAL
  B I Y N   T
TRAITOR ASPIC
  A T N A I O
TWAIN ANODYNE
    O L A E
SPANKING RAZE
  O I G R A O
PUTSCH AUTHOR
  R M T M E M
```

475

```
  S S S B S U
TENANT EXPAND
  C N A D A L
LOSS TRENCHER
  N   U W E S
ADJOURN OBESE
  U E Q   A
SPITE QUARREL
  R S O I   X
DORMOUSE RICK
  M A T T E E
SPARSE EXEMPT
  T T R R L T
```

479

```
  S F O R D W
SPIRAL HEYDAY
  I E D Y N T
ONUS BEMOANED
  C O E M R
HOMONYM BOAST
  I   S D   K
BLOCK SIRLOIN
  S H M S A
ULTERIOR POKY
  I R T O T N
SCORER BIOTIN
  K Y E E P T
```

476

```
  E C   S F C
ACROSS PRIMAL
  L V A R S U
EASE ROADHOGS
  I   O T H H
PRETEND LOFTY
  W G L O
FLOOR MUSKRAT
  E T C N   N
BASILICA NOON
  V M G T A I
PESETA IMMUNE
  S R R C E T
```

480

```
  P J M M E G
MODULE ARTERY
  U S R T E O
UNIT MACERATE
  C A H N T
DEAFAID SIBYL
  R D F T
EBBED BABYSIT
  E E S S M
PATHETIC HEBE
  D A A I O R
PLENTY SENDUP
  E D S M E E
```

481

```
    W   U   D   A   I   H
G A R N E R   M A N T E L
    S   I   A   E   S   L
C H I N   P A N A T E L A
    T   E   D       A
S I D E A R M   S N A I L
    N   R   Y   P   T   R
D I A R Y   M A N A G E R
    Q   U   F   G   N
C U T P R I C E   E A S Y
    I   T   S   A   O   W
T E E T H   N O U G A T
    Y   D   Y   T   S   N
```

482

```
    P   W   T   F   U
B O D E G A   A L P A C A
    L   C   R   M   H
G A L L   T O C C A T A
    R   I   E   R   I
S T U B B L E   S K I R T
        A   E   D   E
S M A R T   M I S T R A L
    A   R   R   P   U
E T H E R E A L   R O P E
    R   T   N   O   A
T I P T O E   M O S A I C
    X   E   W   A   T   R
```

483

```
    P   S   G   C   S   H
D I V I N E   H A T R E D
    Q   L   R   I   R   R
L U R K   M E D I C I N E
    E   A   E   K   I
E T C H I N G   P L E A T
    I   E   E   E
M I D G E   A P P R I S E
    N   H   B   I       P
C O S I E S T   G E R M
    U   P   T   A   U   A
O R I O L E   P I S T I L
    S   T   L   H   T   N
```

484

```
    P   E   H   S   P   N
B O U N T Y   P E A H E N
    U   C   P   A   L   S
T R A Y   E X T R A C T S
    C   D   E   E   L
A P P L A U D   R O B I N
    O   O   P   T   N   N
P U P P Y   W A S T A G E
    L   A   F   L   O
E T H E R E A L   L U G S
    I   D   V   Y   O   L
S C R I B E   H A G G I S
    E   A   R   O   Y   B
```

485

```
    P   V   S   S   C   C
V O Y A G E   A T O M I C
    L   N   S   I   N   N
D I E S   S P L A S H E D
    S       I   S   I   M
S H A L L O W   U S U A L
        E   N   B   T
O R G A N   R E A S O N S
    E   R   K   D       O
E V E N I N G S   P A I R
    E   I   I   A   S
W A L N U T   T A N D E M
    L   G   S       S
```

486

```
    B   V   R   R   I   R
S A L A M I   H A M M E R
    M   R   C   Y   P   T
O B E Y   H U M O R O U S
    O   E   E   O   R
C O N T E S T   E V E N T
        H   T   B   E
A N V I L   P R O D U C T
    E   R   B   U       A
S E T T L A R S   C A M P
    D   I   I   H   A   E
S E L E C T   E X P O R T
    D   S   D   S   A
```

487

```
    T   O   G   G   C   F
F O R M E R   L A Y E R S
    M   I   I   A   L   A
R A F T   P O R T I O N S
    T   P   E   N   C
C O U R S E   E D G E S
    E   D   S   E
S K I L L   J O U R N E Y
    N   I   D   M       I
D I S G U I S E   H I T S
    F   I   S   D   E   H
H E R O I C   A M A Z E D
    N   O   Y   D   R
```

488

```
    C   S   P   S   S   S
T A T T O O   T W E N T Y
    S   A   I   O   G   R
J U L Y   N O V E M B E R
    A   T   E   E   A
E L E C T E D   E N E M Y
        R   R   G   T
T R O U T   B R U S H E D
    A   S   B   A       X
E I G H T E E N   R A T S
    S   I   A   I   E
T E N N I S   T A L E N T
    D   G   T   E   Y   T
```

489

```
G H D   E T C
ARGYLE  SHOWER
O M V   T L N
CORN  IDEALISE
V A   R F U
HELPING  CRUST
A T   B E
ZEBRA  JAVELIN
L A M G   N
FARFLUNG  DEBT
P F M A   E R
SEISM  GIFTED
E N Y   E T D
```

493

```
E M A   A E E
OXFORD  NATIVE
I S V   O E A
PLOT  ELDORADO
E R   E N E
USELESS  TILDE
I E   T T
ABODE  TOBYJUG
R C N   N
BOOMTOWN  HOBO
O I M   E A E
SCONCE  ATTEND
H K T   U E D
```

490

```
P T M   S A B
CLEAVE  WARCRY
E S S   I B O
BASK  SURROUND
S U   L R Z
PERHAPS  REFER
E   C A
SMALL  DOLLOPS
A M C P   I
EMISSARY  DINE
M M I C   U I
BAZAAR  ANCHOR
L N T   T N
```

494

```
R P A   E C
HERALD  BISTRO
T R A   O T E
DOLT  MAVERICK
R A   E A H
STIPEND  ONSET
O T   L G
AGONY  RAVEUP
U Y D R   O
HISTORIC  BUMP
T A E E   A A
LADING  NOBODY
R L S   Y Y E
```

491

```
E N A   S F
EXCEED  COMELY
C X J   O E E
GIST  UNFORMED
T D   F I C
GEOLOGY  UTTER
I E   S O
ICING  BEWITCH
O E V   E R
ALTRUISM  KHAN
D I   N B
CLUMSY  NEARBY
Y D L   G P Y
```

495

```
F F R   B H S
BERATE  IDIOCY
L M C   N G Y
KITE  EGGWHITE
N I   E R H
GESTAPO  SIREN
H T   S S
SPEAK  PIMENTO
L N A   D U
NECKLINE  HONK
N Y D C   U D
STOOGE  AFTERS
Y U D   R S A
```

492

```
R O T   L B P
BANNER  ITALIC
M L E   B R R
GREY  SOYABEAN
O T   A A T
IDEALLY  BREED
R E   S I
IMAGE  HANCOCK
A U C   N A
RHOMBOID  APEX
O E U   B N S
FUNNEL  ONEWAY
T T D   Y W R
```

496

```
D M C   A S S
CINEMA  SQUEAL
D T M   I M F
IDLE  BEDSTEAD
L R   E O R
FAIR  STAID
E C   F A
BOMB  NULLIFY
E I C   R I
SHANGHAI  GENE
O I I   O A I
AVENUE  UNLESS
E E F   S A H
```

497

```
. B . I . R . . C . P .
G E N T L E . B E A K E R
. M . C . C . U . T . R .
H U S H . T Y M P A N U M
. S . . O . . P . S . . .
. E . K E R B . O U T E R
. . . I . Y . K . L . . .
. A L T O . V I C T O R Y
. W . . C . N . N . . . .
S H A M B L E S . I B E X
. I . A . A . M . B . S .
C L E R I C . A D I E U .
. E . E . K . . N . S . S
```

501

```
. R . R . M . V . U . E .
R E T I N A . A W N I N G
. V . . D . Y . L . D . D
N I C E . P I E . E X I T
. L . . O . T . R . N . .
T E N S I L E . G A U G E
. . . I . E . C . C . . .
S T A R E . B A P T I S E
. H . . S . N . . O . . .
P R E G N A N T . S I R E
. E . . R . U . A . O . R
P A P I S T . T E A S E T
. T . P . E . A . R . L .
```

498

```
. T . B . K . S . D . S .
J A V A . I . P R E T T Y
. L . L . S . O . C . A .
B L U E . S C O T L A N D
. E . . I . N . I . Z . .
P R E V E N T . S N E A K
. . . E . G . L . E . . .
S C A L E . R E A S O N S
. O . O . W . T . . A . .
A I R C R A F T . D A T A
. L . I . V . U . U . I .
S E T T L E . C A N N O T
. D . Y . D . E . E . N .
```

502

```
. C . B . A . D . I . O .
H A Z A R D . A B S U R D
. N . C . V . N . I . I .
S A C K . A C C U S T O M
. P . . N . E . . L . . .
D E F E N C E . C A M E O
. . . M . E . T . P . . .
R U G B Y . E A S T M A N
. M . L . E . P . . N . .
S P L A T T E R . H A T E
. I . Z . H . O . E . L .
C R E O L E . O P E N E R
. E . N . R . M . L . R .
```

499

```
. T . C . E . B . C . F .
M O L A R S . A M A Z E D
. W . S . C . S . P . M .
C A G E . A M E R I C A N
. R . P . D . T . L . L .
A D M I R E D . T A K E N
. . . D . S . P . L . . .
P I L E S . C O N S I S T
. M . N . H . S . . T . .
C A R T O O N S . S E A S
. G . I . T . E . C . T .
K E T T L E . S P A C E D
. S . Y . L . S . R . D .
```

503

```
. T . F . S . A . E . M .
U R G E N T . G A M M O N
. E . E . E . O . I . D .
H A I L . N O N E S U C H
. T . . C . Y . S . O . .
P Y R A M I D . G A U N T
. . . I . L . I . R . . .
L I T R E . U N D Y I N G
. N . T . M . H . . O . .
E L D O R A D O . W O V E
. A . A . N . U . E . I .
A W N I N G . S T A R C H
. S . R . O . E . L . E .
```

500

```
. L . E . U . T . E . B .
G A M M O N . R U E F U L
. N . I . C . A . L . S .
. C A R . L A D Y S H I P
. E . E . E . E . . L . .
" T R I V I A L . K E N Y A
. . . E . R . S . N . . .
I N E R T . S T U D I E D
. E . A . E . U . D . . .
S U C C I N C T . B A C K
. T . I . A . T . U . A .
P E P T I C . E F F E T E
. R . Y . T . R . F . S .
```

504

```
. E . A . A . T . T . A .
G N O M E S . H E R E B Y
. R . M . S . U . A . U .
H A L O . I M M O D E S T
. G . . S . P . E . E . .
R E U N I T E . C O P S E
. E . . . K . F . . . . .
P U N C H . M I S F I R E
. N . K . T . C . . A . .
J E T B L A C K . R O B E
. V . A . B . O . A . B .
F E N N E L . F O R M I C
. N . D . E . F . F . E . T
```

505

```
P S P . F E C .
HANKER . ENDEAR
L I O W I R .
FLOP . FLEETING
. E E R . A .
ITEMISE . HOLLY
. O S S P P .
CABBY . FIRSTLY
C I B D . I .
FULLPAGE . HAVE
M I N A U E .
REASON . RESULT
N . E S M H Y .
```

506

```
W L S . P T M .
PEDANT . UNHOOK
A M Y R O U .
FLOP . PLEURISY
. T . T E . S .
GHERKIN . OFFER
. Y C L . I .
BREED . DISROBE
E . S L . R .
RHAPSODY . HAUL
A L B P A . I .
ASHORE . ACCESS
H . T R D K E .
```

507

```
H B O . M A S .
GOKART . UNREAD
M L T L M T .
MIND . ONCEOVER
L . M H U E . .
TYPICAL . TRUNK
. N N V E . .
LAPSE . BARRAGE
F O A R . U .
AFFLICTS . TELL
R E I I A . L .
CANNED . TATTER
Y . T . Y A T .
```

508

```
W H S . S C M .
BATEAU . CRAYON
R E B U L H .
PROD . JEREMIAD
. E E F . I . .
UNHITCH . WHARF
. N T B O . .
FLUFF . BATTENS
A E S R . A .
UNBROKEN . AQUA
C N I O N S .
DETAIN . WONDER
T . L T L E A .
```

509

```
O T . R H A .
ABSENT . EMERGE
L X H A N E .
LINT . OCCUPANT
G R H A D .
MEDICAL . FREAK
. N X B T . .
UNITE . HALYARD
O E D G . E .
OVERLEAP . GAPE
E N F I A O .
SNEEZE . PLIERS
A . E R E T T
```

510

```
O O . S H C .
APOGEE . AVATAR
T R Y Y R .
NINE . VESTMENT
O E O A A .
INSPIRE . SKILL
. H B I . E .
UBOAT . EMIRATE
A S S . I .
UNDERCUT . SIGN
T O R A N H .
DANUBE . TRUSTY
M . T E E B S
```

511

```
I R . Z E E .
ANNALS . INTEND
J N K P E T .
BUCK . IMPERIAL
R Y N . I .
BETROTH . RIFLE
. E D T . .
SCALE . MIDYEAR
H I E A . T .
DOGGYBAG . IOTA
P I O R C E .
DISOWN . AROUND
N . N Y M N D
```

512

```
S F S . E C G .
SPRINT . ASHORE
R L E R A O .
BOWL . LITERATE
U L H M T .
ETHICAL . PIVOT
. N R B N . .
SMITH . VIRGULE
O A T N . I .
MUDGUARD . FIND
S L N I A K .
OSSIFY . NOTOUT
E . O A G E P
```

513

```
  K   P O   U P   N
R E J O I N   S C U B A
N   R   E   U M   P
U N I T   T U R N P I K E
E       I   P     I
O L D T I M E   P O U N D
    R   E   B   P
I S S U E   B O L S T E R
P   E   G   R     N
D I S B U R S E   W I T H
R   L   O   A     R
S I T U P S   O F F S E T
T   E   S   M   T E
```

514

```
  S   V M   S S   Z
S T E A D Y   P H Y S I C
R   R   S   E L   N
R A C Y   T R E E L I N E
N   I   D   A     I
A D V A N C E   U B O A T
    L       L U
A B A T E   W A Y S I D E
A   I   M   Z     E
S T A T U A R Y   S A T E
M   U   R   O     E
M A D D E R   E L A P S E
N   E   Y   T P   T
```

515

```
  D   L S   L T   H
R E C O I L   A B A C U S
M   C   A   P B   M
L U R K   V A S C U L A R
R   I   E   L     N
P E C K I S H   L A D E N
    E   H   R T
P U R E E   C A D E N Z A
N   P   A   M     I
D I S S O L V E   L O G S
Q   A   O   K U   Z
T U C K I N   I N R O A D
E   E   G   N E   G
```

516

```
  S   E A   D C   P
V A N D A L   R E A L L Y
C   I   M   A M   A
S H U T   A M I D S H I P
E   A   N   N H   T
S T O I C A L   F A L S E
    N   C   B F
A M E N D   L E E T I D E
A   U   H   G
F L E E T I N G   C O C K
L   N   V   A O   A
P E D D L E   R E C E D E
T   O   S   Y K   E
```

517

```
    L K   S S   B
D E L U G E   C A L L O W
I   T   Y   A A   U
P Y R E   N O N E V E N T
O   O   O   T     C
C U B I S T S   A N G E R
    N   E   H E
R A I S E   C O N T O U R
N   I   D   P     N
C O N G R E S S   O P U S
I   N   T   A P   S
U N L I K E   C L E V E R
T   A   R   K N   D
```

518

```
    R B   S A   B
P L A I C E   M I R R O R
E   N   T   A I   U
P E E K   R E S E A R C H
B   B   O   H     L
O B V I A T E   F A C E T
    N   H   N S
C H A F E   T E M P L A R
E   E   A   U
A L L R I G H T   H E A L
I   I   A   R     J
D U G O U T   A F F R A Y
M   R   E   L T   X
```

519

```
    H D   A   D
B E L U G A   R O C K E R
O   R   Y   A H   R
W E L L   T U R M E R I C
Y   I   E   E     V
P E R F U M E   R A V E N
    A   E   B L
T R A M P   P O V E R T Y
O   O       G
A L B U M S   Y   E C H O
L   S   T M   S E
R E A L L Y   E X P O R T
R   Y   X N   Y   E
```

520

```
  O   T I   S W   N
E N F O L D   T R I P O D
W   I   O   A T   D
B A I L   L O N G H A U L
R   I   D   H     L
A D D R E S S   B O X E R
    U   E   M L
F E I N T   T I D D L E R
N   N   U   S
O G R E S S E S   I T C H
U   R   H   T     E
B L O U S E   E X E M P T
F   P   R   P S   T
```

521

```
F  W  A     P  S  H
RAGOUT  OCULAR
G  O  H  P  C  R
CELL  ESPECIAL
N  I  Y  U  S
IDOLISE  SMASH
O  T  A  B
STONE  LISSOME
U  G  P  L  A
SNOWSHOE  BOLD
D  A  O  R  U  I
PRIVET  OFFICE
A  E  O  N  F  E
```

525

```
U  A  P  H  G  M
SNIVEL  ECLAIR
E  I  A  T  U  A
YARD  COUNTESS
S  A  P  M
MYSTERY  BELAY
A  D  F  Y
HOBBY  ALLERGY
L  U  S  A  A
IDOLATER  BOLL
H  A  I  E  A
CANTON  UNBIND
T  E  K  P  Y  A
```

522

```
B  E  D  A  G  T
RESUME  GARDEN
F  R  B  A  A  E
MONO  ACTIVATE
U  C  E  I  H
GLOBULE  OTHER
A  E  O  A
FLASK  EPISTLE
A  K  S  E  A
STREAMER  CODE
T  T  A  A  O  D
METRIC  TUREEN
R  Y  K  E  D  R
```

526

```
B  F  S  Y     K
WILLOW  UNSEAL
L  U  E  M  U  I
FLAX  LAMPPOST
O  O  T  Y  R  E
TWINSET  WEARY
O  R  L  M
SPAWN  JAVELIN
A  P  N  M
CORDUROY  CAPE
V  A  O  A  O  A
LARYNX  RUMPLE
L  S  Y  D  B  E
```

523

```
A  A  G  A  L  B
CLINCH  GROCER
K  O  A  A  N  A
DAWN  SAP  GIG
L  T  E  H  L
KINFOLK  GAVEL
E  Y  B  N
WEEDY  BURDOCK
X  E  B  F  A
YOURSELF  VILE
C  A  R  O  I  I
VESTRY  OCCUPY
T  E  L  N  E  H
```

527

```
V  H  W  C  H  E
DECOKE  ORANGE
L  O  L  U  C  R
POMP  LOPSIDED
U  F  E  E  S
WRECKER  ANGST
A  D  C  D
LEARN  WREATHE
N  S  E  O
RECLAIM  FLOW
I  O  B  A  A  D
CHAIR  TANNOY
H  X  E  E  G  O
```

524

```
H  Y  P  F  S  T
AYEAYE  ACUMEN
B  W  R  T  P  L
IRIS  FLAGPOLE
I  E  L  R  E
EDIFICE  DECRY
L  T  S  S
ESSAY  SUBSIST
C  K  B  F  U
TONEDEAF  PUFF
R  O  E  U  A  F
SCRUFF  SPRAIN
H  T  Y  E  T  X
```

528

```
S  R     H  B  G
OPTION  UNITED
R  S  I  T  F  I
DOCK  LACROSSE
U  N  H  C  H
STROLL  FATAL
N  S  L
SCALP  RUSSIAN
A  O  S  P  C
DEBONAIR  ETCH
C  K  T  E
SURETY  M  HAUL
M  R  R  O  E
```

529

```
O   S   CAP   T   F
TRIO    O   LOOFAH
G   F   N   A   U   N
CYST    COINCIDE
    E   O   N   H   A
TWIN    CO   PEONY
    A       T   S   G
STOAT   EYEBROW
    C   V   U   M   E
SHEEPDIP   SLOG
    F   N   D   T   V
BUDGIE   ODIOUS
    E   L   R   M   M
```

530

```
W   L   B   O   P   M
FRIEZE   PRIMER
    E   A   E   N   L
PAWN   FORTKNOX
    T   T   T       D
THEOREM   NAVY
    D   A   D   W
PROBE   AIMLESS
    E   R   P   C   E
OPTIMIST   TEAK
    I   D   N   A   W
KNIGHT   TOMCAT
    E   E   O   E   Y
```

531

```
P   C   W   L   B   T
OUTLAY   ONRUSH
    B   U   S   R   A
GLUE   IRRIGATE
    I   W   Y   G   S
ACRONYM   LABEL
    N   G   V   R
OCTET   BEDTIME
    A   P   S   T   A
ENCIRCLE   TILE
    Y   E   A   R   Y
CONCUR   ABRADE
    N   E   F   N   E
```

532

```
N   S   S   S   P   R
COLONY   WOODED
    B   L   R   O   T   C
MALE   IDOLATER
    L   N   P   U   D
PLUMAGE   OFTEN
    E   E   H   E
SCALE   VACUOUS
    L   R   L   N
SOLDIERY   WAFT
    S   O   F   A   I   A
BEFORE   RANCID
    T   R   R   D   G   R
```

533

```
V   C   A   B   E   N
RAGLAN   ARMIES
    G   A   T   D   I   L
YAWN   ORGANISE
    R   N   E   E   O
SYNONYM   INANE
    B   M   S   C
PREEN   NUMERAL
    E   D   F   N   N
THINAIR   INCH
    I   E   C   O   H
ORANGE   OUTFOX
    E   T   T   F   A   R
```

534

```
A   P   C   H   A   S
BRIE   O   EIGHTY
    C   R   U   A   O   A
RACK   RAVENING
    D   A   E   I   Z
DERANGE   USUAL
    C   E   M   E
ENACT   LANDING
    I   R   O   Y   A
SCREWTOP   LOPE
    E   D   T   O   O   E
STRIFE   LUSTRE
    Y   T   R   E   S   Y
```

535

```
W   K   P   E   U   B
CHOICE   BANGUP
    E   N   R   O   C   P
BEAK   FINALISE
    Z   I   Y   E   A
PENTODE   START
    O   Y   L   O
VSIGN   HUTMENT
    H   E   R   L   E
FOOTBALL   LOUT
    V   H   D   A   Y   R
PESETA   BUREAU
    L   R   R   Y   E   L
```

536

```
K   I   S   A   W   S
WIGGLE   SEAMAN
    N   N   V   S   P   U
UGLI   EMACIATE
    T   N   Y   T   E
BENEATH   TIARA
    L       Y   I   N
OFFER   PROPHET
    X   T   K   A
BISCUITS   NIGH
    N   E   L   O   T   O
INVENT   MARINE
    D   H   E   Y   G
```

537

```
P   D   F   M S   E
GAZEBO  ARTFUL
I   S   R   G   R   P
FLIP  TWILIGHT
O   I   C   V   O
LEFTOFF  WEIRD
S   Y   M   I
APHID  RUSSIAN
O   R   P   S   E
OUZO  LAC  DOSE
S   N   A   O   U   N
FADEIN  VACUUM
L   D   T   Y   E   B
```

538

```
P   T   S   S W
DEVOUT  BRUTAL
E   N   Y   A   I   T
ALMS  LENGTHEN
I   I   D   O   R
STYLIST  PRISM
R   H   W   K
SINCE  TELAVIV
C   L   B   A   B
BYRE  EEL  LIFE
C   R   R   T   A   O
BLIGHT  HAZARD
E   Y   H   Y   E   K
```

539

```
P   F   M   A   T   C
COYOTE  BLITHE
L   R   M   O   L   A
LONG  ENVELOPE
E   N   E   E   L
LACTATE  ORGAN
I   O   D   I
BRIDE  PIQUANT
F   A   S   E   N
COSMETIC  FLOW
R   P   E   A   O   V
SCHEME  SULTAN
E   N   P   T   D   L
```

540

```
C   D   E   M S
BORING  ATTACK
L   L   G   R   O   O
CURL  HARDWARE
M   E   Y   A   G
INSULAR  AWAIT
N   D   M   A
SNUFF  BICYCLE
U   O   M   D   I
ETERNITY  PEST
T   M   S   E   A   T
SELECT  ASLEEP
R   D   Y   R   E   N
```

541

```
C   D   T   A   M   C
PHRASE  DEADLY
O   W   R   A   R   I
SPIN  MAGAZINE
I   I   E   I   I
ANXIETY  EPOCH
N   E   D   A
KNIFE  TRINKET
A   L   D   Y   R
FUGITIVE  DARE
S   G   A   Y   R   A
ZEPHYR  EQUATE
A   T   Y   D   M   A
```

542

```
S   S   P   C   A   C
BURIAL  AFLOAT
B   L   A   N   K   R
JOLT  YEOMANRY
R   B   N   L   E
UNCTIION  VOILA
E   Y   R   I
AGONY  SITDOWN
R   D   V   G   I
TOWERING  CITY
W   N   N   I   A   H
STICKY  NAPKIN
H   Y   L   G   E   N
```

543

```
B   P   A   P   A   M
REFUND  EGGNOG
D   M   V   T   G   R
FLEA  EXTERIOR
A   R   Y   I   S
AMONGST  PETER
O   E   D   V
SALON  MIXEDUP
E   N   P   S   N
TROTTERS  DRIP
I   I   O   E   O   S
HARDEN  NEURON
L   E   Y   T   R   N
```

544

```
L   C   O   A   L
SETOFF  FLORAL
G   C   F   I   U
LINK  HARDWARE
O   A   E   A   E
ONGOING  LISLE
R   D   B   V
ADAGE  CAREFUL
E   A   S   R   R
ABINITIO  TOSS
T   I   E   Q   U   I
TOUSLE  UNBIND
R   T   L   E   A   E
```

545

```
HIKE    COWERED
I  H E  H A H  A
SOANDSO FLINT
P  K G  I E Z  E
ALIBI   CORDON
N    N  E   M  E
ICEAGE  DEFECT
C  L G  N      H
 SEEMLY LANCE
S  C P  I   O  R
TUTTI   SASHIMI
E  O S  U   T S S
MARITIME TYPE
```

549

```
 B  V   T E Y  W
TOMATO  STATIC
 T  R U S C N
STAY    REACHING
 L  I   Y T E
DENTIST DIARY
    R   T P N
PROOF   COUGHED
 E  L   S U S
SCULPTOR SETS
 A  E U I I A
PLAYED  NIGHT
 L  Y   G N E
```

546

```
   L H S  F A
FIBULA   PRIEST
 Z M D  A R  T
GASP DEW  EARN
 R  O  N  T  A
ADVANCE  TRILL
 I  K  M  A
USURP    TORPEDO
 P  S  S  R  R
SHIPPING ABUT
 E  E  N  U W D
GRIEVE   ENOUGH
 E  D  W  L  E
```

550

```
 H  S  CUP  C A
HEALTH  O HART I
 R  I  E P  O R
POEM    EXPLORED
 E  E  R Y  S S
ESCAPES  SIXTH
   D D  C N
PRIME    PROGRAM
 E  I  G A  P
SPARKLED FURS
 E  I  L I  O
GAINED   EATING
 T  G  E S  S S
```

547

```
   C P B  B U
SALIVA   ANNEAL
 P  P N  R C D
MITE    SHEATHED
 T  H D  U L
HAMSTER  HOVEL
    C E  B U
LATEX    CAPSULE
 E  N C  P  A
FREAKOUT SPRY
 I  R V  I O D
MARINE   STAMEN
 L  O Y  M K R
```

548

```
   C B D  L A M
HOMAGE   YELLOW
 B  C C  M A L
GAWK     IMPACTED
 L  M H  R S
TROJAN   KITTY
    V L  W T
LABEL   ROSY UP
 B  R O  U  P
MOURNFUL LADY
 A  U F  D E A
GRILLE   BREATH
 D  E R  E K E
```

551

```
 S  O F  A C P
SAMPLE   PROVED
 F  E E  R M A
MAIN     DROPPING
 R  I N  A U
BINDING  TRUTH
    E G  H E
TRULY    READILY
 E  I D  L  E
ICECREAM THAW
 K  A T  E U R
BOTTLE   TIRING
 N  E R  S N T
```

552

```
 C  U S  S T S
PICNIC   WEEKLY
 N  D A  A R E
HERO     REMEMBER
 M  I P  I V
RAISINS  ANGER
    E G  D A
BEACH    GRILLED
 R  U P  E  F
WARRIORS WIFE
 S  I L  S E E
CENTRE   EXPECT
 R  Y S  D T T
```

Crossword Solutions

553

```
N   L   E   S   H   F
PILOTS   PEOPLE
 C   O   C   E   L   O
SKIM ALE   IVAN
 E   P   D   D   T
FLASHED   WAIST
 U   S   P   Y
BADGE   CONSIST
 R   G   C   C   H
NOTEBOOK   THOR
 U   S   R   E   O   V
UNITED   TURNED
 D   S   S   S   N   L
```

557

```
B   B   C   A   I   T
PATROL   SENIOR
 Z   A   A   S   U   D
BALD TEA   NUDE
 A   A   T   M   D   L
BRACKEN   CABER
 O   R   T   T
CHIME   FOREIGN
 O   P   U   P   A
FOGLAMPS   TANK
 K   A   B   O   A   T
RAPIER   IMPART
 H   N   A   L   E   Y
```

554

```
E   F   F   C   I   C
MALAWI   LONDON
 M   R   S   O   F   U
ABLE   HEADINGS
 O   I   K   N   H
HOUSING   MIDST
 C   G   R   T
ATTIC   WHOEVER
 R   S   T   Y   N
PASSPORT   LOGS
 V   O   A   H   O   A
DEBRIS   MANAGE
 L   S   T   S   G   E
```

558

```
T   C   Z   A
ABSEIL   INVENT
 L   A   P   I   O
BUCK PIP   AFRO
 S   P   Y   T   M
WHISPER   DINAR
 T   D   S   O
CLOUT   MAUNDER
 R   C   V   X
KANGAROO   HEED
 R   E   O   U   M
TIPOFF   RECIPE
 D   N   T   Y   K   T
```

555

```
T   I   S   E   K   E
RAGS A   STARVE
 E  NOD  S   N   E
EAST   DRAGGING
 L   L   Y   A   T
SLEEVES   PRESS
 I   U   O
WINGS   UNROLL
 C   H   P   T   A
BITTERLY   BIT
 C   E   I   I   O   E
SLEEPS   NEWEST
 E   N   M   G   S   T
```

559

```
F  IMP     A   N
CUBS A   SODIUM
 N   R   N   I   J   M
EDNA   CONFUSED
 E   A   K   S   R
DISLIKE   STOOD
 N   E   G   U
ISSUE   FOOLISH
 I   N   T   G   I
ESCAPING   ZERO
 T   B   G   L   A   I
WEALTH   EUROPE
 D   E   T   S   D   E
```

556

```
Y   Z   A   T   P
ONCE R   REGARD
 G  RAT  U   I   I
ALSO   INTENDED
 A   S   H   S
OPERATE   GIFTS
 E   V   T
SASH   SEESAW
 E   E   T   S   I
AQUARIUS   OWN
 U   R   P   E   A   N
FENCES   LARGER
 L   H   Y   S   S   R
```

560

```
T   Y   A   S   F
COMA R   FAIRLY
 G  CAT  A   L   A
OATH   INCREASE
 T   S   T   N   H
WEBSITE   STAIR
 U   S   L   R   N
TRUCK   PACKAGE
 O   H   G   N   E
APPEALED   EVER
 E   S   I   I   P   Y
DARTED   NEEDED
 N   S   E   G   R   S
```

561

```
. S D S . L E B . . .
M I N U E T . O Y S T E R
. L . C . R I O . T . S .
L I N T . I . S P I R I T
. C . . N . E . M . D .
C A B B A G E . B A B E L
. . U . Y . W . T .
S T A R K . T I M E L A G
. H . G . B . N . . L .
M O U L D I N G . G L U T
. R . A . L . . A . M .
B A R R E L . L O V I N G
. X . Y . Y . . E . A .
```

562

```
. U . R . O . A . P . C .
E S C O R T . B E E T L E
. A . T . T . A . R . O .
O B O E . O A F . O A T S
. L . . M . T . X . H .
P E L I C A N . A I D E D
. . N . N . D . D .
M A G I C . P R A E T O R
. C . M . A . Y . . R .
S C R I B B L E . R I D E
. E . C . B . Y . A . A .
U P D A T E . E L I C I T
. T . L . Y . . D . N .
```

563

```
. S . U . W . E . C . T .
S H A G G Y . A B O A R D
. E . L . S . G . N . U .
P R A Y . I C E . F I S T
. R . . W . R . E . T .
S Y N O N Y M . . T O Y
. E . . U . G . A . T .
A B A T E . . S K I R T
. . W . A . E . . . O .
A P P E N D I X . L O U T
. E . I . O . U . E . C .
B A N G E R . A P A T H Y
. . H . N . L . D . Y .
```

564

```
. B . M . C . B . C . C .
D A D A . I . E C H O E D
. N . . K I T . G . A . R
N A M E . I M A G I N E D
. N . . Z . N . R . A .
H A P P I E R . S M I L E
. . A . N . H . A .
F I F T H . R U N N I N G
. R . T . F . N . . A .
M O V E M E N T . S I T E
. N . R . A . . E . I .
T E N N I S . R E M O V E
. D . S . T . S . E . E .
```

565

```
. P . H . W P . S .
T A X I . U . A F R I C A
. R . P E N . L . O . A .
A C T S . D E L I V E R Y
. E . . R . S . I . C .
F L O O D E D . A D D E D
. . . C . D . G . E .
S T A C K . V I A D U C T
. O . U . B . R . . A .
U M B R E L L A . M E L T
. A . R . A . F . A . V .
A T T E N D . F A R M E D
. O . D . E . E . S . S .
```

566

```
. C A T . A L . S . S .
. H . U . N . A T T A C H
. O . B A G . M . R . R .
D I N E . R E P E A T E D
. C . . I . S . N . E .
P E N C I L S . A G E N T
. . H . Y . C . E .
A T L A S . P A R R O T S
. H . R . S . P . R .
T E A C H E R S . T E A R
. M . O . N . U . I . D .
P E D A L S . L I C K E D
. S . L . E . E . K . R .
```

567

```
. C . H . S . S . T . C .
C O R O N A . T E E T H E
. L . O . N . A . M . A .
L U S T . C A T A P U L T
. M . . T . E . O . E .
E N V I O U S . T R O T H
. . D . M . E . A .
L O G O N . W A L L A B Y
. B . L . W . R . . E .
G E R A N I U M . G A G S
. Y . T . N . U . A . G .
B E H E A D . F A T C A T
. D . R . Y . F . E . R .
```

568

```
D O N E . U L T I M A T E
I . Y . E . I . M . T . A
R E L A X E D . P A T H S
E . O . P . R . R . Y .
C O N V E N T I O N A L .
T . . R . O . V . C . C
O L D . I M A G E . T W O
R . R . M . S . M . . N
. N E V E R T H E L E S S
F . A . N . . N . R . I
A D M I T . R E T U R N S
R . E . A . A . S . O . T
M I D D L I N G . A R M S
```

569

```
L   H E A L S   D       E
C U R E     M   T W E L V E
A   R   U   E   C       E
A B L E   S E T T L I N G
E       I   A   L
P R E S E N T   R A Y S
        U   G   F   E
A P A R T   P R O D U C E
    L   F   K   A       R
V O C A T I O N   S E A L
    U   C   N   T   E   D
A G R E E D   I D E A L S
    H   S   S   C   N   E
```

570

```
    T   R   L   P       A
S H R I N E   I S L A N D
    R   C   T   Q   E   I
B O L E   T O U C H I N G
    N   U   E   O       A
B E W I T C H   P U P P Y
    N   E D S
V A L V E   B E S E E C H
    L   I   S   A       R
T W O T I M E D   H E A L
    A   I   I   E   E   B
C Y G N E T   N E A R B Y
    S   G   H   D   D   Y
```

571

```
    S   P   I   E   A   E
R E F O R M   V E R I F Y
    C   R   A   E   T   F
S E E K   G A R R I S O N
    D   I   Y   S       R
R E M A I N S   S T A T E
    B   E   V   R
S W O O P   R E C Y C L E
    I   V   P   T       A
I M P E T I G O   D U P E
    P   P   X   O       T
A L K A L I   P O W W O W
    E   R   E   N       P
```

572

```
    S   H       D U T
S Q U I R M   R U N O U T
    U   D   U   E   M   R
C A V E   G O S S A M E R
    L   S   N   E
A L I M O N Y   I N A N E
    A   D   E
C A C H E   F O N D A N T
    P   A   R   G       I
V I T R E O U S   S E C T
    A   A   W   L   A   K
G R U N G E   E A G L E T
    Y   I   L   D   E   L
```

573

```
    S   L   L   A   M   R
M E R I N O   G E Y S E R
    C   N   Y   I       G
C O R K   A L L T H E R E
    N   L   E   U       E
E D U C A T E   P L A T E
    A   Y   D   K
B U T T Y   O U T S I Z E
    N   E   C   N       E
H E D G E H O G   A J A R
    A   O   U   E   M   L
E S P R I T   O R I S O N
    Y   Y   E   N   D   T
```

574

```
    G   P   S   P   S   G
D R Y R O T   L A W Y E R
    O   A   Y   U   A   N
P O N Y   L A M B S K I N
    V   I   P   T       A
T E A C O S Y   Y I E L D
    H   H   R   K
O N I O N   D A M A G E D
    E   W   D   K       N
T I T M O U S E   G A G A
    G   E   S   O   O   A
S H R I E K   F L A N G E
    N   Y   F   T       E
```

575

```
    L   O   F   H   A   F
F O R M A L   E R R O R S
    A   I   O   L   R   E
U N I T   A P P E A L E D
    E   T   S   N   Z
A D O P T E D   A G R E E
    R   D   M   E
A C T O R   R E A D I L Y
    H   D   A   N       I
R E T U R N E D   M O T H
    W   C   G   I   A   R
B E T T E R   N A I L E D
    D   S   Y   G   L   S
```

576

```
    P   C   S       A   K
M E M O R Y   T E N N I S
    N   L   O   Y   D
M A D   B A R I T O N E
    A   E   E   H       E
E N D U S E R   V I N Y L
    N   F   W   N
S T U D Y   W A R G A M E
    A   E   T   S       E
S K I R M I S H   T I N T
    I   D   R   I   H   I
S N O O Z E   N O U G A T
    G   G   D   G   S   L
```

577

```
  B U I   L S M
M A R G I N   A L W A Y S
M   L S   R   I   S
O B E Y   E I G H T I E S
O     C   E   C   L
F O R G E T S   S H I F T
    R   S   P   E   U
O C E A N   L E A D I N G
L   C   O   R
R E S E A R C H   K I T E
A   F   D   A   E   O
I N S U R E   P O E T R Y
  S   L   R   S   P   Y
```

578

```
  C L   H   S C P
B A N A N A   T R A G I C
  M   W R A   T   G
G E T S   B R I G H T E R
  R     O   D O   O
H A R M F U L   C L U N G
    E   R   W   I   O
S C R E W   H A T C H E D
  I   T   S   T
A R T I S T I C   D R E W
  C   N   A   H A   Y
H U N G E R   E C H O E D
  S   S   S   D   L D
```

579

```
  R A C   S G U
M A N U F A C T U R I N G
  I   T U A   O   I
I N D U S T R Y   W A V E
  M   I S   T   E
O P I N I O N   T H I R D
  R   N   P     S
S E A L S   G U E S S E S
  V   E T   M U
T I E S   R E P U B L I C
  O   S I   K   W D
A U T O M A T I C A L L Y
  S   N   L   N Y   E
```

580

```
  R S   P   B E C
H A W K E R   R O U T E S
  T I   O O   R   N
S H O P   J E A L O U S Y
  E     E D   P   U
P R O D U C E   G E E S E
    A   T C   A
F R A Y S   S H I N I N G
  A L   W A   O
D I V I S I O N   H A V E
  S G   N N   O E
M E T H O D   E A S I L Y
  S   T Y   L T   S
```

581

```
  B F   I     D S
B E L O N G   G L O W E R
  L L   N U   D   A
F L A K   O U T B O A R D
  O     B S   C
S W A D D L E   W I G H T
    E   E G   N
S C A M P   B A C K L O G
  H E   J R   R   B
D O W N T U R N   S A T E
  I T   N I   L   A
S C R I P T   S T U D I O
  E A   A H   R   N
```

582

```
  A E   F   S   F
U N E V E N   A B S E I L
  T I   U I   A   A
K I L N   M A R T I N E T
    C   B Y   C
F O R E V E R   S T E A L
  U     R B
S T O R M   B A R G A I N
  C A   S N   E
I L L F A T E D   W A S H
  A F   R S   G   L
A S S I Z E   A V A T A R
  S A   W W   W   B
```

583

```
  D I   D A   O C
P I E R C E   G A B B L E
  A O   C L   L   D
F L A N   L O O P H O L E
  I     A W   N
P S Y C H I C   B O G U S
  K     M B
S E D G E   R A I L W A Y
  L     B D   A
D E C K H A N D   P O S E
  T E   G E   D   H
S O U R C E   B L O W U P
  N B   L T   G   T
```

584

```
  S P   G   H E   P
S A V O U R   E M I G R E
  G T   A N   O   T
C O D A   V O C A L I S E
    T   I E   S
R I P O S T E   C O M F Y
  C     Y O
P E S K Y   S E N D O F F
  L     H O
F O R E H E A D   L Y R E
  L V   A A   L   O
A L L I E D   S T A B L E
  Y L   Y H   R   E
```